THE EVOLUTION OF
SCOTLAND'S SCENERY

View from Bealach na Bà (Pass of the Cattle) on the Kishorn–Applecross road.
Torridon Sandstone wall of Meall Gorm on right. *Photograph by W. A. Sharp.*

The
EVOLUTION
of
SCOTLAND'S
SCENERY

J. B. Sissons

OLIVER & BOYD
EDINBURGH AND LONDON

OLIVER AND BOYD LTD

Tweeddale Court Edinburgh 1
39a Welbeck Street London W.1

First Published 1967

© 1967 J. B. Sissons

Set in Monotype Plantin and printed in
Great Britain by R. & R. Clark Ltd

PREFACE

THE grandeur and beauty of Scotland's scenery have been extolled in countless publications. Only one book, however – *The Scenery of Scotland*, by Archibald Geikie – has been entirely devoted to explaining how the scenery of the country as a whole came into existence. Since the third edition of Geikie's book appeared in 1901 much new information has become available and, particularly during the last ten years or so, the surface forms of Scotland have been increasingly studied and ideas about their origin and evolution have changed considerably. The present book therefore seeks to describe and explain the surface features of the country in the light of the evidence and ideas now available.

In presenting this material every attempt has been made to use as few technical words as possible. Apart from one or two elementary geological terms (used mainly in the first chapter) the meanings of the various terms that are used are indicated as they are introduced. For those unfamiliar with the study of landforms it is hoped that this book will help them to understand how the surface features of a particular country have come into existence. In this respect it may be pointed out that there is a growing belief, particularly among geographers and geologists, that landform study has now advanced to such an extent that the subject can be comprehended only by a few specialists. This belief is incorrect, however. The subject depends entirely on simple facts obtained by observation and measurement in the field and in the laboratory, and the amateur, suitably advised, is often just as capable of collecting these facts as the specialist. In the following pages the author has tried, firstly, to present the principal facts available and, secondly, to indicate the inferences that it seems possible to draw from them. It will be appreciated that often the facts have been, and still are, interpreted in different ways by different people, and that the interpretations based on them here are inevitably coloured by the author's views.

The author wishes to express his gratitude to Professor J. W. Watson for insisting that this book be written and to the University of Edinburgh for granting the leave of absence that made this possible. He is particularly grateful to Miss E. L. Duncan for her care and patience in drawing all the maps and diagrams. To his wife he is grateful for encouragement and for assistance in many ways.

It must be mentioned that the permission of the Controller of H.M. Stationery Office has been obtained for the reproduction of Plates VB, XA, XI, XII, XIXB, XXB, XXIA and XXIIA and of Fig. 52. Figs 46, 73, 79 and 81 are reproduced from *Trans. Inst. Brit. Geogr.* by permission of the Council of the Institute. The sources of other Plates and Figures are given in their captions.

J. B. SISSONS

Edinburgh
December 1966

v

CONTENTS

1

Preglacial evolution

'FROM the tops of the mountains to the shores of the sea, all the soils are subject to be moved from their places, by the natural operations of the surface, and to be deposited in a lower situation; thus gradually proceeding from the mountain to the river, step by step into the sea.' Thus wrote James Hutton towards the end of the eighteenth century when he introduced the concept of changing scenery. Some of the changes in Scotland, such as the erosion of parts of the coast by the sea, the formation of gullies on mountain slopes or the spreading of gravel on valley floors by rivers in flood, may be seen in operation today. Others, such as the conversion of the fertile farmlands of Culbin to a sandy desert during the latter part of the seventeenth century, are recorded by historical evidence. Farther back in time the landforms themselves record the changes. They show that even during man's brief occupance of Scotland sea-level has varied considerably in relation to the land, at times almost severing the country by extension of the estuaries of Forth and Clyde and at other times standing lower than at present along most of the coastline. A mere 10 000 years ago large glaciers were still decaying in many corries and valleys in the mountains. They were the last significant representatives of vast masses of glacier ice that had covered Scotland intermittently during several hundred thousand years and that may yet accumulate again. The glaciers have had a profound effect on the landforms both in lowlands and uplands, producing in the latter most of the more striking elements of the scenery. Earlier events in the evolution of the present land surface are recorded by the plateaux at different levels and by various elements of the drainage pattern, while the rocks themselves record the great volcanic outpourings and related events of parts of the west that occurred around sixty million years ago. Still older elements of the scenery that, in their origin, date back hundreds of millions of years and have been exhumed from beneath a cover of later rocks, can be identified here and there, either as hills emerging from the surrounding sediments or as valleys from which the cover rocks have not yet been completely cleaned out.

Inevitably the production of later elements of the scenery has resulted in the destruction or obliteration of many of the earlier ones. This has been particularly true of the seventy million years or so of Tertiary time, during which Scotland has been repeatedly uplifted and its surface more and more deeply eroded. The corresponding Tertiary sedimentary accumulations are absent from the land surface (except for tiny patches) and presumably lie, as yet wholly uninvestigated, beneath the surrounding seas. During the Quaternary glaciations that followed erosion again prevailed. Not only were the solid

1

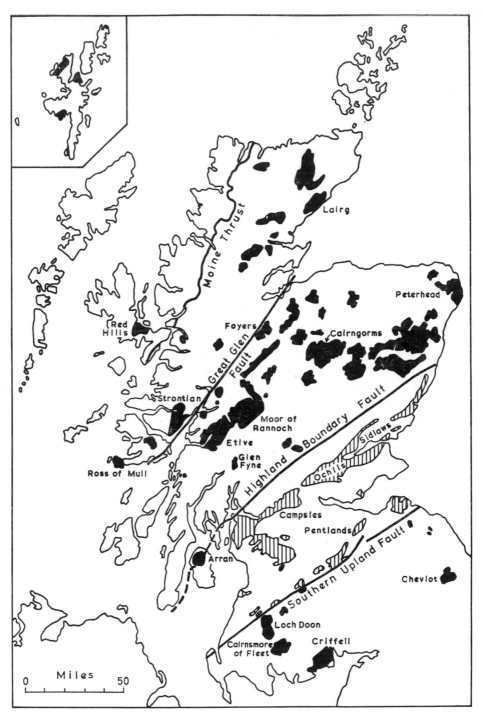

FIG. 1. Principal outcrops of granite and (in Central Lowlands) principal outcrops of volcanic rocks.

rocks deeply gouged in many valleys and some lowlands, but each glacial advance resulted in most of the materials that had been laid down by its predecessor being swept away or obliterated. Consequently depositional landforms and the sequences of deposits that are essential for the establishment of a reliable story of successive events are widely available only for the very latest of the changes that have affected the surface of Scotland. Here, fortunately, they abound and include not only the materials laid down by glaciers and glacial rivers during the later stages of the last glaciation, but also marine, estuarine and lacustrine deposits that accumulated during lateglacial and postglacial times. These deposits (so far as they have been investigated) enable a detailed picture of successive changes to be built up and permit events to be measured in thousands or even hundreds of years over a period extending back for some 13 000 years. The situation is very different, however, for the early part of the glacial story and for preglacial events. For the latter we have to think in terms of millions or tens of millions of years and, since the landforms are mainly erosional, we can usually scc only the end-products of the destruction that has been wrought over vast periods of time. Consequently the sequence of events in preglacial times is far from firmly established and one can only seek to decipher some of the more important elements that contribute to the present scenery.

Rocks and scenery

Whatever uncertainties may exist regarding the evolution of the land surface there is no doubt that one result has been a striking correlation in many areas between rock type and scenery, a correlation that applies both to altitude and form of the ground. Within the Central Lowlands there is a close correspondence between hills and igneous outcrops. Volcanic rocks are responsible for the long belt of hills that extends from coast to coast as the Sidlaw Hills, Ochil Hills, Campsie Fells (and associated hills) and the Kilpatrick Hills. Similar rocks form the high ground on the borders of Ayrshire and Renfrewshire, the northern part of the Pentland Hills, and the Garleton Hills in East Lothian (Figs 1 and 2). The volcanic rocks reach their greatest altitude in Ben Cleuch in the Ochils (2363 feet), where the lava beds attain their maximal thickness; they fall in altitude northeastwards towards Montrose as the lavas become thinner and increasingly

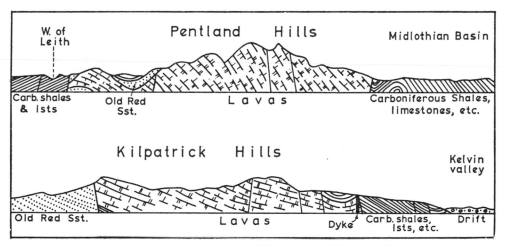

FIG. 2. Sections across the Pentland Hills and the Kilpatrick Hills to show relations between geology and relief. Based on Geological Survey maps. Base lines represent sea-level.

interbedded with sedimentary rocks. The surfaces of the volcanic uplands are often very irregular in detail with numerous steps corresponding with the edges of the inclined and faulted beds of lava. Occasionally, as on the steep hill slopes west of Stirling, the truncated lava flows form steps one above the other that continue for many miles. Between Bridge of Earn and Dundee the Earn and Tay correspond approximately with the axis of an anticline whose central part was long ago downfaulted. Now, through differential erosion, the Old Red Sandstone between the faults has been largely removed to form low ground bordered by steep fault-line scarps away from which the lavas dip northwestwards in the Sidlaws and southeastwards in the Ochils. Some of the gaps in the volcanic hills also reflect the geological controls. Thus the deep gap that runs from Johnstone to Dalry corresponds with a belt of sedimentary rocks downfaulted amidst the lavas, while the Neilston gap a few miles away exhibits a similar relationship. The major gap at Stirling is no chance feature but occurs at a weak point in the line of volcanic hills where lava beds of quite different ages are separated by the Ochil fault.

Further variety in the scenery of the Central Lowlands is provided by the innumerable outcrops of intrusive igneous rock. While some of these outcrops have little or no apparent effect on the relief, many others form striking features. Hundreds of volcanic necks occur, some forming low knolls and others giving rise to isolated steep-sided hills from a few hundred yards to about a mile in diameter and circular or oval in plan. Among the more conspicuous are North Berwick Law and the Bass Rock in East Lothian (Plate IA); Arthur's Seat and the Castle Rock in Edinburgh; Largo Law, Kellie Law, Carnbee Law and the pointed summits of East and West Lomond hills in Fife; Dumgoyn and Dumfoyn at the western end of the Campsies and, close by, Dungoyach rising abruptly from the floor of the Blane valley; Dumbarton Rock commanding the Clyde estuary; Neilston Pad, Lochlands Hill near Beith, Loudoun Hill near Darvel, and Mochrum Hill near Maybole. In a somewhat different category geologically, but even more prominent than any of these, is the island of Ailsa Craig that rises steeply to 1100 feet at the entrance to the Firth of Clyde. Hills of rather more rounded outline are associated with laccolithic intrusions. Among these are the Tinto Hills rising to over 2000 feet, Black Hill in the Pentlands (which contrasts sharply with the craggy lava hills near by) and Traprain Law in East Lothian.

Intrusive sheets of igneous rocks, up to several hundreds of feet thick, form many other hilly areas in the Central Lowlands. Typically these sills give rise to asymmetrical features with steep scarps on one side and more gentle slopes on the other. Individual scarps can rarely be followed continuously for long distances since usually they are repeatedly offset by faults, so that isolated slabs tilted in various directions result. Among the many features associated with such intrusions are Craigie Hill near Kilmarnock, much of the high ground north of Dalmellington culminating in Benbeoch, Salisbury Crags in Edinburgh, and the Isle of May and Inchcolm in the Firth of Forth. Many prominent features correspond with the outcrop of a particularly thick sill that underlies a large area of the Central Lowlands and that is in many respects similar to the well-known Whin Sill of northern England (Francis 1965). It appears as the inclined sheets of rock crowned by Stirling Castle and Wallace's Monument, and southwards from Stirling produces long dip slopes cut off by steep scarps. It is associated with hilly ground around Kirk o'Shotts and again near Torphichen in West Lothian. The sill provides the rocky promontory through which the northern approaches to the Forth bridges have been excavated and forms much of the higher ground in the hilly country south of Cupar. It attains its greatest altitude (almost 1500 feet) in White Craigs overlooking Loch Leven, where, as a resistant capping to the sedimentary rocks beneath, it crowns a scarp as much as a thousand feet high (Plate IB).

Among the sedimentary rocks only some of the conglomerates of Old Red age give rise to prominent hills. Thus on the Highland border Strathfinella Hill overlooking the Howe of the Mearns exceeds 1300 feet and a considerable area of upland between Crieff and Callander culminates in Uamh Bheag at 2181 feet. On the opposite side of the Central Lowlands conglomerates and sandstones form the southern part of the Pentland Hills. For the most part, however, the Old Red sediments, mainly sandstones, are associated with low ground, such as the belt of lowland that includes the Howe of Fife and the Loch Leven basin, and the continuous strip of lowland that extends almost across the width of Scotland from the Howe of the Mearns through Strathmore, Strath Allan and the Carse of Stirling, to the southern end of Loch Lomond. The Carboniferous sedimentary rocks nowhere form striking features and, except where strongly influenced by glaciation (Chapter 5), usually correspond with subdued and gently-undulating ground. Here and there modest features appear, such as the Camp Ridge that borders the Mid-lothian Basin on its eastern side and that probably stands higher than its surroundings owing to beds of limestone brought up in an anticline. It is also noticeable that most of the outcrops of Coal Measures are associated with relatively low ground, a result probably of the prevalence of shales and weak sandstones in these sediments coupled with the rare occurrence of limestones. The landforms developed on the Carboniferous rocks of the Central Lowlands are thus very different from those associated with rocks of the same age in much of northern England. Karstic features are lacking in the limestones of central Scotland and no prominent scarp and dip slopes are associated with either limestones or sandstones. One reason for these differences is that the more resistant beds in the Scottish sediments are very much thinner than those in northern England, while a contributory factor is the severe disruption of the Scottish sediments by innumerable faults and by igneous rocks.

Large areas of the Southern Uplands are typified by smooth rounded hills whose form, despite statements to the contrary at invervals since 1880 (A. Somervail), is still often attributed to rounding by over-riding glacier ice. Rather does it appear that geological factors are of prime importance, in that the Ordovician and Silurian greywackes and mudstones usually occur as steeply-inclined thin beds whose individual outcrops are consequently narrow and thus do not favour the production of large structurally-controlled features. Furthermore, weathering of these rocks rarely results in the production of boulders but instead produces mainly flattish small stones and lesser debris that contribute further to the rounded appearance (Plate IIB). In the southwest, variety is introduced by the large granite masses, the higher parts of which stand well above the surrounding sedimentary rocks to culminate in Cairnsmore of Carsphairn, Cairnsmore of Fleet and Criffell. The Loch Doon granite mass, however, forms a basin that is surrounded by a ring of rugged mountains, including Merrick and the Kells Range, whose existence reflects the superior resistance of the baked sedimentary rocks around the granite margin (Fig. 3). Igneous rocks also help to vary the scene in the Tweed basin. South of the Teviot, volcanic necks are represented by hills such as Scaw Law, Maiden Paps, Rubers Law, Black Law, Lanton Hill and Dunion Hill, while lavas give rise to craggy hills around Kelso and to the rough Border uplands drained by the Kale and Bowmont waters. Intrusive rocks also form the Dirrington laws and – most conspicuous of all – the Eildon Hills culminating in triple peaks that stand a thousand feet above the floor of the Tweed valley at Melrose.

In the Highlands and islands some granite masses are associated with high ground, as in northern Arran, the Cairngorms, the uplands culminating in Lochnagar and Mount Keen, and the mountains bordering upper Loch Etive with Ben Cruachan and Ben Starav as their highest points. In the Northeast some of the most conspicuous hill masses

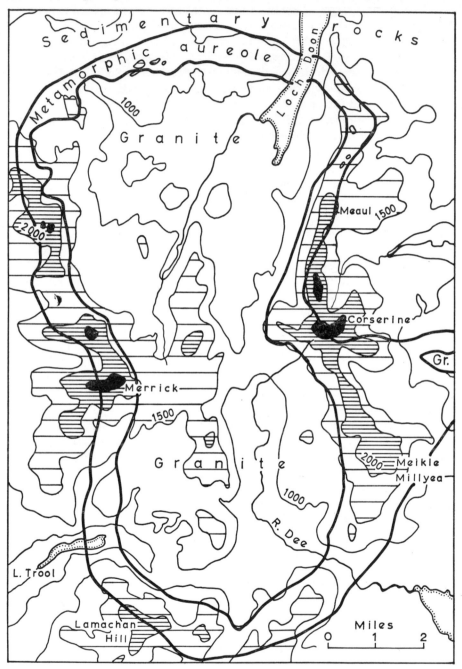

FIG. 3. Correlation between geology and relief in and around the Loch Doon granite area. The high ground corresponds closely with the metamorphic aureole.

PLATE I. A. The Bass Rock. B. Scarp of White Craigs and Bishop Hill, Kinross-shire. *Photographs by Aerofilms.*

PLATE II. A. Stac Polly, Ross-shire. *Photograph by W. A. Sharp.* B. Smooth slopes of the Lowther Hills broken by gullies and small scars. *Photograph by Aerofilms.*

are formed of granite, among them Ben Rinnes, Bennachie and the Hill of Fare. On the other hand, large areas of low ground in the Northeast are floored with the same rock, and Rannoch Moor in the heart of the southwestern Grampians is to a considerable degree a great granite basin surrounded by mountains composed mainly of metamorphic and volcanic rocks that rise 2000 feet or more above the basin floor. Where the granite forms high ground in the Highlands it is often associated with smooth upper slopes and rounded summits, a characteristic not usually evident from the valley floors, where rough rocky slopes are often the most obvious features. D. E. Sugden (1965) found that in the Cairngorms the pseudobedding in the granite is parallel with the smooth slopes, even where these are as steep as 20 degrees, but that it is abruptly truncated by the walls of glacial troughs and corries. This suggests that the smooth slopes are the result of erosion under nonglacial conditions and that in preglacial times the Cairngorms were dissected by deep V-shaped valleys with quite steep but smooth slopes that merged upwards into rounded summits and plateaux.

The junction of the Highlands with the Central Lowlands is emphasised by the belt of resistant metamorphosed grit that forms the Highland border zone. Its influence is seen in the narrow rocky valleys by which one enters the Highlands and in the peaks of Ben Lomond, Ben Ledi and the Perthshire Ben Vorlich. Quartzite has proved similarly resistant to denudation. In the Northwest it forms a protective white capping to mountains such as Ben More Assynt, Ben Eighe and Ben Leagach, and is particularly imposing in the peak of An Teallach. Elsewhere in the same area it appears as great tilted sheets that slope down eastwards from summits such as Canisp, Spidean Còinich, Sgùrr Bàn and Beinn Spionnaidh through a vertical interval of 2000 feet or more. Quartzite forms the highest ground in Islay and Knapdale, and in Jura, almost wholly composed of quartzite, it culminates in the Paps of Jura. Between Glen Nevis and Glen Coe it corresponds with much of the high ground, including the summits of Sgùrr a' Mhaim, Am Bodach and Binnein Mòr. In the central Grampians the most imposing quartzite mountains are Schiehallion and Ben-y-ghlo, and from here to the Banffshire coast a discontinuous belt of quartzite is associated with a series of lesser ridges. Among the most notable hills of this rock in Northeast Scotland are Ben Aigan overlooking the Spey opposite Rothes, and Mormond Hill inland from Fraserburgh.

Outcrops of limestone in the Highlands are often distinguishable by the carpet of green vegetation with which they are covered. In some areas, as near Durness and Inchnadamff, they are characterised by swallow holes, underground streams and caves (Plate XIXA). In the Grampians the limestones, being less resistant than adjacent rocks, usually correspond with cols or long depressions. Such relationships are strikingly displayed in Shetland, where several of the voes as well as the long north-south depressions in Mainland correspond with limestone belts, the most marked examples being the valleys that extend from Weisdale Voe and Loch of Strom to Dales Voe.

Lavas and associated volcanic rocks form the highest part of Ben Nevis and much of the rugged scenery in and around Glen Coe, including the Three Sisters. Lavas also cover a wide area between Loch Melfort and Loch Creran extending inland to the Pass of Brander. Here they produce quite different scenery, for they nowhere form mountains, giving rise instead to a seemingly-endless sea of irregular ridges and hollows with innumerable craggy outcrops (Plates XVII and XVIIIB). The Tertiary lavas of Mull, Skye, Morven and Eigg (Fig. 4) produce further variety. Most of them are horizontal or gently inclined, so that the more resistant sheets often form successive steps one above the other on the hill sides, the development of these steps having been greatly facilitated by rapid weathering of the vesicular tops and bottoms of the flows. Especially around the margins of the islands shales and clays appear from beneath the lava beds in many places and, being unable to support the weight of the rocks above, have facilitated the development of landslips and the consequent production of great lava escarpments that reach more than 2000 feet above sea-level in northern Skye. Among other remarkable features developed in the volcanic rocks of the western islands are the precipitous ridge of the

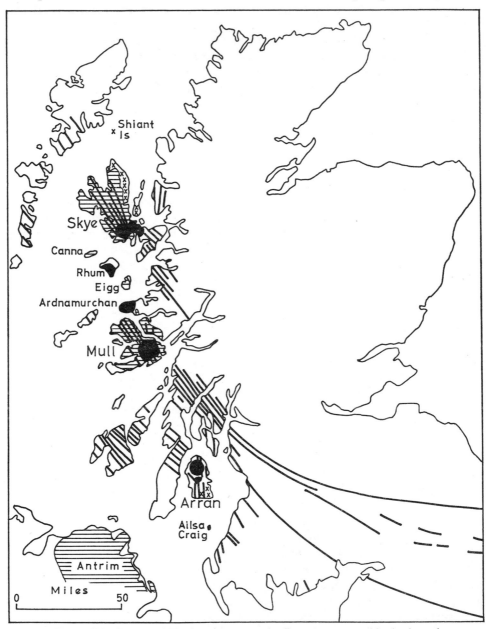

FIG. 4. Distribution of Tertiary igneous rocks. Lavas represented by horizontal shading, central intrusive complexes by solid black, and main areas with sills by crosses. A few of the numerous dykes are also shown. Based partly on J. E. Richey and H. H. Thomas 1930.

Scurr of Eigg, the basalt columns of Fingal's Cave in Staffa, and the great columnar cliff of Eileen Mhaire in the Shiant Islands (Plate IVB).

In Orkney, much of Caithness, and a broad zone fringing the Moray Firth, Old Red sandstones and mudstones form smooth hills or gently-undulating lowlands and plateaux (Plate XVIB). Variety is introduced in Caithness by the coastal cliffs (Plate XXA), while a thick series of sandstones not represented elsewhere in Orkney forms the high ground of Hoy that terminates westwards in the 1100-foot cliff of St John's Head and the 450-foot sea-stack known as the Old Man of Hoy. Among the Old Red rocks the conglomerates form the most distinctive inland features and account for the prominence of hills such as Morven, Smean and Maiden Pap in Caithness, the Ben Griams in Sutherland, and Meall an Tuirc and Cnoc Fyrish in Ross-shire.

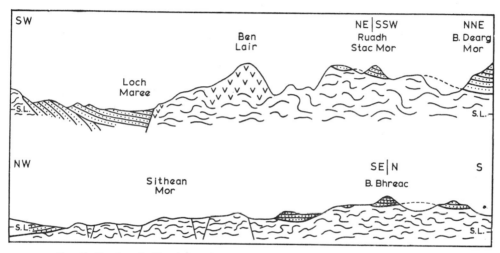

FIG. 5. Sections in Northwest Scotland showing how the present surface of the Lewisian Gneiss is in part an ancient land surface revealed by the removal of Torridon Sandstone. After A. Godard 1965.

Some of the most spectacular scenery in Scotland occurs near the northwest coast in the country west of the Moine Thrust. The ancient complex of the Lewisian Gneiss forms the basement rock and its innumerable lines of weakness have been exploited by erosional agencies (especially glacier ice) to produce a remarkably irregular and barren landscape (Plate VIIIB). The horizontal or gently-dipping beds of Torridon Sandstone that rest unconformably on the gneiss form mountains and ridges that often end in great stepped buttresses and cliffs (Frontispiece and Plate IIIA). In some areas, as in Applecross Forest, the gneiss is concealed and both mountains and low ground are formed of Torridon Sandstone. In other instances, as around Stac Polly and Suilven, the gneiss forms the low ground and the steep sandstone slopes of the mountains rise abruptly above it (Plate IIA). Some of the sandstone mountains, such as Quinag and Cul Mòr, have a tiny outlier of quartzite capping the very summit, while from the summits of others (as mentioned above) the quartzite falls away eastwards in great dip slopes. The removal of the Torridon Sandstone has exposed the ancient land surface developed on the underlying gneiss and, around the margins of the sandstone this land surface, somewhat modified, still survives in places (Fig. 5). Thus at Slioch the nearly horizontal beds of sandstone envelop three prominent hills of gneiss, one of them over 2000 feet high, and it appears that the deep trench of Gleann Tùlacha and Lochan Fada is an ancient feature from which the sand-stone has been cleared out (Peach *et al.* 1913a).

One of the most prominent results of differential erosion has been the production of linear features, and often these impart a marked grain to the land surface. In the Southern Uplands many minor valleys trend in a southwest and northeast direction with the strike of the Ordovician and Silurian rocks (Fig. 6). On a smaller scale glaciation has resulted in parts of the Southern Uplands in the production of parallel ridges and hollows con-trolled by the rock outcrops. This effect is especially clear in the metamorphosed sedi-ments adjacent to the Cairnsmore of Fleet granite as seen in Plate IXA. Linear features related to rock structures may be seen in many parts of the Highlands. They are especially evident in the parallel coasts of peninsulas, bays and islands on the eastern side of lower Loch Linnhe and in northern Kintyre, Knapdale and Jura. Northwesterly-trending lines of weakness have been emphasised in the Lewisian Gneiss of the northwest coast-lands and in Harris and Lewis. The general trend of the whole east coast of the Outer Hebrides is apparently related to a major fault-line beneath the adjacent sea, while the Great Glen fault, in addition to being followed by Loch Linnhe and the glen itself, is parallel with the straight coast between the Beauly Firth and Tarbet Ness and may also have had some influence on the location of the east coast of northern Caithness (Plate IVA). The major faults that trend roughly parallel with the Great Glen fault (Fig. 7)

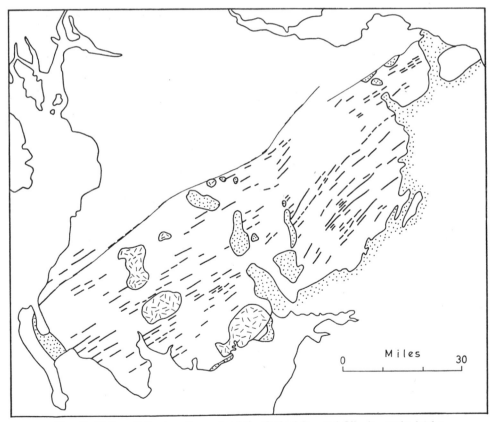

FIG. 6. Valleys following the grain of the Ordovician and Silurian rocks in the
Southern Uplands (together with those along the Southern Upland fault).
Other rocks shaded. After D. L. Linton 1933.

also frequently correspond with major valleys, large lake basins or with important coastal indentations (Chapter 3).

Sufficient has been said to make it clear that in most of Scotland there is a striking correlation between rocks and scenery. It is not clear, however, what particular properties of the rocks – whether joints, grain size, porosity, chemical composition, or other characteristics – have rendered them relatively resistant or weak, for very little research has been devoted to this subject, although unsubstantiated generalisations abound. The problem is complicated by the fact that some of the landforms have in part evolved under considerably warmer climates than prevail at present. In a study of northern Scotland, A. Godard (1965) has observed that, among the granitic rocks, it is the medium-grained ones that form the highest ground. He found that the least permeable granites, which one might expect to form high ground, in fact form relatively low ground. He also found that there is a tendency for the relative relief to be inversely related to the proportion of biotite in the rocks. Godard's conclusions are tentative but at least they indicate the need for further investigation of a neglected topic.

Cover rocks and ancient landforms

As we have seen, the removal of the Torridon Sandstone from the underlying Lewisian Gneiss has resulted locally in the exhumation of an ancient land surface. Exhumation on a much larger scale has taken place, however, as a result of the removal of Old Red and younger rocks. Often this has resulted in the reappearance in modified form of ancient erosional landforms. In other instances the ancient land surfaces were so modified by faulting or warping before exhumation that they now appear as features that are partly structural and partly erosional. The main trends of much of the coastline of Scotland appear to have been determined by the stripping of these cover rocks, and many major and minor features of the land surface reveal the same influence.

On the broadest scale this influence is seen in the relatively low average altitude of the Central Lowlands, surfaced mainly by Old Red and younger rocks, as compared with the Highlands and Southern Uplands on either side. The fault-line scarps that bound the lowlands are usually steep and abrupt, losing their identity only where rocks of similar resistance are juxtaposed. The Solway Firth represents another large area where younger rocks are at a low altitude. On the Scottish side of the firth much of the coast between the mouth of the Nith and Abbey Head closely follows a narrow outcrop of Carboniferous rocks. Farther west most of Loch Ryan, along with the low ground around Stranraer, corresponds with a structural depression occupied by Carboniferous and New Red sediments. Gravity measurements imply that these sediments continue below the waters of Luce Bay, the broad outline of which is probably determined approximately by the extent of these rocks. Whether or not Wigtown Bay exhibits a similar relationship is uncertain, but basins with the same general trend and occupied by Carboniferous or New Red rocks (or both) largely determine the courses of the rivers Nith and Annan (Fig. 6). They include the Sanquhar, Thornhill and Dumfries basins crossed successively by the Nith; the Lochmaben basin; and, most impressive of all, the narrow valley of the upper Annan beginning abruptly at the Devil's Beef Tub. In much of the Tweed basin there is again a general correspondence between low ground and the sedimentary cover rocks (Old Red and Carboniferous) except southwards where the resistant members of the Carboniferous strata increase in thickness and form much of the hill country along the southeastern border of Roxburghshire. In the Lammermuirs Lauderdale appears

Fig. 7. Rock outcrops of the Highland margins. Main outcrops of Old Red
Sandstone shown by dots and small outliers by crosses; contemporaneous
volcanic rocks shown by horizontal shading. Solid black areas represent
Permian and Mesozoic strata and vertical shading Tertiary igneous rocks.
Some major faults are also shown.

to be an ancient valley from which the Old Red strata have not yet been completely removed.

The Old Red sediments are widely preserved around the eastern and northern margins of the Highlands and the various scattered outliers of these rocks, some of them as much as twenty miles distant from the main outcrops, imply that formerly they were much more extensive (Fig. 7). As the Old Red rocks were removed a surface of considerable relief was revealed, part of it representing the ancient land surfaces upon which the Old Red accumulated and part of it a result of later faulting. At many places modified remains of this exhumed surface can be identified, and those adjacent to and north of the Great Glen have been mapped in detail by A. Godard (1965). In southern Caithness the quartzite ridge of Scaraben and adjacent lesser quartzite hills are ancient features with patches of Old Red breccia representing cemented exhumed screes clinging to their slopes. The Findhorn valley for several miles above Drynachan Lodge partly follows a strip of Old Red let down between parallel faults. Southwest of Elgin the valleys of the River Lossie and the Black Burn in part correspond with pre-Old Red valleys. A small patch of Old Red conglomerate lies on the floor of the Fiddich valley near Dufftown, another rests on the floor of one of the Isla headstreams, and a third occurs in the bottom of Glen Tervie south of Ben Rinnes (Hinxman *et al.* 1902). A small patch of Old Red rocks has been found near the head of the Water of Feugh valley (Bremner 1942) and a

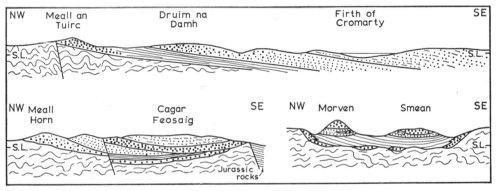

FIG. 8. Sections showing the Old Red conglomerates (large dots), sandstones (small dots) and mudstones resting unconformably on the folded and metamorphosed Highland rocks. Horizontal scale approximately half an inch to a mile. After B. N. Peach *et al.* 1912, C. B. Crampton *et al.* 1914 and H. H. Read *et al.* 1925.

much larger down-faulted outlier corresponds with the deep valley that leads from the Don past Rhynie towards Huntly. Some of these remnants are very small indeed (in some instances only a few hundred yards across) and this leads one to suspect that a considerable number of other valleys have an ancient origin that cannot be demonstrated owing to the complete removal of these rocks.

A narrow strip of Old Red sediments adheres to the west coast of Kintyre for several miles and strongly suggests that the trend of at least part of this coast is related to the present or former distribution of these rocks. More important, however, in determining the trends of considerable parts of the mainland coast north of the Highland fault is the distribution of New Red, Jurassic and Cretaceous sediments. Tiny patches of Jurassic strata follow part of the east coast of the Black Isle and its continuation beyond the entrance to the Cromarty Firth, sometimes appearing only in near-shore skerries (Fig.

7). On the east coast of Sutherland a much longer, but nevertheless narrow, strip of Jurassic (with some Triassic) rocks, bounded inland by a fault, clings to the coast. Such occurrences strongly suggest that the main outlines of these coasts have been determined by the partial or complete stripping of these weak rocks from the relatively resistant rocks beneath. This suggestion is supported by the glacial evidence, for ice-transported blocks of Jurassic, as well as Cretaceous, rocks are found over a wide area of Caithness and the Orkneys and in a long coastal belt on the southern side of the Moray Firth (Chapter 4). This wide distribution, along with the abundance, variety and size of the transported materials, indicates that a large area of Mesozoic sediments (probably the fullest sequence in the Scottish area) underlies the Moray Firth, and it seems very probable that erosion of these rocks from the underlying resistant rocks has resulted in the main coastal trends of this large embayment. The glacial evidence along the east coast of Aberdeenshire and Kincardineshire is less adequate, for here the ice usually moved seawards. However, at some places the ice moved onto the land after crossing the present sea area and here the glacial debris includes various Jurassic and Cretaceous rocks. This suggests that here also these rocks are present beneath the sea-bed and, perhaps along with Old Red sediments, may have helped to determine the coastal outline.

On the west side of Scotland the outcrops of Mesozoic rocks are small but numerous on the mainland coast and in the islands between Mull and the entrance to Loch Broom (Fig. 7). They clearly represent the remains of strata that were once much more wide-spread. They are exposed in the west of Skye only a dozen miles from the Outer Hebrides and in the Shiant Islands they approach within five miles, yet they have not been found in the outer islands themselves. This suggests strongly that the east coast of the outer islands, and the steep submarine slope that follows it, to a considerable extent represent in their existence today the result of the removal from the Lewisian Gneiss of the relatively weak Mesozoic rocks (whose distribution in turn may be related to a submarine fault). On the opposing mainland coast the corresponding landform is represented by the steep western face of the Highlands extending for 130 miles southwards from the vicinity of Cape Wrath. Although now greatly dissected by fjords and often broken up in the north into isolated mountains, this feature when reconstructed across the numerous but narrow gaps that breach it, appears as the most prominent mountain wall in the British Isles with an abrupt, sometimes precipitous, ascent from the coast or from narrow coastal lowlands or hill country to altitudes of 2000 to 3000 feet above sea-level. At many places outcrops of Mesozoic strata may be seen at or near the base of this feature. In Morven and Ardnamurchan the Mesozoic rocks appear from beneath the Tertiary lavas and related igneous rocks. In the Broadford area of Skye they lie at the foot of the mountainous ground that reaches 2400 feet in the easternmost part of the island. Farther north, along the coast of the mainland, as far as the entrance to Loch Broom, a dozen small patches of these rocks, some resting in simple unconformity on the rocks beneath and others affected by faulting, are scattered over the low ground in front of the mountain wall. Still farther north Enard Bay and Eddrachillis Bay may perhaps owe their abnormal depths to the relative ease with which Mesozoic rocks have been removed (p. 52). This evidence suggests that the mountain wall in its main outlines is an ancient feature ex-humed from beneath a cover of Mesozoic rocks. Whether the trend of the feature was determined originally in part by faulting or whether it is in ancient origin essentially an erosional feature developed on the eastern margin of a Mesozoic tectonic downwarp is uncertain. It does appear, however, that the Mesozoic sediments were adequate to bury the scarp, for in places they are still thousands of feet thick where preserved beneath the

Tertiary lavas. One may infer further that much of the erosion of the Mesozoic rocks has taken place since the lavas were ejected, for to argue otherwise would be to attribute to a remarkable coincidence the fact that they are preserved extensively on land only where protected by the Tertiary igneous rocks.

On the eastern side of the Northern Highlands the Mesozoic rocks are banked against a steep slope in the Black Isle, and in eastern Sutherland they are everywhere backed by a fault-controlled slope that rises rapidly to altitudes of 1200 to 2000 feet above sea-level. It seems, therefore, that we may regard the Scottish mainland north of the Great Glen as a block whose main outlines and steep marginal slopes on east and west were established in Mesozoic times and which now, through Tertiary uplift and erosion, have been exhumed and modified. The area between the northern Highlands and the Outer Hebrides represents a tectonic depression established and developed in Mesozoic times* and now in broad outline revealed by Tertiary erosion. Within this depression the only high ground is associated with the Tertiary igneous rocks.

It has been frequently maintained that Tertiary igneous activity was associated with the development of a great rift valley along the western side of Scotland and it has been suggested that this rift continues southwards through the western part of the Irish Sea to pass between Wales and Ireland. As T. N. George (1966) has pointed out, however, the geological evidence does not support the concept of a simple rift. The fault or faults required to define the eastern margin of the supposed rift are not known to exist; parts of the igneous province were greatly depressed by faulting and warping but other parts were uplifted by thousands of feet; and Arran and Ailsa Craig are separated from the other centres of Scottish Tertiary igneous activity by the Highland outposts of Islay, Jura and Kintyre. Rather does it appear that in its main area of occurrence – in Mull, Morven, Ardnamurchan, Skye and adjacent smaller islands – Tertiary igneous activity took advantage of the tectonic feature already developed in Mesozoic times. Parts of this feature were greatly modified by faulting and warping that preceded, accompanied and followed the outpourings of lava (in places thousands of feet thick) and the intrusion of thick sills and of great masses of granite and gabbro. Many of the present landforms within the trough reveal the influence of these structures, as witness the northwesterly-trending valleys and coastlines of northern Mull and western Skye. The boundaries of the trough do not appear to have been seriously modified by this activity, however, and in their exhumed form today still exist as long linear sub-parallel features.

Erosion surfaces

Although we have emphasised the importance in the present land surface of ancient features exhumed through differential erosion, this is not intended to imply that erosion during Tertiary times has been relatively unimportant. On the contrary, this exhumation is in itself a demonstration of the importance of Tertiary erosion, while the destruction wrought on the early Tertiary igneous rocks provides further impressive proof (p. 21).

A major consequence of this erosion has been the production (and dissection) of the plateaux and benches that are such a prominent feature of wide areas of Scotland. In the west, owing to high precipitation (including its effects through glaciation), the plateaux are often severely dissected, although a general accordance of level of peaks and ridges is apparent in the view from most high points (Plate VIB). In the east the

* Old Red sediments have not been found in this large area and Carboniferous ones are known only in the extreme south at Inninmore Bay in the Sound of Mull.

plateaux are usually very prominent, and nowhere more so than in the eastern Grampians, of which it has often been said that there is far more flattish ground on the hill tops than on the valley floors (Plate IIIB). It has long been recognised that plateaux and benches at different altitudes can be identified in many parts of Scotland and it is generally agreed that these relate, in downward sequence, to successive periods of relatively stable base-level that alternated with periods when uplift prevailed. Beyond this point, however, agreement ends and current (and past) views tend to fall into two main categories. On the one hand, some authors emphasise the importance of marine erosion in the production of the various erosional levels. They state or imply that the erosion surfaces are essentially horizontal and assign to them small altitudinal ranges or even specific altitudes. Authors of the other group, however, emphasise the subaerial origin of erosion surfaces, often assign a considerable range of altitude to individual surfaces, and favour (or do not discount) the view that they have been warped. Although these two interpretations as expressed in their extreme forms are completely at variance with one another, it appears that elements of each are necessary to account for the erosion surfaces (and original drainage system) of Scotland.

The view that marine planation has been an important agent in fashioning the land surface of Scotland was popular more than a hundred years ago, but current views stem mainly from the work of S. E. Hollingworth (1938). In a cartographic study of various areas of western Britain Hollingworth suggested that in Southwest Scotland erosion surfaces of marine origin occur at 2600-2700, 1070, 730-800, 560 and 400 feet. In a more detailed study W. G. Jardine (1959) identified surfaces in Southwest Scotland at 2600-2800, 1900-2000, 1700-1800, 1350-1400, 1000-1100, 750-850, 600-700, 450-500 and 200 feet. Although apparently sympathetic with a marine explanation, he refrained from committing himself. T. N. George (1955) favoured Hollingworth's views in a study of river evolution in the ground drained by the Nith, Annan and upper Clyde and illustrated horizontal surfaces at 2650, 2300, 1670, 1070 and 600 feet. More recently George (1965, 1966) has argued strongly in favour of the marine origin of erosion surfaces. Although mentioning the possibility of warping, he nevertheless uses projected profiles to suggest the existence of horizontal surfaces over a wide area including Harris, Skye, Mull, Jura and adjacent parts of the western mainland. In this area the three main surfaces recognised are at around 3200, 2400 and 1600 feet and are considered to have been cut by the sea. George suggests that here and elsewhere in Scotland a major submergence took place in mid-Tertiary times and drowned a surface of varied relief. Thus he writes (1965) that by mid-Tertiary times the Central Lowlands are 'likely to have been significantly developed by subaerial erosion. Later submergence, when the whole of Scotland was drowned, and the pulsed uplift that followed . . .' are reflected in the successively lower erosion surfaces.

However much one may agree with the view that marine erosion has played an important part in the Tertiary evolution of Scotland, one must recognise that the interpretation outlined above encounters certain difficulties. Thus it introduces into Scottish Tertiary history a great submergence for which there is no geological evidence. This absence of evidence is particularly difficult to explain in view of the claim that considerable dissection preceded submergence, for one would expect to find at least some valleys now in course of exhumation from Tertiary marine deposits. Another weakness is the emphasis on horizontal erosion surfaces. While it is true that a surface whose individual small remnants maintain horizontality over a large area is difficult to explain except by marine erosion, it does not follow that a surface of variable altitude is not of marine origin. In

FIG. 9. Part of H. Fleet's (1938) map of erosion surfaces in the Grampians. 'Grampian Summits' shown by solid black, 'Grampian Main Surface' by close vertical shading, 'Grampian Lower Surface' by wider shading and 'Grampian Valley Benches' by dots. Triangles represent prominent residual hills.

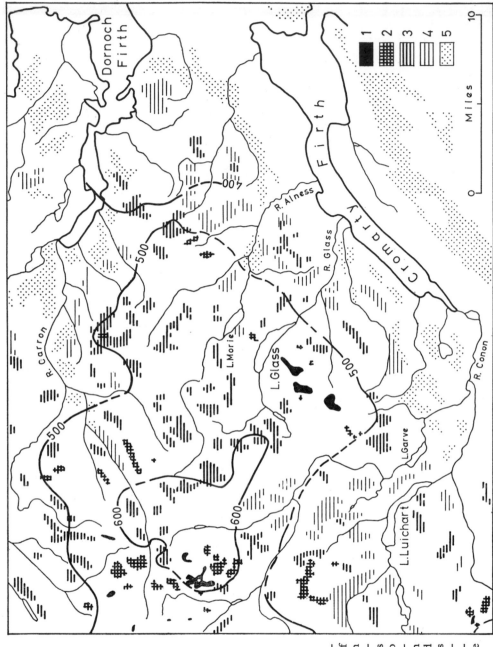

Fig. 10. Part of A. Goddard's (1965) map of erosion surfaces in the Northern Highlands. The various types of shading, 1 to 5, represent successively lower erosion surfaces. Generalised contours in metres reveal the considerable variations in altitude of one of these surfaces (no. 3).

fact it is hard to believe that Scotland, with its long history of warping and faulting (which, as the disruption of the Tertiary igneous rocks shows, certainly continued far into the Tertiary), has in the last phase of its history been uplifted through thousands of feet without significant distortion.

A different type of interpretation, involving the integration of summits, plateaux and benches into surfaces with a considerable range of altitude, has been preferred by various writers. A. Geikie (1901) laid great stress on the 'table-land' of the Highlands and Southern Uplands. B. N. Peach and J. Horne in numerous publications up to 1930 recognised a High Plateau at 2000 to 3000 feet with residuals such as the Cairngorms and Ben Nevis rising above it, and an Intermediate Plateau with an upper limit at about 1000 feet. For a large area of the Grampians these conclusions were supported and amplified by H. Fleet (1938). He recognised extensive erosion surfaces at 2400-3100 feet (Grampian Main Surface) and 1500-2100 feet (Grampian Lower Surface), along with a more restricted one (Grampian Valley Benches) at 750-1000 feet (Fig. 9). Above the Grampian Main Surface rise mountains and mountain groups such as the Cairngorms, Lochnagar, Ben Alder and Ben Lawers. Erosion surfaces mapped by J. M. Soons (1958) in the Ochils at 1500-1900 and 750-1000 feet appear to accord with two of Fleet's surfaces. In a brief description of erosion surfaces in Southeast Scotland A. G. Ogilvie (1930) suggested the existence of features at 1500-2000, 500-1000 and 100-500 feet.

By far the most detailed work on erosion surfaces in Scotland has been carried out by A. Godard (1965) as part of a study of the northern mainland and many islands. He recognises surfaces at altitudes of about 2300-3100, 2000-2300, 1300-2000, 600-1000 and 300-600 feet. Some of these altitudes are similar to those assigned by Fleet to surfaces in the Grampians, and the similarity becomes more apparent when it is pointed out that the surface identified at 2000-2300 feet is a poorly developed feature. It is somewhat misleading, however, to summarise Godard's detailed work by means of overall altitudinal ranges (thus giving the impression of merging erosion surfaces), for in any limited area the height range of a particular erosion surface is much less than its full range in northern Scotland as a whole. In other words, each surface varies considerably in altitude, a variation that is attributed to original form, subsequent modification and warping (Fig. 10).

The results of such work, though inevitably based in part on subjective assessments, are nevertheless much more convincing than reconstructions of fragments of the present land surface into a succession of horizontal or near-horizontal steps. The view that the erosion surfaces are mainly of subaerial origin also carries conviction. On the other hand, it must not be forgotten that the presence of a series of extensive subaerial surfaces implies the existence (or former existence) of a correlative series of marine surfaces. It may also be observed that the subaerial surfaces provide only a part of the story of Tertiary landscape evolution, for it is still necessary to invoke marine submergence to account for the initiation of the drainage system.

One view that is widely held about erosion surfaces (by exponents of both the subaerial and marine interpretations) is that the remnants that now remain have survived with relatively little modification since the time they were first formed in relation to higher base-levels. While this may often be true of the very lowest features (such as the feature shown in Plate XXA), it becomes increasingly improbable as one ascends to higher altitudes. As Hutton pointed out long ago (in the words that open this chapter) the whole land surface is exposed to constant attack by the elements. On many mountains recent destruction is recorded by the great quantities of frost-shattered rock in course of movement down their slopes (Plates XIV and XVIA). This movement is slow, yet when we remember that the highest parts of Scotland have been exposed to the elements for tens of millions of years, during a great part of which time they have probably been subjected to the active chemical weathering of a much warmer climate, it becomes impossible to accept that parts of the original high-level erosion surfaces still survive. This conclusion also follows from the description earlier in this chapter of some of the results of differential erosion. The term 'differential erosion' does not mean (as is often unintentionally implied) that weak-rock lowlands and valleys have been deeply excavated while erosion surfaces on adjacent resistant rocks have survived with little modification. Rather does it mean that the land surface as a whole has been affected in proportion to the relative resistance of the rocks of which it is composed. Thus the excavation of the Old Red sandstone belt that borders the Highlands (from Strathmore to Loch Lomond) to a level some 3000 feet below the highest summits of metamorphosed grit that now overlook it, does not mean that 3000 feet of sandstone have been eroded away while the highest parts of the grit country have remained at their original altitude. Instead it merely shows that the thickness of sandstone removed to produce the lowland is 3000 feet more than the thickness of grit removed from the summits. For example, 1000 feet of grit may have gone while 4000 feet of sandstone have been removed.

An important aspect of erosion surface development that has been almost neglected in Scotland (and in the rest of the British Isles) is the process of slope retreat unaided by active undercutting by rivers or the sea (Sissons 1960a). The results of this process are evident in upland basins such as those of Loch Shin, Rannoch Moor or Loch Doon, and in many lowlands such as Strathmore or the Howe of Fife. To maintain that these areas have been excavated by wandering rivers (or by glacier ice) would present insuperable difficulties. Equally one cannot argue that the valleys of Scotland have been excavated by the rivers that occupy them. To do so would be to require the rivers to have wandered over large areas when at high levels and to have become more and more restricted in their wanderings as incision progressed, to finish on the narrow (and, preglacially, even narrower) valley floors many of them occupy. The erosion actually carried out by rivers is extremely small and is comparable with the slot produced by a saw cutting through a large block of wood. The rest of the material (although carried away by the river) is removed from the valley slopes by soil-creep, land-slipping, rill-wash, gullying and related processes, which together cause the slopes to retreat away from the river itself. The higher slopes overlooking many of the larger valleys in the Highlands and Southern Uplands are set back several miles from the rivers. The descent to the valley floors often occurs as a series of steps separated by steeper slopes, the steps being some of the erosion surfaces mapped by various workers (e.g. Fig. 10) and recording in their *initiation* periods of relative stability during the intermittent uplift of Scotland. In their present form, however, they demonstrate the importance of slope retreat in valley widening.

Following the views of W. Penck and L. C. King, these stepped valley slopes enable us to envisage a continuously-evolving land surface. With each major period of Tertiary uplift new steep slopes were initiated by river incision. During each period of relative stability retreat of these slopes resulted in the production of gentle slopes (erosion surfaces) between their base and the river that had initiated them. With further uplift both erosion surfaces and the slopes behind became separated from the rivers by new steep slopes, but continued to evolve as before. Thus each erosion surface has tended to extend at the expense of the one above it and to be encroached upon by the one below it. The same process may be envisaged as applying to marine features cut into the margins of the intermittently-rising land mass, with the consequence that, except at low levels, the original marine platforms and cliffs have now been replaced through slope retreat by subaerial features. Where marked contrasts in rock resistance exist, successive waves of slope retreat have moved relatively rapidly over weak rock outcrops but more slowly where they have encountered resistant rocks, with the consequence that intervening erosion surfaces have been extinguished and the high steep slopes that bound weak rock lowlands have come into being. It may also be observed that we cannot assume automatically that the highest erosion surfaces that exist today are the highest that ever existed in Tertiary times, for one or more high surfaces may have been completely destroyed by the encroachment of slopes of later origin. This appears to have happened at least in the central Grampians (p. 28) and much of the high ground of Scotland generally is probably well below its early Tertiary level.

The clearest evidence of great erosion in Tertiary times in at least part of Scotland is provided by the intrusive and extrusive rocks shown by potassium-argon dating to be some 55 to 60 million years old. The way in which the lavas rest on the folded, faulted and subsequently worn down Cretaceous and earlier rocks shows that considerable erosion took place in early Tertiary times before the lavas were ejected (George 1966).

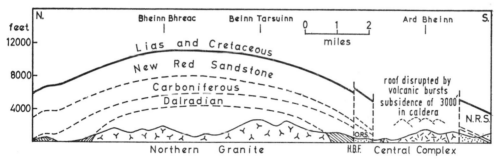

FIG. 11. Diagrammatic and reconstructed section across Arran suggesting the great thickness of rock removed by Tertiary erosion. Since uplift and erosion were doubtless contemporaneous, it should not be assumed that the domed surface existed in this simple form as a landscape feature. After T. N. George 1966.

Later erosion is demonstrated by the truncation of the dipping lava beds and especially by the granites intruded deep beneath a former ground surface and now themselves exposed and deeply dissected. In some areas such as northern Arran or Rhum the thickness of rock removed from above the level of the present highest summits certainly amounts to thousands of feet (Fig. 11). Proof of this severe erosion is limited to the areas of Tertiary igneous activity where it may have been excessive in ground uplifted relative to its immediate surroundings. Yet it would be surprising if considerable erosion, resulting in the complete destruction of early Tertiary land surfaces, has not taken place elsewhere in Scotland. One other piece of related evidence is provided by the northwest-southeast mid-Tertiary dykes, some of which were injected, according to potassium-argon dating, about thirty million years ago. Since these dykes cross hill and valley alike, rising in the Southern Uplands to 2000 feet above sea-level, it is clear that the valleys below this altitude (at least where dykes are present) had not been excavated when the dykes were injected. In fact it seems probable, in view of the absence of associated lava flows, that the ground surface was considerably above its present level at that time.

Tertiary deposits

Deposits of Tertiary or possible Tertiary age in Scotland are of very limited extent. In the Northeast patches of gravel composed of rounded quartzite pebbles and flints occur at altitudes of 300 to 400 feet above sea-level inland from Buchan Ness and near Fyvie and Turriff. They are generally thought to be of Pliocene age and are said to rest in places on a rock platform, perhaps of marine origin (Flett and Read 1921). Rocks that are deeply weathered have been observed at a large number of scattered localities in the Northeast, although it is not known if the weathering took place in interglacial or preglacial times. Granite in Aberdeen has been seen to be weathered through a thickness of 30 feet, and even at 40 feet patches of decomposed granite have been observed. On the other hand overlying glacial till was found to contain numerous undecayed stones, thus implying that the deep weathering pre-dates at least one period when the area was ice-covered (Phemister and Simpson 1949, Fitzpatrick 1963).

That a far warmer climate than the present one prevailed in early Tertiary times is indicated by the deep soil horizons intercalated with some of the Tertiary lava beds, for their highly aluminous character suggests a lateritic origin under sub-tropical conditions. The associated plant remains, which include magnolias and proteas, further emphasise the difference from today. For much of the rest of the Tertiary direct evidence of Scotland's climate is lacking, but analogy with the Continent suggests that conditions were distinctly warmer than at present. For the late Tertiary suggestive evidence is provided by Godard. At many points in Northwest Scotland he has discovered ancient red soils preserved on his lowest erosion surface in fissures in the Cambrian Limestone. As a result of X-ray analysis he finds these soils to be comparable with the Mediterranean *terra rossa*, which are mainly relict soils related to a wetter and slightly warmer climate than the Mediterranean area experiences now. It is therefore suggested that when the lowest erosion surface was formed the climate of Scotland was still considerably warmer than it is today and, from comparison with the Continent, Godard favours a mid-Pliocene age for this surface. He also suggests that uplift and dissection of the surface were accompanied by a change to cool wet conditions and describes deposits associated with this phase that occasionally exceed 30 feet in thickness.

Origin of the drainage system

While a major result of Tertiary erosion has been the development of valleys along belts of relatively weak rock, there are nevertheless many valleys whose origin cannot thus be explained. The latter are often markedly discordant to known geological structures and it has long been accepted that the streams that occupy them are the direct descendants of the streams that first flowed on an early land surface. Since, despite the present complexities of relief, these streams in many parts of the country form simple patterns (Fig. 12), it is also accepted that they have been initiated at or above the present levels of the local summits and that the surface on which they developed was of relatively simple form. It is now also generally held that such a surface is most easily provided by marine agency. Beyond this point, however, present views diverge.

Attempts to explain the initiation of the drainage of Scotland (or of part of it) fall into three main categories. H. Mackinder (1902) believed that the original drainage of the southern half of the country consisted mainly of southeastward-directed streams that flowed from the Grampians across the site of the Central Lowlands (not then excavated) to the Southern Uplands. Here, he suggested, some of the original streams curved round

PLATE III. A. Torridon Sandstone of Sàil Ghorm rising above lower
ground formed of Lewisian Gneiss. B. Dissected plateau of the Cairngorms. *Photographs by Aerofilms.*

PLATE IV. A. The Great Glen. *Photograph by Aerofilms*. B. Cliff of columnar Tertiary basalt, Shiant Is. *Photograph by Tom Weir*.

towards the east, the Nith perhaps being continued by the Tyne and a river that followed the line of Loch Goil, and the Gare Loch perhaps being continued by the Tweed. This seems to imply reversal of much of the Clyde, a view that was advocated by J. W. Gregory (1915), who continued the reversed Clyde through the Biggar gap to join the Tweed. Various other writers favoured Mackinder's interpretation, among them B. N. Peach and J. Horne (1930) and F. Mort (1918), the latter envisaging a system of initial rivers flowing southeastwards across Kintyre, the Firth of Clyde, the western Southern Uplands and the Solway Firth. These interpretations are no longer current, for they fail to explain the many discordant streams that do not flow southeastwards (Linton 1933). Mackinder's view is also now regarded as unacceptable since he required the streams to have been initiated on a surface of low relief produced by subaerial erosion. As A. Bremner (1942) pointed out, the uplift and tilting of a subaerial surface would not produce a new drainage system but would cause the rivers that already existed to incise their courses.

A second group of interpretations has laid particular emphasis on eastward-flowing discordant streams. In an early attempt H. M. Cadell (1886) carried the initial headstreams of the Forth across the present site of Loch Lomond. Much later Bremner (1942) argued that the earliest streams of a large part of Scotland flowed eastwards, their sources lying close to the present west coast of the mainland or even farther west. Following a view long favoured for much of England and Wales, he suggested that the streams were initiated on a Cretaceous cover as it emerged from beneath the sea. During emergence faulting and warping took place, producing such features as the Minch, Moray Firth, North Channel and Irish Sea and causing the streams to depart from the simple eastward pattern in some areas. This view was in part anticipated and has since been modified and elaborated by D. L. Linton (e.g. 1933, 1940, 1951a). He has concluded that the original drainage of most of the Grampians and of much of Scotland farther south was dominated by eastward-flowing streams, now partly dismembered and represented by the eastward-directed parts of such streams as the Isla–Deveron, Avon–Don, Feshie–Geldie–Dee, Tummel–South Esk, Lyon–Tay, Bran, Lochay–Almond, Earn, Devon–Leven, Forth, Tweed and Solway–Tyne. In some areas, and especially in southern Scotland, these original eastward-flowing streams are considered to have been trunk streams and to have received tributaries from one or both sides. Linton has suggested that the initial streams may have commenced to flow on a cover of chalk, which in turn rested on an almost plane surface cut across the varied rocks beneath. He has sought to reconstruct this old surface on the assumption that the most easterly high points of the present land surface approximate to it. Thus he represents the base of the chalk as sloping towards the east or north of east over the whole of eastern Scotland descending, for example, from around 4000 feet in the Caingorms to 1500 feet in northeastern Aberdeenshire, and from 3500 feet in the central Southern Uplands to 2700 feet in The Cheviot. In the west, however, it is suggested that the Tertiary volcanic activity was associated with the development of a great rift valley.

In certain respects this attractive hypothesis needs to be modified. As we have already seen (p. 15), the geological evidence shows that a simple rift valley did not develop in western Scotland in Tertiary times, although faulting and warping were very important. In the Southern Uplands the discordant streams show far more relation to the present distribution of high ground than to an eastward-tilted surface and, of the many discordant streams, only a part of one (the Tweed) flows eastwards. In the Grampians some of the most important discordant streams do flow eastwards but others, equally discordant, flow in different directions, the most notable being the group directed southeastwards to Strathmore (Fig. 12). As Linton (1951a) has pointed out, the pattern of discordant streams draining to the Moray Firth is 'markedly centripetal' and 'strikingly divergent' from any streams that could have developed on his postulated initial chalk surface. A partial explanation of this anomaly is provided by the glacial evidence (p. 81), which shows that chalk still exists today on the floor of the Moray Firth. This is very significant, for it means that a former chalk cover is not to be envisaged as sloping regularly in one main direction but as being more closely related to the flanks of the basin-like depression whose lower parts now form the Moray Firth.

The difficulties encountered in attempting to fit the drainage of Scotland (and of other parts of Britain) into an essentially-unidirectional initial pattern have led to a third type of interpretation, first proposed by S. E. Hollingworth (1938) and subsequently elaborated by T. N. George (1955, 1965). According to this view a major submergence in mid-Tertiary times resulted in the drowning of a land surface of varied relief. During subsequent intermittent emergence marine erosion surfaces were cut and on these, as they were exposed at successively-lower levels, a new drainage system was initiated. One advantage of this interpretation is that it can readily explain the varied directions of flow of discordant streams. Another is that it can account for the simple fact that most discordant streams flow away from areas of high ground. On the other hand, the interpretation has been marred by frequent references to essentially-horizontal erosion surfaces and by the introduction of an unsubstantiated submergence in mid-Tertiary times. Furthermore, since this submergence is considered to have drowned a land surface already considerably dissected, one either has to return to the long-abandoned views of last century and invoke improbably-extensive marine planation of resistant rocks in order to eliminate this varied relief, or one has to accept that the rivers developed during later-Tertiary emergence would not constitute an entirely new system but would often utilise the valleys already fashioned before submergence.

While it has been necessary to indicate certain weaknesses in the three interpretations that have been put forward to account for the initial drainage of Scotland, it is certainly not intended to suggest that these interpretations should be totally rejected. The last two in particular have contributed greatly towards our understanding of the Tertiary evolution of the country and it appears that, if we omit from each the unsatisfactory aspects mentioned above, they may be combined into a single, more satisfactory interpretation.

A striking feature of the present drainage of Scotland is that the divide between the streams flowing to the North Sea on the one hand and to the western seas on the other is, except for local modifications by river capture and glaciation, a simple linear feature that usually coincides closely with the line of highest ground. This fact has been generally ignored in reconstructions of the original drainage of the country. Yet it seems probable that the present watershed is likely to accord approximately with the line of the original watershed, for the latter must have had an original altitudinal advantage and it would tend to be the last part of the land surface to be lowered by waves of slope retreat initiated by coastal cliffing or intermittent river incision.

The location of the initial watershed is suggested in Fig. 12, where it has been drawn to separate different systems of discordant drainage. In the Northern Highlands it is never far from the present drainage divide or from the line of highest ground, the most important discrepancies being where severe glacial erosion has occurred (Chapter 3 and Fig. 13). This initial watershed separates discordant streams draining to the Moray

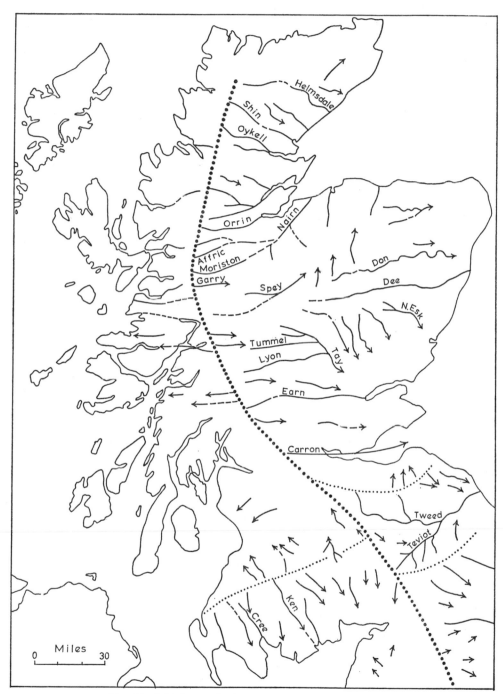

FIG. 12. Initial watersheds and initial drainage of Scotland.

Firth from those draining to the west coast. The latter group is poorly represented in the Northwest, however, owing to the development of structure-guided valleys. In the Grampians the initial watershed passes through the Ben Nevis area. From its vicinity several important discordant streams flow eastwards and with them has been included a reversed River Leven.* A few discordant streams draining westwards from this water-shed are shown in Fig. 12 and it may well be that others flowing southwestwards formed part of the original drainage but cannot now be identified since they accord with the grain of the rocks. In the Central Lowlands differential erosion and glaciation have resulted in the destruction of most of the initial drainage system, but a few discordant elements survive, such as the Carron continued by the Firth of Forth and the upper Devon (per-haps continued by the Leven). In view of the extremely effective differential erosion in the Lowlands, it appears very significant that the Carboniferous sediments in the vicinity of the border of Lanarkshire with West Lothian and Midlothian should correspond with a broad area of quite high ground, considerable parts of which exceed 800 feet. Especially noticeable is the fact that a large part of this high ground is formed of Coal Measures, which elsewhere in the Central Lowlands are associated with low or very low ground. The reason for this apparent anomaly may well be that in the past, as now, this tract has formed the watershed between drainage to the east and west coasts.

If this proposed initial watershed is continued into the Southern Uplands it passes through the Tweedsmuir Hills and close to the belt of high ground on the border of Dumfriesshire with Roxburghshire. As can be seen in Fig. 12, it separates quite different systems of discordant streams. The fact that Merrick in the western Southern Uplands, Broad Law in the centre, and The Cheviot just over the Border in the east are of similar altitude (2764, 2754 and 2676 feet respectively) does not mean that the original surface of southern Scotland was approximately horizontal, for to suggest this is to ignore the consequences of differential erosion. While Merrick is formed of metamorphic rocks and The Cheviot of granite, Broad Law is composed of much weaker sedimentary rocks. The consequence of such rock differences is seen in the westernmost part of the Southern Uplands, where the highest point of the plateau developed on the sedimentary rocks stands 900 feet below the highest point of the Merrick range. We may therefore infer that the Tweedsmuir Hills (with Broad Law as their highest point) were originally far higher relative to Merrick and The Cheviot. Despite differential erosion they still constitute the largest area of high ground in southern Scotland and it is difficult to avoid the conclusion that they lie on the line of the primary watershed.

The watershed we have now identified as running through the length of the Scottish mainland is of such simple form that it seems to be adequately explicable only as the axis of an upwarp. Its continuation as the well-known Pennine axis of uplift accords with this interpretation. We may therefore imagine that when Scotland began to emerge from beneath the sea it was the land in the vicinity of this line that appeared first and that from this line the earliest Highland rivers began to flow eastwards and westwards. Emergence need not, of course, have taken place at one time along the whole of the line. Furthermore, it appears that warping in other directions also occurred. The way in which the dis-cordant streams of the western half of the Southern Uplands flow on the one hand to the Solway and on the other towards the Central Lowlands suggests the location of one axis

---

* The gradient of most of the floor of the Leven valley is so slight that it has permitted the con-struction of the eight-mile-long Blackwater Reservoir. The rapid descent of a thousand feet from this gently-sloping valley floor to Kinlochleven is clearly a relatively recent development in the history of the drainage and strongly suggests that formerly the Leven flowed eastwards to be continued by the Tummel.

of warping. The divide separating the two systems of streams is a simple linear feature, the only significant departure (apart from relatively recent modifications such as are associated with the Nith (p. 42)) being some of the Clyde headstreams, which commence a few miles south of the line (Fig. 12). It may also be assumed that accentuation of the ancient North Sea downwarp has continued during Tertiary time (it is known to be still in progress at least in the southern part of this sea). This appears not to have been a simple eastward tilting, however, for the presence of chalk and earlier Mesozoic sediments beneath the Moray Firth suggests that downwarping in and towards this area has taken place. More important than these movements, however, are the major dislocations that occurred in parts of the west of Scotland in association with Tertiary igneous activity.

Two aspects of the Tertiary lavas appear particularly significant in the present context. Firstly, their base, although extremely variable, lies far below the Highland summits to the east. Secondly, the presence of lake and swamp sediments between some of the lava beds, the absence of intercalated marine sediments, and the evidence of weathering of some lava flows before later flows covered them, all show that the lavas were poured out over a land surface. This evidence may be interpreted in two ways. On the one hand, we may assume that when the lavas began to be extruded, they flowed out over a land surface situated then, as now, far below the Highland summits. This would mean that already in early Tertiary times the mainland of Scotland (or at least a large part of it) occupied in relation to sea-level very roughly the position it now occupies. Such an interpretation is untenable, however, for the mid-Tertiary dykes show that much of the dissection of Scotland has taken place in the later Tertiary. Furthermore, the deep and relatively narrow valleys that dissect the uplands, although often greatly altered by glaciers, nevertheless emphasise the importance of late Tertiary uplift and dissection. One must therefore adopt the alternative view that the land surface over which the lavas flowed stood, at the time they began to be extruded, at a much higher level relative to Ordnance Datum than it does now, perhaps standing as high as the present Highland summits although in a lowland of the time. The present position of the lavas is therefore a result of major earth-movements not, however, through the formation of a simple rift valley (p. 15), but by continued or renewed downwarping of a Mesozoic trough accompanied by severe dislocation by faulting. There is a hint in the variable altitude of an elevated Quaternary marine platform that (quite apart from land movements related to glacial loading and unloading) instability in this area has continued into Quaternary times, and it may be that some of the coastal scarps that bound the lava plateaux have originated as fault scarps rather than by differential erosion controlled by faults.

The evidence of erosion of chalk and earlier Mesozoic rocks before the Tertiary lavas were ejected (p. 21) strongly suggests that contemporaneously similar erosion took place over the highest parts of the Highlands with consequent partial or complete removal of cover rocks and exposure of the metamorphic and igneous rocks beneath. In seeking a surface on which the earliest streams began to flow one must therefore go farther back to a time when a cover of chalk and other Mesozoic rocks probably existed. While there is no proof that such rocks ever extended across the Highlands, an implication of the view that the surface on which the Tertiary lavas began to be extruded stood, at the time of extrusion, at a much higher level than it does now, is that the thick sequence of Mesozoic rocks that in places exists beneath the lavas was then also at a much higher level, thus rendering their former extension across the Highlands more probable than their present altitude suggests. This accords with the view that the great dissected west-facing mountain wall that bounds the Northern Highlands is in its broad outlines a feature exhumed from beneath the Mesozoic strata (p. 14).

It thus appears that the earliest rivers probably began to flow on a cover of chalk and other Mesozoic rocks and were already well established when the volcanic activity began in the west of Scotland. Not only have these cover rocks now gone from the higher parts of Scotland, but the surface on which they rested has probably long since disappeared. A hint of such destruction may be gleaned in the very highest part of the country, namely the central Grampians, for here, although several important discordant streams flow eastwards, there is no indication in the present land surface of the initial eastward slope on which these streams must have commenced to flow.

On the other hand, over the remainder of the country there is usually a close relation between the general direction of slope of the ground and the direction of the discordant streams. In part this doubtless reflects the influence of warping, as suggested above, but it appears that an additional factor is involved, namely marine erosion during uplift. The way in which the cover rocks, ranging in age from Old Red to Cretaceous, occur along the coastlands bordering the Highlands and Southern Uplands has been remarked upon earlier in this chapter. If we consider the distribution of these rocks along with their inferred distribution beneath the surrounding seas and with their widespread occurrence in the Central Lowlands, it is evident that we can regard the older rocks of the Highlands and, to a considerable extent, of the Southern Uplands as constituting ancient masses exhumed in broad outline from beneath the cover rocks. The remarkably close relationship between much of the present coastline and the known or inferred presence of the cover rocks implies that in relatively recent geological times the sea has been a very selective agent of erosion. We may therefore infer that in times past, when sea-level was higher, it operated in an equally selective manner. Hence we may imagine that, as Scotland emerged intermittently from the beginning of Tertiary time, marine erosion operated at successively lower levels on the deformed surface of the cover rocks. Where, as was usually the case, these rocks were relatively weak they were removed quite rapidly and the sea then cut much more slowly into the far more resistant rocks thus exposed. When uplift occurred streams were extended seawards, their courses being discordant to the structures of the old resistant rocks but often conformable in a general way with the dip of the cover rocks. Meanwhile the original marine erosion surfaces were, by slope retreat, extended as subaerial features and in turn consumed by later-developed retreating slopes, while slopes initiated by river incision were also wasting back from the valleys. Throughout the evolution of the land surface differential erosion was of major significance, in some places resulting in the reappearance (and modification) of ancient features dating back to Mesozoic or earlier times, and in many places producing valleys and lowlands along fault lines or outcrops of relatively weak rock. The final part of this evolution, in late Tertiary times, appears to have been associated with relatively rapid uplift that allowed the formation of deeply-incised V-shaped valleys that have since been greatly refashioned by glacier ice.

2

Glacial erosion and early ideas about glaciation

ALTHOUGH the main elements of the relief of Scotland were fashioned before the country was overwhelmed by glacier ice, the latter produced an immense variety of new forms, both large and small, and imposed on the country most of the scenic features that now delight the tourist. In many uplands valley slopes were steepened and spurs truncated while valley floors were deepened, often in an extremely irregular manner, to produce rocky barriers alternating with basins now filled with lakes. In the western Highlands a coastline that in preglacial times probably possessed only a few major indentations was transformed to the intricate pattern of fjords that exists today. Frequently the valleys established in Tertiary times were linked by new valley segments, many of which cross major watersheds and greatly facilitate communications through the mountains. Glaciers also bit deeply into the higher slopes of numerous mountains to produce the hundreds of corries that now fret the uplands, especially in the west. Beyond the mountains some lowlands were etched out by the ice into thousands of seemingly-chaotic rocky knolls and hollows, while on others was imposed a remarkably regular system of parallel ridges and depressions. Often the latter features are in part composed of materials deposited by the glaciers themselves. Such deposits, usually comprising stones and boulders set in a matrix of sand, silt and clay, are widespread, especially in certain lowlands, and often completely conceal the solid rocks beneath over considerable areas.

Today everyone accepts that these deposits, as well as the corries, fjords and related erosional features, are due essentially to the action of glacier ice. Yet only a hundred years ago such views were novel and were still being hotly denied by some eminent geologists. Less than a hundred and fifty years ago the idea that Scotland had once been covered by a great thickness of ice had not even been suggested.

The introduction of the glacial theory

As long ago as the closing years of the eighteenth century J. Hutton realised that the glaciers of Switzerland had been much more extensive in the past and that they had transported large blocks of granite for a great distance, but he did not apply the idea to Scotland. The same views were repeated by J. Playfair in 1802 and again in 1822. A much stronger hint was given in a remarkable paper by J. Esmark first published in Norway in 1824 and subsequently republished in the *Edinburgh New Philosophical Journal* in 1827. Esmark realised that Norway had been covered by a great ice-sheet that had transported boulders and other debris, smoothed rock surfaces and excavated the fjords.

He made no reference to Scotland, but it is interesting to note that in 1827 R. Jameson, for half a century Professor of Natural History in the University of Edinburgh, was suggesting to his students the possibility that the transported blocks of rock that occur widely in Scotland had been carried by glaciers.

Apart from this suggestion, which was not followed up, Esmark's views, far in advance of current thought, were ignored and the emphasis was on submergence and great floods of water. The idea of submergence had had a very long history and, at a time when scientific thought was not completely disentangled from the teachings of the Church, it was possible to cite the Noachian deluge, while support could also be derived from the opinions of Aristotle, Eratosthenes, Strabo and Plutarch that the mountains of Greece had been under water. The concept of great floods of water was strongly advocated by J. Hall who, in a paper published in 1815, supported his view with a careful study of the country in and around Edinburgh. He described the ridges and grooves that characterise the landscape of the Lothians, noting in particular that many hills, such as North Berwick Law in East Lothian and the Castle Rock and Corstorphine Hill in Edinburgh, present steep faces towards the west and gentle slopes towards the east. Such features he termed 'craig and tail', recognising that the agency that had produced them had come from the west. He noted too that often the rocks were scratched, and in the vicinity of Corstorphine Hill he measured the direction of these striae at more than a dozen points, concluding correctly that the agency that had inscribed them had moved towards a direction ten degrees north of east. This agency he referred to as a 'diluvian wave' and he wrote of 'the operation of immense torrents', apparently imagining great waves of the type that are associated from time to time with oceanic earthquakes (i.e. tsunami). Striae were also measured by Imrie in the Campsie Fells and were described in a paper published in 1814. He found that their general direction was from west to east and that large blocks of rock, themselves scratched, were sometimes scattered over the surface of the ground. He therefore concluded that the rocks had been impelled over the ground by a current of water from the west. Similar views were expressed by others. However, considerable dissatisfaction came to be felt about the transport of large masses of rock in this way, particularly when low ground intervened between the source area of the boulders and the place at which they were found. Such was the case, for example, with the boulders of Highland rock found in the Campsie Fells and Pentland Hills. Hence a variant on the simple submergence hypothesis was introduced, invoking ice-bergs that, floating in the sea, could carry pieces of rock from one part of the country to another, distributing them over the submerged land surface as they melted. By 1840 this view was widely accepted.

In that year, however, the idea of a great ice-sheet was brought to Britain by Louis Agassiz. Working in Switzerland with Venetz and Charpentier, who had proved that the Swiss glaciers had been formerly much more extensive, Agassiz greatly extended their ideas to include many other parts of Europe. When he came to Britain he travelled widely and found abundant evidence of the former existence of glacier ice. At the same time as he published his paper on former glaciers in Scotland, Ireland and England his converts, W. Buckland and C. Lyell, also published similar views, the former dealing with various parts of Scotland and the latter specifically with Angus. Agassiz described transported boulders, moraines, and rocks that are smoothed, polished and scratched, and explained the widespread clay with striated stones as deposited beneath glacier ice, invoking not only valley glaciers but also a great ice-sheet. He argued also that glacier ice had provided the barrier that held up the former lakes of Glen Roy and adjacent glens to produce the famous 'parallel roads'.

These brilliant reinterpretations of evidence that had long been known were not generally accepted for more than twenty years. The initial result in Scotland of the promulgation of Agassiz' views was a series of papers presenting the evidence for valley glaciers in various parts of the Highlands and islands and in the Southern Uplands. Moraines and scratched and polished rock surfaces were described in the Cairngorms, the western Highlands, Skye, Cowal and by Ben Wyvis, as well as in the high ground of the Southern Uplands by Loch Skene. Such valley glaciers were readily visualised and the evidence for them was identical with the well-known evidence in the Alps where valley glaciers descending from the high mountains could actually be seen. A great ice-sheet, perhaps thousands of feet thick, grinding over Scotland in the manner envisaged by Agassiz, was an entirely different matter, however, and was for a considerable time completely rejected. Instead submergence and ice-bergs continued to be invoked. This rejection was not as unreasonable as it may seem today, for no authenticated landing had yet been made on Antarctica, while little was known of the great Greenland ice-sheet. Furthermore, many of the loose surface materials of Scotland consist of sand and gravel, clearly sorted and deposited by currents of water, while the clay with boulders that on Agassiz' view was laid down beneath an ice-sheet was known to contain marine shells in places, sometimes to altitudes of hundreds of feet above present sea-level.

The first sign of a change of view came when R. Chambers (1853) pointed out that 'waves of translation' and floating ice-bergs could not have produced the ridge and trough forms of the Lothians and elsewhere. He invoked instead a former wide extension of circumpolar ice, although he still linked this with the notion of submergence. Much more important were A. C. Ramsay's recognition of the erosion of rock basins by glacier ice (1862) and T. F. Jamieson's discourse on the ice-worn rocks of Scotland (1862), along with the latter's convincing demonstration of Agassiz' idea that the 'parallel roads' of Glen Roy and neighbouring glens are due to glacier damming (1863). The final blow to the old ideas was struck in 1863 when Archibald Geikie described at length some of the widespread evidence for the former existence in Scotland of both ice-sheets and valley glaciers. Although at this time Geikie still favoured deep submergence to explain the water-sorted deposits of sand and gravel, he soon abandoned this hypothesis, and his paper marks the turning point from the old ideas to those still accepted today. A few die-hards, amongst whom the most outspoken was D. Milne-Home, retained the old notions for many years, but the great majority of Scottish workers turned whole-heartedly to the idea of ice-sheets and set out to prove their former existence in a convincing manner. The officers of the Geological Survey, along with T. F. Jamieson in Aberdeen, led the way, and were ably supported by the many enthusiastic members of the Glasgow and Edinburgh Geological Societies. The culminating point of this 'golden age' was attained in 1894, when there appeared the third edition of James Geikie's *Great Ice Age*, the first three hundred or so pages of which are devoted almost entirely to Scotland. At that time Scotland led the world in this field of study and the essential foundations of our more detailed knowledge of today had been firmly laid.

Glacial erosion

The belief that glacier ice is a powerful erosive agent was perhaps held by Playfair in the early years of last century when he wrote: 'For the moving of large masses of rock, the most powerful engines without doubt which nature employs are the glaciers'. Certainly Esmark was clear about the great erosive action of glacier ice, and the matter was elaborated for Britain generally by Ramsay. In Scotland James Geikie in particular followed Ramsay in his emphasis on the erosion of rock basins by ice both on land and beneath the western seas. In recent years D. L. Linton above all others has added to our knowledge concerning the extent to which the landscape of Scotland has been bitten into by ice. Yet opinions have by no means always been unanimous.

One point that early caused concern was that a substance apparently so weak as glacier ice should have eaten deeply into solid rock, sometimes of the most resistant type. The point was expressed succinctly by John Ruskin when he wrote that ice can no more erode rock basins than the custard can deepen the pie-dish! Consequently the alternative concept grew up that glaciers are essentially protective agents, the land around being subjected to the ravages of such agencies as frost and rivers. This concept, however, gained little support in Scotland. Instead there was put forward, particularly by J. W. Gregory (1913), the idea that the Scottish fjords are essentially a result of the movement of the land along faults.

While these alternative views are no longer current, they contain more than an element of truth. Many of the major glacial troughs of Scotland closely follow lines of faulting and shattering in the rocks and form straight steep-sided trenches, of which the most remarkable is the Great Glen. The old arguments of glacial erosion as opposed to glacial protection are now replaced by the modern emphasis on the selectivity of glacial action, which recognises that in some places ice erosion was severe while in others, sometimes close by, its effects were slight. This is well exemplified by the deep trench of Glen Clova cut into a gently-undulating peat-covered plateau that seems hardly to have been affected by glacier ice. In a similar manner the plateau of the Cairngorms is sharply cut off by steep-walled valleys and corries, while in the heart of the smooth rounded hills of the Southern Uplands lies the deep glacial gouge now occupied by Talla Reservoir. On a less impressive scale selectivity is clearly demonstrated in the lowlands of the Outer Hebrides by straight depressions that run in different directions and mark the lines of faults, dykes, shear planes and other lines of weakness picked out by the ice. The variability of ice erosion is also shown by the occurrence beneath glacial deposits at many places in Aberdeenshire of rotten rock that was clearly formed before ice last covered the area (p. 22).

The importance of erosion in many Highland valleys reflects in part the length of time they have been occupied by glaciers, for during the waxing and waning of each of the successive ice-sheets that have covered Scotland the valleys were occupied by ice while the surrounding uplands were largely ice-free or covered with slowly-moving caps of ice. Even when the country was largely or entirely covered by an ice-sheet, selective erosion continued, for just as today the Greenland and Antarctic ice-sheets include streams of faster-moving ice controlled by buried valleys, so in Scotland in the past we may envisage similar actively-moving ice-streams related to the hidden valley system, with more slowly-moving ice over the intervening uplands.

The processes by which glaciers erode are generally considered to be of two main types: abrasion and plucking. The results of these two processes were clearly described by J. D. Forbes in 1845 in the Coruisk valley of Skye, where the *roches moutonnées* show the usual smooth abraded slopes facing up-valley abruptly terminated by craggy plucked slopes facing down-valley. Such features are common on the floors and sides of many Highland valleys, so that looking downstream smoothed, polished and striated surfaces tend to prevail, while a view in the reverse direction presents a very irregular aspect. On the lee side of a *roche moutonnée* the ground is often lower than on the opposite side, so that a series of such features often produces a succession of steps in a valley floor. Such steps may merge together into major features attaining heights of several hundred feet: often they correspond with bands of particularly resistant rock or occur at valley junctions, although in some instances the reason for their location is not readily apparent. Steps tend to become greater in amplitude up-valley and the last and often the largest is the ice-plucked backwall of the corrie at the valley head.

The effects of ice action on the rocks can be examined in detail on many a rock exposure, especially in the west of Scotland. Where the rock is fine-grained much of its surface may be fashioned into gently-curving swells and depressions that are mostly aligned with the direction of ice movement, and it may be scored with innumerable striae that often run roughly parallel with these corrugations. Especially on the lee side of the rock (in terms of ice movement) the trend of the corrugations and striae is frequently more variable and may even be perpendicular to the prevailing direction, showing how the basal ice adjusted itself to the rocky obstruction as it flowed around, over and past it. The individual striae may themselves show the actual direction of ice movement (of two possible directions) in the way that they deepen, perhaps to end suddenly where the inscribing stone retracted into the ice that had till then held it in place. Numerous crescentic gouges perhaps six inches to a foot long and approximately perpendicular to the striae may scar the surface of the rock. Each increases in depth with the direction of former ice movement to about half an inch or an inch whereupon it ends sharply in a small vertical face.

Smoothed rock surfaces may be interrupted by shallow steep-sided depressions where blocks have been plucked out by the ice. Often these depressions are wedge-shaped, for they tend to be located where lines of weakness such as joint and foliation planes intersect at an acute angle. Bands of shattered rock facilitated the task of the ice and often form straight grooves in the rock surface. Plucking is particularly effective on the lee side of masses of rock, however, and here the intersecting flat faces controlled by joint, fault or foliation planes show where blocks have been removed by the ice. The importance of such structural weaknesses in glacier plucking was demonstrated by A. Harker (1901) through detailed observations in Skye. He found that in the Cuillins boulders from the basic dykes and sheets are surprisingly numerous as compared with those of gabbro, even though the latter is the prevailing rock. Thus in the corrie of Tairnealear the minor intrusions occupy no more than a twentieth of the ground surface, yet boulders derived from them comprise between a third and a half of the total. Harker therefore concluded that the well-jointed rocks of the minor intrusions were particularly susceptible to plucking and were often picked up as boulders, whereas the more massive gabbro was usually ground down by abrasion to produce the finer constituents of the glacial drift.

The process of plucking in Scotland, as elsewhere, was probably facilitated in many places by weathering that took place preglacially as well as during interglacials and interstadials. The relevance of such weathering processes can be appreciated by an examination of many rocky slopes in the Highlands today, where the frost-widened joints make one realise that, were glaciers to develop again, innumerable blocks would be readily available for removal. Since glaciers have repeatedly grown and decayed during Quaternary times in Scotland the importance of weathering in the intervening milder periods may well be considerable in many localities.

On the other hand, it seems unlikely that during these milder periods river erosion has been of much assistance to the glaciers in their task of excavation. The ineffectiveness of the Scottish rivers in this respect is certainly suggested by the very limited amount of erosion of solid rock they have achieved since the last glaciers disappeared. Mountain streams that tumble down over glaciated rock slopes have in some places affected these slopes to only a slight degree and ice-smoothed rock and even striae may sometimes be seen beneath the water. Many Highland streams do flow through considerable rock gorges for limited distances but these gorges often appear to be largely the work of glacial torrents (Chapter 6). It seems likely, therefore, that meltwater rivers, flowing both subglacially and proglacially, have in some localities assisted the work of erosion carried out by the ice itself. In addition water running down valley sides beneath glacier margins doubtless assisted the processes of rock disintegration, as it has been shown to do at the present time beneath glaciers in Norway and elsewhere.

Although we might mention other processes that may have assisted the glaciers in their erosive activity, we cannot avoid the conclusion that deep excavation by the ice itself has taken place on a vast scale in many Highland valleys as well as in certain other localities. The basins cut in solid rock, sometimes to depths of hundreds of feet, allow no other conclusion. The immense erosion that such basins demonstrate has given rise to speculation as to factors that may have assisted the glaciers in their task. One view that has received some currency on the Continent takes into account the probability that the cold conditions associated with the growth of glaciers would result in deep freezing of the ground. It is argued that as the glaciers subsequently extended over the frozen ground they would protect it from extremes of climate, with the result that the frozen ground would thaw out and thus make available shattered rock for removal by the glaciers. Yet it is difficult to see how this process could help at all in the excavation of rock basins once they had been initially established, for the lakes that occupy these basins, especially the deeper ones, would effectively protect the rock beneath from the extremes of climate. A more feasible suggestion has been made by W. V. Lewis (1954) and D. L. Linton (1963). This takes cognisance of the fact that the removal of surface rock may result in expansion of the rock beneath and cause it to part along extensive sheet joints. This tendency is utilised in quarrying operations and it is recorded that in one quarry in Vermont the bursting apart of the rock became so active that the quarry became too dangerous to work. Although noted particularly in igneous rocks, there seems no reason why expansion should not take place in other types of rock as pressure is released by removal of the rock above. Hence, as rock is removed under a glacier, we may imagine the rock farther beneath parting and thus facilitating the process of plucking. The fact that the weight of the glacier itself bears down on the rock will not prevent the process, for the density of ice is only about a third of that of the rock removed. The process need not be retarded as it extends downwards and, in fact, we can argue that it would be assisted by the increasing concentration of ice-flow along the depression as it was deepened.

While uncertainties exist concerning the exact manner in which glaciers erode, and the two processes of abrasion and plucking do not seem adequate to explain some phenomena (such as the vast ice-transported masses of rock described on p. 82), there is no doubt that glacial erosion has been extremely effective in many parts of Scotland. The various types of landform that have resulted from this activity will now be considered separately, for convenience, although it must be emphasised that in any one area several or all of them may be present together.

3

Landforms produced
by glacial erosion

Glacial troughs

THE results of glacial erosion are most strikingly displayed in the mountains of the western Highlands and of some of the islands. Here the deepening and widening of valleys by glacier ice, often assisted to a considerable extent by landslipping on the oversteepened slopes, has so greatly reduced the divides that only small areas of the Tertiary plateaux survive. On the other hand, in the eastern Grampians plateaux are often extensive and glacial excavation, although locally very important, has in general been less severe. A similar contrast exists in the Southern Uplands. In the area around Loch Doon, including the Merrick and Kells ranges, the scenery is locally almost as harsh as that of the western Highlands, with rough-walled valleys and large areas of ice-scraped bare rock, thus differing markedly from the smooth, rounded slopes of the Lammermuirs and Moorfoots in the east.

The general difference between east and west in the Southern Uplands also in part reflects a difference in rock type, for it is in the igneous and metamorphic areas of the west that the effects of glacial erosion are most evident. The sedimentary rocks, however, are by no means everywhere characterised by smooth forms for, particularly towards the highest ground, steep ice-eroded valley walls become increasingly common. The deep trough of Talla has already been mentioned. Near by is the Meggett valley with its roughened slopes and open aspect, and also the straight U-shaped trench of the Moffat Water where glacial erosion has been greatly facilitated by a linear belt of shattering in the rocks. Here some of the tributary valleys hang markedly above the main valley, the most noteworthy example being associated with the waterfall known as the Grey Mare's Tail, where the discordance in level between tributary valley and main valley amounts to 700 feet, suggesting this much glacial excavation along the shatter belt. The main valley of this region, that of the Tweed, also reflects the geological controls, for where it lies along the strike of the rocks it is often quite broad with spur ends truncated, whereas when it cuts across the rock outcrops it is often irregular and constricted.

Similar alternations of broad and constricted portions characterise the valley of the Dee upstream from Banchory, the narrow parts tending to correspond with the more resistant rocks such as granite. As in the Tweed basin, the results of glacial erosion become increasingly apparent in the upper parts of the valleys heading in the highest ground. Thus the Dee itself occupies a deep ice-eroded trough near its source in the Cairngorms, and is joined by streams that flow for the first few miles of their courses in similar troughs such

35

as glens Geusachan, Luibeg and Derry. On the northern side of the Cairngorms other major glacial troughs include Glen Einich and remote Glen Avon. To the south of the Dee, Glen Callater and the upper part of Glen Muick, which is cut in the Lochnagar granite mass, rank as major troughs and with them may be grouped the deep gouges in which the main headstreams of the North Esk flow. Glen Clova too has been greatly deepened by ice in its upper part and D. L. Linton (1963) estimated that this deepening amounts to as much as a thousand feet. Down-valley, however, the intensity of glacial excavation rapidly diminishes, for the tributary valleys become less and less discordant in level with the main valley, and the long profile of the latter approximates more and more closely to the profile that we may assume had been established in preglacial times.

Although the glacial troughs of the Southern Uplands and eastern Grampians provide ample proof of the effectiveness of glacial erosion, they cannot compare with those of the western Highlands in numbers and depth or in variety of form. In the east and south of Scotland well-developed troughs are restricted to a few areas. Furthermore, rock basins, steps and bars are not usually numerous even in these areas. On the other hand all these features abound in the west. This area of great erosion is limited eastwards and north-wards approximately by a line following the course of the A9 road from Dunkeld to Dalwhinnie and thence northwestwards past the head of Loch Laggan to the Great Glen. Much of the mainland north of the Great Glen lies in the region of intense erosion, the principal areas to be excluded being peripheral ones such as Caithness and eastern Suther-land. Included also in this region are the mountains of Arran, Mull, Rhum, Skye and Lewis and Harris.

Within this western region are situated almost all the large lakes occupying basins eroded by the ice. Between the basins rock bars may form massive rocky outcrops rising from the valley floor (Plate VIIB), or the valley may constrict sharply between steep walls of resistant rock, the river tumbling over falls or rapids in the bottom of a gorge. Such is the nature of the marked constriction of the Pass of Leni in the Teith valley which corre-sponds with the important belt of schistose grit that follows the Highland edge and gives rise to distinct features in other valleys near the upland margin. Thus the grit is associated with the rocky barrier at the outlet of Loch Katrine, the large rock lumps on the floor of the Earn valley between St Fillans and Comrie, and the steep wooded slopes of the Pass of Birnam by Dunkeld. Upstream from Dunkeld the Tay valley opens out in mica-schists but at Killiecrankie suddenly narrows again where a belt of quartzite and other rocks crosses it. Still farther on the valley broadens once again around Blair Atholl, where it is cut in metamorphosed limestones and associated metamorphic rocks. This alternation of broad and narrow valley segments is seen again in the adjacent Tummel valley, where the constrictions at the lower end of Loch Tummel and at Dun Alastair are mainly associated with a belt of quartzite that, owing to faulting and folding, crosses the valley twice.

This influence of the rocks on valley form means that the steep-sided U-shape, so often emphasised in text-books as characterising glacial troughs, is by no means a ubiquitous feature, for a given valley may vary in cross-profile from a V-shape to a narrow, steep-sided U to a broad, open U. These variations are well illustrated in Glen Nevis. The lowest four miles of the glen, near Fort William, have a steep-sided U form, but at Poll-dubh, where the valley is cut in granite and associated contact-hardened sediments, this changes to a V-shape for a short distance. Thereafter the U-shape is resumed for a couple of miles only to be followed upstream by a V-shaped notch that is cut in the bottom of a more open feature. This notch is ice-marked almost to its base but its form suggests that glacial meltwaters may well have played a considerable part in fashioning it. Still farther upstream the name 'glen' is no longer applied to the valley, which now becomes a broad open U, often with only moderate slopes.

The best U-forms appear to be developed where the rocks show no marked contrasts in their resistance to glacial erosion. The radiating valleys cut in the granites of northern Arran with their smooth sweeping curves are a case in point. In this area F. Mort (1914) estimated from the hanging valleys that in glens Iorsa and Rosa glacial deepening amounts in places to between 500 and 800 feet. Some of the most striking glacial troughs are those developed along lines of faulting and shattering in the rocks. The Pass of Brander, flanked on one side by the 3000-foot slope of the Ben Cruachan mass, is a good illustration. This line of weakness is continued northwestwards by a part of Loch Etive and then by Glen Salach leading to Loch Creran. Particularly important in parts of the Highlands are the lines of faulting that run north-northeast and south-southwest with the cleft of the Great Glen as the prime example of an associated feature. A similar fault determines the trend of the straight trench-like valley of Strath Glass, while another controls the canyon-like Meig valley as well as a whole series of aligned features extending for forty miles from the head of Loch Duich to central Ross-shire (Plate VA). In the Grampians faults with the same trend accord with Glen Strae, the lower part of Glen Etive, and the deep trench occupied by Loch Ericht. By no means all straight glaciated troughs are related to lines of weakness in the rocks, however, as witness the absolutely-straight, thirty-mile-long valley of the Tummel.

Glacial breaches

An important aspect of glacial erosion that is well represented in the Highlands is the breaching of preglacial watersheds to produce new valleys where perhaps only shallow cols existed previously (Linton 1951b, 1963). Many of these valleys now form ice-gouged hollows that cross divides at considerable altitudes and bear no relation to the main valley systems. Many others are major troughs cut deeply into watersheds that we may reasonably presume were unbreached in preglacial times. In some areas the breaches are so numerous that it is sometimes difficult to determine which are the ice-deepened preglacial valleys and which are the new ones cut entirely by ice in glacial times.

An example of a simple high-level breach is the pass utilised by the road that leads from Bridge of Balgie in Glen Lyon to Loch Tay. This pass is about two miles long and a thousand feet deep and lies exactly at right-angles to the trend of the two major valleys, opening out at both ends on their flanks a thousand feet or so above their floors. The gap is clearly related to times when both the Lyon and Tay valleys were deeply filled with ice and is the result of ice spilling over southwards at a high level into the Tay valley. The ground on either side of the gap reaches well over 3000 feet above sea-level and the form of the ground suggests that the original col was probably situated at about 2500-2600 feet, implying that in the production of this trough the ice cut down about a thousand feet. Many other troughs cut by ice moving at a distinct angle to the trend of the major valleys occur between the Lyon, Tay and Earn valleys, and between the Earn valley and the Highland edge. In origin they relate to times when much or all of this area was covered by an ice-sheet whose upper layers were moving outwards from the Grampians towards a direction between south and east. Once well established, the deeper breaches were able to function at times of less extensive ice cover, so that we may visualise periods when broad glaciers occupying the major valleys were linked by much narrower bodies of ice flowing through the various interconnecting gaps.

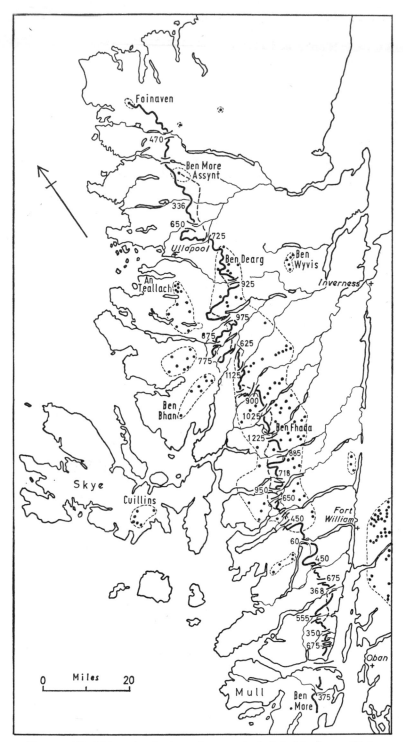

FIG. 13. Glacial breaches in the main watershed of the Northwest Highlands, based on G. H. Dury 1953. Present watershed shown by continuous line and line of highest summits (where different) by broken
line. Summits closely approaching or exceeding 3000 feet shown by
dots (except where coinciding with watersheds). Altitudes of floors
of glacial breaches given in feet.

PLATE V. A. Strath Conon, Ross-shire. *Photograph by Aerofilms.* B. Glacially-smoothed and striated rock, Coire Lair, Ross-shire. *Geological Survey photograph. Crown Copyright reserved.*

PLATE VI. A. Tarbert, Harris. *Ministry of Defence (Air Force Department) photograph. Crown Copyright reserved.* B. Highland summits with Ben Nevis on the left. Glacial breach containing Lochan Meall an t-Suidhe in foreground. *Photograph by Aerofilms.*

High-level breaches are of widespread occurrence in the Highlands, especially in the west. They vary from features that are merely gaps in a steep-sided ridge – as, for example, where ice has spilled over from one corrie to another – to linear cols with flattish floors often peat-covered and sometimes containing a shallow rock-basin lake (Plate VIB). Many of these cols lie at altitudes exceeding 2000 feet and testify to the erosion carried out by the overriding ice at high levels in the mountains. Many other breaches, however, are major valleys with floors cut down almost to the level of the glacial troughs that follow long-established valleys, while in some instances the new valleys have been eroded to even greater depths than these older valleys. A remarkable example in the latter category is provided by the straight trench occupied by Loch Treig cut clean across the main west-east Grampian watershed. On either side of this trench the mountains rise well over 3000 feet above sea-level, but the surface of the loch is at less than 800 feet, while the deepest point on its floor is only 350 feet above sea-level. A broad col appears to have existed over the site of this breach in preglacial times, but even so the amount of ice erosion involved is immense, and Linton (1951b) concluded that it was certainly 1500 feet and may have been as much as 1800 feet. The Loch Treig trough, however, is only one of a series of breaches in the main Grampian watershed. Some of these, like the Treig valley, are almost straight features excavated along major lines of faulting and shattering. They include Glen Tilt and the trench containing Loch Ericht, in each of which as much as 1200 feet of down-cutting by the ice may well have occurred.

Another group of important through valleys breaches the main watershed of the Northern Highlands (Dury 1953). Here, between western Sutherland and Mull some thirty deep gaps, as well as a large number of lesser ones, have been cut through the mountain line (Fig. 13). The floors of many of the gaps lie 2000 feet or more below the adjacent mountain summits and although this figure is not a measure of the amount of glacial erosion that has occurred, this erosion must have been considerable, probably exceeding a thousand feet in some cases. Inevitably some of these gaps provide the principal route-ways between east and west. The one between lochs Eil and Shiel, which is followed by the road and railway from Fort William to Mallaig, rises to only 60 feet above sea-level at the present divide. Even lower is the comparable feature on the floor of the glacial trough that is now the Sound of Mull, for here the submerged breach is some 200 feet below sea-level. A basic reason for the development of this long line of breaches is that for considerable periods the highest part of the ice-sheet was situated slightly to the east of the mountain backbone of the Northern Highlands, with the result that ice seeking to escape westwards from the ice-shed had to force its way through the mountain barrier.

The ice-gouged gaps shown in Fig. 13 are by no means the only large ones in the Northern Highlands, for there exist scores of others that, together with the ice-deepened valley system inherited from Tertiary times, form a complex interconnecting system of routes where glacial erosion was especially effective. The part of this ice-route system lying between Fort William and Mallaig is illustrated diagrammatically in Fig. 14. In this map the shaded areas could well be taken to represent the pattern of valley glaciers at times when these were of considerable thickness. At certain other times the ice was still thicker and probably the whole of the area shown was beneath an ice-sheet. At such times the most rapid erosion would still take place along the valleys, for here the ice would be thickest and moving most rapidly.

In Fig. 14 the east and west valleys, in part inherited from Tertiary times, are clearly evident. These valleys would be joined in preglacial times by other lesser valleys, some of which, through glacial breaching of their heads, are now linked to form continuous

E.S.S.—D

ice-ways. Glacial modification and initiation of valleys has been so intense in this area, however, that it is not always clear whether certain valleys are essentially of glacial origin or date from preglacial times. A similar system of valleys exists in the Southwest Grampians between lochs Awe and Lomond. Here also intense glacial deepening of pre-existing valleys has taken place and new ones have been cut by the ice as well. Consequently an interconnected pattern of glacial troughs exists, which includes the valleys occupied by the various fresh water and sea lochs. Again it is not always clear which are new valleys and which are old ones. Linton and Moisley (1960) have argued that the valley occupied by Loch Lomond is essentially a product of glacial times, involving as much as 2000 feet of down-cutting by the ice.

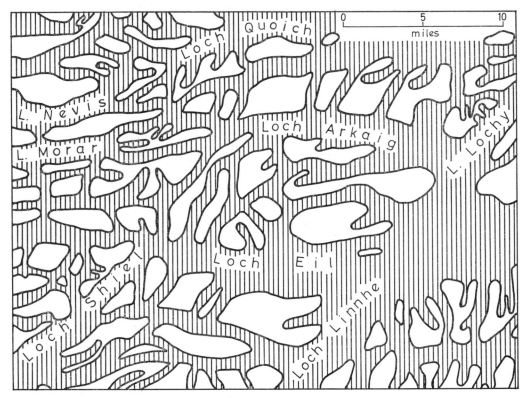

FIG. 14. The interconnected valley system between Fort William and Mallaig, emphasised by shading the main valleys and the numerous lesser valleys that link them.

Whatever uncertainties may exist about the origins of some valleys, there is no doubt that in the western Grampians and Northern Highlands there was a strong tendency towards the development of a system of valleys radiating from the areas of maximal ice accumulation. Where suitably-aligned valleys already existed the ice utilised them and deepened them. Where they did not exist the ice cut new ones, breaching pre-existing watersheds as it did so. In the Grampians the ice for long periods moved outwards from the area of Rannoch Moor and the high ground to the south. The related pattern of radiating valleys is brought out by the arrangement of the major rock basins as shown in Fig. 18. Among the more important elements of this valley system are Loch Leven, Glen Coe and the lower part of Loch Etive leading towards the west; Loch Awe and upper Loch

Fyne southwest; Loch Long south-southwest; Loch Lomond south-southeast; Loch Katrine east-southeast; Loch Voil, Loch Earn, Glen Dochart, Loch Tay, Glen Lyon, Loch Rannoch and the Tummel valley between east and northeast; and Loch Ericht and Loch Treig approximately north-northeast.

We must not, however, over-emphasise this radial tendency, for many glacial troughs do not conform to such a simple pattern. Thus Loch Etive alone trends in three distinctly different directions, while the upper section of the loch is at right-angles to the Pass of Brander, and this pass is itself at right-angles to the general trend of Loch Awe. These marked differences in trend reveal the importance of lines of weakness in the rocks. It must also be borne in mind, however, that the pattern of glaciated troughs we now see is the end product of a long and complex series of ice movements. Directions of movement varied very greatly at different times in many uplands. Thus the series of glacial troughs that leads outwards from the basin of the Moor of Rannoch through the surrounding mountain rim testifies to the importance of this basin as a centre of ice accumulation. This radial movement could only occur, however, at times when ice nourished on the adjacent mountains had accumulated to a sufficient thickness in the basin. At times of limited ice cover the movement of ice was essentially into the basin, not out of it. That such conditions prevailed during the closing stages of the last glaciation is shown by the moraines on the floor of the basin that were deposited by glaciers nourished on the mountains to the west. Changes in the directions of ice movement are also well illustrated in some of the islands and were caused by the varying strengths of different ice masses. In northern Arran the radial system of troughs demonstrates the importance of local ice accumulation in the mountains during times when glacial conditions were of moderate intensity. When, however, conditions were more severe, ice from the Highlands filled the Firth of Clyde, covered Kintyre, and extended far to the south across the floor of the Irish Sea. At such times Arran was completely overwhelmed by Highland ice and a simple radial flow could not exist. The Highland ice produced through valleys across the high ground, such as that occupied by Loch Tanna and the one at the head of Glen Iorsa, and was very probably responsible for the great width and depth of Glen Iorsa itself. In eastern Mull the influence of ice from the Highlands is seen in the deep breaching of the mountain mass, as well as in the depression, in part structurally controlled, that curves round the eastern and southern sides of the mountains and includes lochs Spelve, Uisg and Buie. Yet at times of limited ice cover the mountains of Mull nourished their own glaciers, and these glaciers flowed out radially, often in quite different directions from the movement of the Highland ice. Thus moraines show that at a late stage of the last glaciation these local glaciers occupied Loch Spelve and the head of Loch Buie. Such changes in the patterns of ice flow are similar to changes that occurred in many other mountain areas of Scotland. Such variations must have taken place on many occasions with the repeated waxing and waning of glaciers during Quaternary times. Hence the complexity of the pattern of glacial troughs is not surprising.

Outside the western areas of intense, but nevertheless selective, glacial erosion the breaching of watersheds is generally less common, although locally very significant. Such breaching occurred in the Cairngorms and resulted from the partial encirclement of these uplands by the ice-sheet centred in the Southwest Grampians. Since the external ice pressure was greatest on the southern and southwestern sides, the local ice, deflected from a simple radial flow, was forced northwards across the high ground. The straight gash of the Lairig Ghru, bordered by mountains exceeding 4000 feet but with its col at little more than 2700 feet, is the most impressive breach. Another is represented by the trough linking

Glen Derry with Glen Avon, and this is continued beyond Glen Avon by a further trough in which the Water of Caiplich rises. On the eastern side of the main mountain mass another major northward-directed breach joins the Gairn valley with Glen Builg and the Avon valley (Fig. 15). Where the two latter meet, the River Avon turns abruptly through a right-angle to flow through a breach some 800 feet deep. As Linton (1954) has pointed out, it is evident that the upper Avon was formerly part of the River Don (a continuous valley still links them), but the breach in the northern watershed of the original river was cut down so deeply by the ice that the upper Avon abandoned its original east-northeast course to follow its present one.

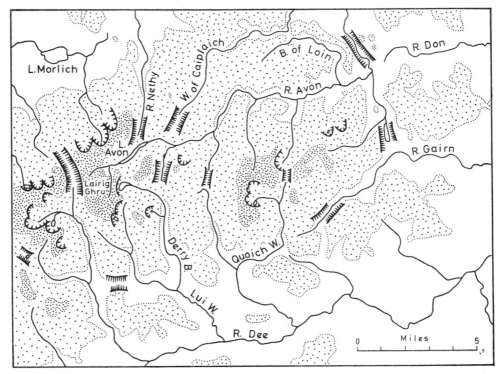

FIG. 15. Corries and principal glacial breaches in the Cairngorms. Land above 1200 and 2400 feet distinguished by shading.

In the Southern Uplands the granite basin between lochs Doon and Dee resembles the Rannoch Moor basin in that it was for long periods a major centre of ice radiation. The surrounding mountain rim has been similarly breached at various points, although less impressively, and the rocky trough leading from Loch Dee to Loch Trool provides one of the neatest examples. In the Tweedsmuir Hills a glacial breach connects the Talla valley with that of a tributary of the Yarrow, while another leads from the head of the Yarrow to the trench of the Moffat Water. Of similar modest dimensions is the Dalveen Pass in the Lowther Hills. Much more significant is the marked constriction in the Nith valley between the basins of Sanquhar and Thornhill, for it appears that before this breach was produced the upper Nith flowed in the opposite direction and, along with its many tributary streams, belonged to the drainage of Ayrshire. One other major gap that may be in part a glacial breach is the one at Biggar, which forms a broad flat-floored depression running approximately west-east for seven miles between the Clyde and the Tweed.

Selective glacial erosion also operated in the line of volcanic hills that parallels the northern margin of the Central Lowlands (Linton 1963). These hills were repeatedly overwhelmed by ice from the Highlands that moved up the preglacial valleys on their northwestern flanks, breaching their heads and linking them with valleys leading in the opposite direction. In this manner Glen Eagles is connected with Glen Devon in the heart of the Ochils, while the Endrick and Carron lead in opposite directions from the mid-point of a valley in the Campsie Fells. Strathblane lies in another breach that now separates the Campsie Fells from the Kilpatrick Hills. At its highest point the floor of this trench reaches an altitude of only 300 feet and its gently-curving course clearly reflects the gradually-changing direction of the ice-stream as it was forced round towards the east by the eastward-moving ice on the southern side of the volcanic hills.

Major rock basins

As Ramsay recognised more than a century ago, proof of the ability of glacier ice to cut down deeply into the rocks is most clearly supplied by rock basins. The dimensions of many of the basins on land are to a considerable extent revealed by the lakes that fill them. All the really large lakes in Scotland occupy rock basins, although in some instances the lake surface is above the rock lip owing to an additional barrier provided by deposits of various kinds. Among the lakes that are partly or wholly in depressions of other origins the two largest are probably Loch Leven in Kinross and Lake of Menteith, both of which appear to occupy hollows in glacial deposits.

The principal fresh-water lochs of Scotland, as well as many minor ones, were intensively studied in the early years of the present century under the leadership of J. Murray and L. Pullar. As a result of their survey it was established that by far the deepest loch is Morar with a maximal recorded depth of 1017 feet, this being followed in order by Loch Ness 754 feet, Lomond 623, Lochy 531, Ericht 512, Tay 508 and Katrine 495 feet (Fig. 16). In terms of surface area Loch Lomond leads with 27·45 square miles, followed by Ness 21·78, Awe 14·85, Maree 11·03, Morar 10·30 and Tay 10·19 square miles. By far the largest rock basin, as measured by volume of water, is that of Loch Ness with 263 000 million cubic feet, and this is succeeded by Loch Lomond with 93 000 and Loch Morar with 81 000 million cubic feet.

In most instances these figures tend to be minimal because of deposition in the lakes during and since the disappearance of the glaciers. Some lakes, especially the largest ones, are fairly flat in their deepest parts owing to the accumulation of sediment. Deltas and alluvial fans have also diminished the size of most lakes. For example, Loch Tummel had been reduced to half its original area by river deposition at its upper end before its level was raised by the building of the dam for the hydro-electric station. On the other hand, Loch Rannoch would be larger but for a mass of coarse gravel laid down by glacial rivers at its outlet end. Lochs Voil and Lubnaig differ in surface level by only 9 feet although they are 5 miles apart. During high floods the flat alluvial ground between them is largely submerged and, along with Loch Doine, they form a single sheet of water, thus temporarily reconstituting the long narrow lake that existed in earlier times. Lochan na h'Earba, south of Loch Laggan, has been split into two parts by the building of an alluvial fan, although the fact that the two lakes have a single name can hardly be taken as evidence of the recency of this event. In the Southern Uplands St Mary's Loch and Loch of the Lowes, originally one sheet of water, have been separated through the meeting of alluvial fans built out by streams from the opposing valley sides.

While some rock-basin lakes have been reduced in area or divided, it is likely that other

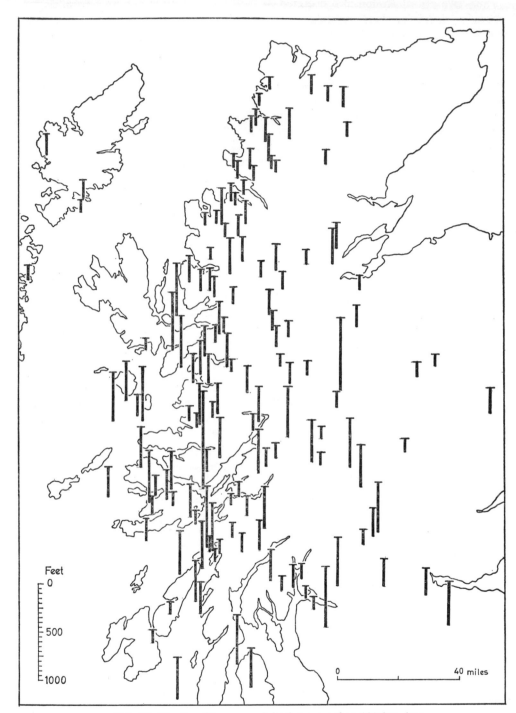

FIG. 16. Depths of known rock basins more than 120 feet deep.

rock basins in Highland valleys are completely hidden beneath superficial deposits. The River Glass between Invercannich and Struy falls only 15 feet in 6½ miles as it meanders over the flat alluvial deposits of its valley floor, and this may well be the site of a former lake that occupied a rock basin now buried. Loch Insh in the Spey valley is the remnant of a much larger lake that formerly extended up the valley at least as far as Kingussie. Farther downstream towards Aviemore a rocky barrier forms isolated hills rising several hundred feet above the valley floor and it seems likely that this barrier marks the lower end of a rock basin now buried beneath the abundant drift deposits of the Spey valley. In the glacial troughs radiating from the high ground south of the Dee lochs Muick, Callater and Lee occupy rock basins, the last having been considerably reduced in size by the deposition of alluvium at its upper end. In comparable locations in Glen Clova and Glen Isla no lochs occur, but flat-surfaced deposits on the valley floors suggest that they once existed and that rock basins are probably hidden beneath.

Most of the larger lakes of Scotland are long in relation to their width and the term 'ribbon lake' is very appropriate. Loch Shin, for example, is 17 miles in length but averages only half a mile in width, while fault-guided Loch Shiel is 17½ miles long but at no point attains a width of a mile. Some lakes occupy a single rock basin that descends fairly regularly to its deepest point and then rises again. This simple type includes those of lochs Ness, Lochy, Monar, Morar, Lungard, Morie, Glass, Tay, Treig and Katrine. Some of these lie partly or wholly along major shatter belts and their simplicity indicates the ease with which the ice eroded the broken rock as compared with the more resistant rock on either side. The most striking example is Loch Ness, which, except where deposits opposite the mouth of the River Foyers slightly raise its floor, is one great trough with a depth of more than 600 feet for much the greater part of its length. In other instances, such as Loch Katrine, variations in rock resistance have been insufficient to produce significant irregularities in the floor of the basin. Morar, the deepest basin of all, with the lowest point on its floor 987 feet below sea-level, *appears* to have derived no special assistance from lines of weakness in the rocks, for it is aligned nearly at right-angles to most of the complex rock structures. One wonders, however, if it is significant that Loch Beoraid, only a few miles to the south, occupies a deep fault-guided trough that is almost exactly parallel with Loch Morar.

By no means all the rock basin lakes occupy simple depressions. Loch Shin, for example, conceals half a dozen minor basins beneath its waters and Loch Shiel perhaps a larger number, while some very irregular basins occur in the Outer Hebrides. Loch Langavat in Lewis has at least eight rock basins and Loch Obisary in North Uist fifteen. To a considerable degree these irregular lake floors reflect the variations in the rocks, the minor basins in lochs Langavat and Obisary, for example, often corresponding with the strike of weak bands of rock or with shear planes or fault lines. However, this cannot always be the full explanation, for the several small basins of Loch Shiel are in part cut in the same types of rock as the single great basin of Morar. The difference here may be related partly to the fact that Loch Morar lies parallel with the westward ice movement that prevailed in this area whereas most of Loch Shiel is at a distinct angle to this direction.

The effect of the configuration of the ground on the excavation of rock basins is seen in their frequent occurrence in glacial breaches. Their presence here is in fact convincing evidence that these breaches were scooped out by the ice as it was forced more rapidly through a relatively narrow passage. Among the more important basins in such locations are those of lochs Treig, Ossian, Ericht and Garry in the Grampians and of Loch Frisa in Mull. Among smaller basins at higher levels we may cite Lochan na Lairige in the breach

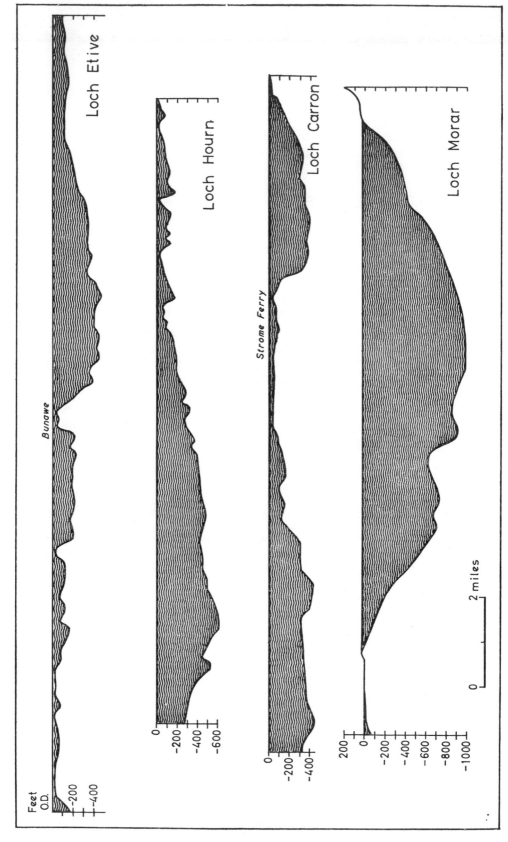

Fig. 17. Long profiles of certain fjords along with that of the near-fjord of Loch Morar. The profiles are constructed along the line of greatest depth and thus vary in direction. The open sea lies to the left of each profile.

between Glen Lyon and Loch Tay, Loch Tanna (partly drift-dammed) in a north-south col in the mountains of Arran, and lochs Calavie and Mhoicean in breaches leading out of the Monar basin in central Ross-shire. Small high-level breaches in the Mamore Forest southeast of Ben Nevis contain shallow rock basin lakes at altitudes as high as 2400 feet, while at the same altitude a rock-bound lakelet lies in a minor glacial breach near the head of the Keltie Water north of Callander.

The effect of relief on glacial erosion is also seen in the extent or depth of many lakes. Loch Tay commences exactly where Glen Lochay and Glen Dochart join, for here the combined power of the ice-streams moving down these valleys was sufficient to initiate overdeepening. Immediately to the south Loch Earn begins in a similar position. The reverse situation is provided by Loch Avon in the Cairngorms: the ice that flowed through the striking glacial breach of The Saddle and down Strath Nethy as a distributary of the Avon ice reduced the erosive power of the latter and caused the overdeepening represented by the rock basin of Loch Avon to come to an end. The deepest part of some lakes is related to geological factors. Thus a major line of faulting may affect only part of a lake, such as the middle reach of Loch Tay or the head of Loch Luichart. In other instances the deepest part occurs where the valley is narrowest. Loch Maree, which is for the most part aligned along a major fault, has its deepest point where the valley is most constricted between Ben Slioch and Meall a'Ghubhais. The same influence is evident in lochs Loyal, Ericht and Lomond. The contrast between the northern and southern parts of Loch Lomond is extreme, for whereas the long narrow trough of the former descends to almost 600 feet below sea-level, the latter is almost everywhere less than 100 feet deep. The southern part is dotted with islands, most of which are due to highly resistant beds of grit or conglomerate, but a considerable area is floored with easily-eroded Old Red sandstone. It is evident from both the depth and width of the lake that the erosive capacity of the ice was immensely greater in the narrow northern trench than in the southern part where the ice spread out towards and beyond the margin of the Highlands. Since the trench is itself, at least in large part, the result of ice erosion, it appears that the more deeply a trench is eroded by ice the more will the ice be channelled through it and the more will erosion take place. Glacial erosion thus appears to be a cumulative process and its highly selective and effective operation in the upland valleys is the result.

It has been stated from time to time in the literature that rock basin lakes tend to be deepest towards their heads. This is certainly not a valid generalisation so far as the larger Scottish lake basins are concerned, for 35 per cent are deepest at their upstream ends, a similar percentage are deepest towards their outlets, and the remaining 30 per cent achieve their greatest depth at approximately their mid-point. It therefore seems that the local effects of geology and relief are far more important within the compass of a single rock basin than is the supposed diminution of ice erosion with increasing distance from the source of a glacier. A similar generalisation is often made about fjords and they are said to have a 'down at heel' form with the deepest part towards the head. This is true of Loch Etive (Fig. 17), but here the considerable depth of the inner part of the loch is a result of the restrictive influence of the high ground (contrasting with the much more open aspect of the lower reach of the loch) greatly assisted by a major shatter belt. Loch Etive is exceptional, however, and the great majority of the Scottish fjords have their deepest part (typically 300 to 600 feet below sea-level) towards the seaward end. This is hardly surprising, for the volume of ice flowing along a fjord usually increased towards its mouth owing to successive increments from tributary valleys.

At the mouths of fjords, however, there is usually a rapid shallowing of the water and a barrier or threshold occurs. This feature is repeatedly stated in elementary text-books to be a mass of morainic debris deposited at the snout of a glacier occupying the fjord, yet this is quite incorrect. It is true that at the entrances to some fjords, such as Loch Etive, there are large deposits of gravel laid down by meltwater rivers close to glacier snouts, but even in these instances the shallowing of the loch is essentially a result of the rise of the solid rock floor. Fjord basins are, in fact, rock basins eroded by the ice and differ in no way from other rock basins except in that they are filled with salt water. The gradation between fresh- and salt-water basins is well illustrated on the Scottish coasts. Thus the surface of Loch Maree is only 31 feet above sea-level, of Loch Morar 30 feet and of Loch Lomond 27 feet, while lochs Shiel and Hope are only 12 feet above, so that only a modest rise of sea-level would convert all these fresh-water lochs into fjords. The situation is even more critical in the case of Loch Etive, for this loch only just manages to achieve fjord status. At the narrow entrance at Connel, rock is so close to cutting off the loch from the sea that a reversible tidal waterfall – the Falls of Lora – is produced. During the ebbing tide the water in the loch is unable to escape sufficiently rapidly through the narrow passage to keep pace with the fall of the tide outside, so that a difference in level of several feet is produced and causes the waterfall (or, more accurately, rapids). During the rising tide the reverse situation develops.

The main reason for the existence of a rock bar at the entrance to most fjords is the rapid diminution in ice erosion where the ice escaped from the constricting valley walls. It was not produced, as has been sometimes suggested, by a glacier being caused to float in the sea and thus ceasing to erode. The results of ice spreading out in the Loch Lomond basin have already been mentioned. In two other near-fjords – lochs Morar and Maree – the consequences were similar. All three lochs become wider as they begin to emerge from the high ground and islands appear above their waters. In a similar manner the constriction at the entrance to Loch Alsh is interrupted by rocky islands, while a small group of islands marks the mouth of Loch Broom. At the mouth of Loch Torridon the only visible evidence of the rock bar away from the margins of the loch is an isolated rock that rises 8 feet above high water. In Little Loch Broom the entrance is visibly guarded only by a solitary rock that is awash at high tide.

Most of the larger fjords contain more than one basin and the rocky barriers between often correspond with narrows sometimes utilised by ferries, as at Kylesku, Strome Ferry and Ballachulish. The floors of the fjords are thus typified by considerable irregularity both on a large and a small scale, as shown by the long profiles in Fig. 17. Irregularity in cross profile is common also. Thus while rocky islands appear at the mouths of some fjords, deep ice-gouged hollows may be hidden beneath the sea close by. Immediately south of the island group at the entrance to Loch Broom is a trough whose floor is 400 feet below sea-level, while the rock bar revealed by shoals at the mouth of Loch Hourn is cut through abruptly by a trench that goes down to 600 feet below sea-level and merges with a much larger trench that follows the Sound of Sleat. Thus while rock thresholds are typical of fjord entrances they are, in some instances, themselves deeply breached.

The radial pattern of the fjords along the west coast of Scotland reflects both the movement of ice and the influence of geological factors. Northwards from Loch Torridon the dominant southeast to northwest trend of the coastal indentations and of the larger rock basins immediately inland corresponds with the principal rock structures. Since the prevailing direction of ice movement approximately followed the trend of these structures the excavation of glacial troughs and their rock basins along southeast-northwest lines was of frequent occurrence. Farther south on the mainland, as far as Loch Sunart, the general westward movement of ice that prevailed is less evident in the trend of the fjords, for here the ice usually flowed across the grain of the rocks. Southwards from Loch Linnhe a north-northeast to south-southwest trend is very obvious both in the large rock basins and in various indentations of the coast. Although these features usually correspond with lines of weakness in the rocks, the coastal indentations from the Sound of Kerrara to West Loch Tarbert are of modest dimensions. To a considerable extent this reflects the moderate altitude of the coastal belt and the consequent less effective channelling of the ice. It probably also reflects the variable direction of ice flow, for it seems that at times of very extensive ice cover the dominant flow was towards southwest and south-southwest, whereas at times of more limited cover a movement directed more towards the west occurred, the consequences of the latter being seen in east-west valleys with small rock basin lakes (such as Scamadale and Tralaig) in the country between Oban and Kilmelfort.

Beyond the zone of fjords, although in places overlapping it, is another zone in which much larger rock basins occur. The delimitation of these outer basins in Fig. 18 is some-what less accurate, owing to the spacing of the soundings, than the representation of the fjord and lake basins, but this does not materially affect the pattern depicted. The three greatest basins – around Arran, south of Mull, and between northern Skye and the main-land – are each many times larger than Loch Ness, the greatest lake basin. Most of the larger sea-bed basins descend to 600 feet below sea-level in their deepest part, and some considerably exceed this depth. In the Sound of Jura, the Firth of Lorne, and between Lismore Island and Mull 700 feet is exceeded. Between Skye and Rhum a sounding of 834 feet has been recorded, and in the Inner Sound of Raasay a depth of 1062 feet has been obtained (Robinson 1949). This depth is the greatest recorded in British coastal waters and is not encountered again until the margin of the continental shelf is passed well beyond the Outer Hebrides.

The distribution and shape of most of the basins show that they are to a considerable degree the result of concentrated flow of ice through the passages between islands and between islands and the mainland. Where the islands have considerable relief, as in Skye, Rhum, Mull, Jura and Arran, the effect is especially marked, partly because of deflection of the invading ice by the high ground, and partly because, except at times when these islands were overwhelmed by invading ice, the local ice itself added to the effectiveness of the mountain barriers. Consequently emphatic overdeepening occurs in the trench between Rhum and Eigg, which descends to over 500 feet below sea-level, and again between Rhum and Canna, where a depth of 780 feet is achieved. The most striking example is the great basin that commences in Loch Fyne south of the rock bar at Otter Ferry and extends along the floor of the lower loch to split into two branches, one of which follows Kilbrennan Sound and the other the Firth of Clyde (Fig. 18). At the entrance to lower Loch Fyne a depth of 660 feet has been recorded, while the bottom of the trench in the Sound of Bute is more than 500 feet below sea-level for many miles, and in the narrowest part of Kilbrennan Sound 500 feet is again exceeded. Towards their southern margins the two branches of the basin gradually fade out and the barrier marking their limit is a broad belt of relatively shallow water only 100 to 200 feet deep extending from southern Kintyre to Arran and thence across to the coast of southern Ayrshire.

In part the great size of some of the sea-bed basins may be explained by the vast streams of ice that flowed along them, for each of the major ones was supplied by several or many glacial troughs on land. It appears also, however, that geological factors were often particularly helpful. Although little is known directly of the geology of the sea floors along the west coast of Scotland, certain inferences may be made from adjacent land areas.

Fig. 18. Principal rock basins of Scotland and adjacent seas. The approximate extent of certain rock basins whose existence is not firmly established is shown by vertical shading.

Thus the important Camasunary fault of Skye apparently passes between Rhum and Eigg and parallels the east coast of Coll, perhaps corresponding with the elongated basin off this coast. The Great Glen fault was used to advantage in the excavation of the two basins in Loch Linnhe, and along its probable continuation past Colonsay to Islay another basin has been created (which is in turn continued by Loch Gruinart in Islay). The basins in the sounds of Sleat and Jura, Kilbrennan Sound and the Firth of Lorne are approximately parallel with the strike of the rocks, and although the rock structures are often complicated they doubtless facilitated glacial erosion in these passages. Structural control is also indicated by the way in which the regularly-curving coastlines of eastern Mull and northeastern Arran (from the northern tip to Brodick Bay) parallel almost exactly the curving margins of the Tertiary igneous masses. The manner in which a narrow strip of relatively soft rocks, comprising Old and New Red Sandstone and Carboniferous sediments, borders the sea along the whole northeast coast of Arran suggests that similar soft materials underlie the adjacent sea floor. This suggestion is strengthened by the presence of sediments belonging to one or more of these rock groups over much of southern Arran and most of southern Bute, on the southern tip of Argyllshire at Toward Point, on Great Cumbrae and along the length of the Ayrshire coast from near Wemyss Bay to Girvan. It is therefore highly probable that similar relatively soft rocks underlie the Firth of Clyde and the Sound of Bute, thus helping to account for the major ice-eroded basin as well as for the lesser troughs in the narrower part of the firth. It is possible that the red sandstones extend some distance into lower Loch Fyne and have facilitated its excavation, for the glacial deposits in northern Kintyre in places contain pieces of red sandstone for which there appears to be no adequate source on land (Peach *et al.* 1911). There is also the possibility that the floor of the Sound of Jura and the sea bed between Jura and Colonsay are in part composed of Old Red Sandstone. Glacier-transported pieces of this rock are scattered freely over Oronsay and Colonsay (Craig *et al.* 1911) and fragments of the same rock may be picked up in Jura, while the narrow strip of Old Red Sandstone that fringes half a dozen miles of the coast of western Kintyre hints strongly at its underwater presence.

The deep basin that occurs on either side of Raasay and extends towards the Minch is also in an area where geological factors appear to have favoured glacial erosion. The Sound of Raasay may be along the line of a major fault and several other important faults enter the Inner Sound from the lands on either side. The most important of these crosses the island of Raasay obliquely and its trend where it intersects the east coast strongly suggests that it continues close to this coast off the northern shore of the island and alongside the island of Rona. It is just off this coast that the sea floor descends to over 1000 feet below sea-level when not far away northern Raasay rises to 800 feet above sea-level. The submarine slope between is steep, with an average gradient of 1 in 3 in places, although the eastern side of the submarine trench is seldom steeper than 1 in 7 (Robinson 1949). A fault control of this deep trench therefore seems likely and it may well be that the Raasay fault, on the east side of which the Mesozoic rocks have been dropped down at least 2500 feet, has caused these relatively soft rocks to form the floor of part of the Inner Sound and thus aided its excavation by glacier ice. It is also necessary to point out, however, that in Raasay the Mesozoic rocks have been strengthened by the injection of igneous rocks, so that, if this applied also to the Mesozoic rocks presumed to floor part of the Inner Sound, the task of the ice might have been rendered less easy.

It may well be that the excavation of the northward extension of the basin bordering Raasay, as well as of some of the much smaller sea-bed basins off the northwest coast shown in Fig. 18, was also aided by the presence of Mesozoic rocks. Apart from their existence beneath the lavas of northern Skye, these rocks appear in the Shiant Islands a few miles from the coast of Lewis, as well as in a dozen small patches along the coast of western Ross-shire, so that their occurrence on parts of the intervening sea floor may reasonably be anticipated. Certainly some very favourable geological factor seems neces- sary to account for the depths achieved within a few miles of the northwest coast, as in the entrances to Eddrachillis Bay (510 feet), Enard Bay (660 feet) and Gruinard Bay (700 feet). These depths are much in excess of those found on the adjacent land where even in the fault-assisted Loch Maree basin only 336 feet below sea-level is reached and this where the ice was greatly constricted by high ground.

The deep basins of the sea floor along the west coast thus point to powerful erosion by the ice assisted in many places by favourable geological circumstances. Doubtless the belts of weaker rock and the lines of faulting had already been exploited to some degree by erosive processes in preglacial times and the major coastal indentations initiated. The principal closed basins on the sea bed, to the extent that they are true rock basins, could not have been formed preglacially, however, unless considerable movement along faults took place. An essential result of ice erosion in this western area was greatly increased fragmentation of the land areas. Skye and Mull, now separated from the mainland by narrow straits, were part of it before the Ice Age. The chain of islands including Seil, Luing, Shuna, Lunga, Scarba, Jura and Islay was almost certainly a peninsula of the mainland, a status that Knapdale and Kintyre with their deep gaps at Lochgilphead and Tarbert just manage to retain. It is quite possible that Arran was linked to Kintyre, and it is clear that the Kyles of Bute are essentially a product of glacial erosion. In other places, as in Knapdale and Kintyre, severance was not quite achieved. Bute is almost split in three places, one instance being the long hollow southwest of Rothesay containing Loch Fad, which is part rock basin lake and part drift-dammed. Jura is nearly bisected at Loch Tarbert, and two other Loch Tarberts, East and West, almost meet in the centre of Harris (Plate VIA). Another glacial breach, between Salen and Loch na Keal, almost severs northern Mull from the remainder of the island, while Skye is almost breached in several places as, for example, between Portree and Loch Snizort.

The description of the sea-floor basins of the west would be incomplete without reference to the long series of basins that extends almost the whole length of the Outer Hebrides along their eastern side and reaches almost 800 feet below sea-level near Barra Head. J. Geikie (1894) believed that these basins were excavated by basal ice that was deflected by the Outer Hebrides to flow parallel with their length. This explanation is difficult to reconcile with the striae, *roches moutonnées* and related features that show that the ice-sheet moved across the Outer Hebrides in a direction almost exactly per- pendicular to their trend. One wonders therefore if the excavation of the basins was performed by ice moving in the prevailing direction, its task being facilitated by the presence of weak Mesozoic rocks (p. 14), or whether some nonglacial cause was wholly or partly responsible for them. Owing to this uncertainty the basins are not shown in Fig. 18.

While the narrow fjord basins of the west coast have as their counterpart in the east the series of fresh-water lake basins from Loch Katrine to Loch Naver, the group of deep sea-floor basins is also balanced by a series in the east. The basins of this latter group are small, however, in comparison with those of the west. This difference was brought about partly by the fact that ice accumulation was always greater in the west and partly by the occurrence of high ground close to the west coast, resulting in steeper ice gradients and more rapid flow. This more rapid movement was further facilitated by the ease with which the ice could escape to the Atlantic Ocean with its relatively warm waters, whereas in the east the Grampians presented a major barrier to movement and the North Sea is relatively shallow and is (and doubtless was) colder than the Atlantic. Furthermore, at times of very extensive ice cover, the northern North Sea was largely occupied by the Scandinavian ice-sheet, which further retarded the rate of evacuation of the ice in eastern Scotland.

The existence of a deep basin in the Inverness Firth is suggested by the record of a borehole put down in Inverness. This bore, located on ground close to sea-level, passed through 319 feet of superficial deposits but failed to reach rock. Direct evidence is lacking in the Cromarty Firth, although ice erosion is indicated at least at the entrance to the firth where the Sutors represent the visible part of a narrow steep-sided trench in which the sea is 200 feet deep. In the Forth valley three quite distinct deep basins have been found. In one of these, excavated in the Old Red Sandstone underlying the Carse of Stirling, boreholes show that the buried rock surface descends to more than 350 feet below sea-level. A second basin underlies the Devon valley on the south side of the Ochils and its floor is as low as 336 feet below sea-level (Soons 1960). The third basin underlies the lower course of the River Carron and then continues beneath the waters of the Firth of Forth, its rock floor having been proved by mining operations to descend to 675 feet below sea-level. Farther down the Forth valley rock lies no more than 200 feet below sea-level (Drysdale 1956) so that the amount of downcutting achieved by the ice is at least 475 feet. This evidence of completely closed rock basins clearly disproves the old idea, still unfortunately current, that the deep hollows are river-cut valleys related to preglacial sea-levels hundreds of feet below present sea-level. The major trench of the Forth valley is continued southwestwards and then westwards by a drift-filled hollow that passes Kirkintilloch and Bearsden and leads directly into the estuary of the Clyde. The rock floor descends to at least 240 feet below sea-level between Bearsden and Clydebank and at one point in Dumbarton it is known to be 224 feet below sea-level. It is not certain that either this trench or the smaller trench that follows the Clyde in Glasgow are definitely closed basins, but the probability is high. Taken together, these various deep gouges in the Forth and Clyde areas demonstrate the importance of selective glacial erosion in the Central Lowlands associated with the movement of ice towards an easterly point.

Glacial roughening

In many areas the overriding ice produced a highly-irregular relief that, when viewed from the ground, may at first seem totally chaotic. On the other hand, in certain other areas it imposed a remarkably regular pattern of smooth ridges and hollows on the landscape. The irregular type is most strikingly developed on the Lewisian Gneiss of the northwest coastlands and the Outer Hebrides, and is also very characteristic of volcanic rocks. On the other hand, it is not developed to any significant degree on the limestones, sandstones and shales of Carboniferous and Old Red age such as cover wide areas in the Central Lowlands. These sediments have been instead frequently moulded by the ice into broad swells and depressions that are often composed in part of material deposited by the ice (and are therefore considered in Chapter 5).

The irregular type of relief where well developed forms innumerable small hills, often with large areas of bare rock at the surface, separated by depressions often containing small lakes or accumulations of peat. The term 'knock-and-lochan topography' has been aptly applied by Linton (1959) to relief of this type. The individual hills vary from massive protuberances of rock several hundred feet high to small rocky knolls. They often have the form of *roches moutonnées*, with ice-abraded surfaces on their flanks and upper parts and rough ice-plucked slopes on their lee sides. These *roches moutonnées* may give an alignment to the relief, but the extent to which this is evident depends largely on the trends of the lines of weakness in the rocks in relation to the direction of ice movement. It is very well seen on the west coast near Loch Sween, where the ice at times flowed parallel with the trend of the beds of quartzite, epidiorite and limestone, etching out innumerable small parallel depressions separated by straight narrow ridges (Fig. 19).

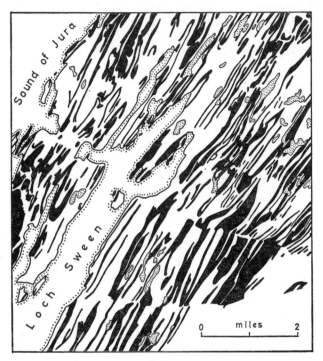

FIG. 19. Coasts and lakes parallel with rock outcrops in the Loch Sween area, Argyllshire. The solid black areas are outcrops of epidiorite and mostly correspond with ridges. Based on Geological Survey One-Inch sheets.

Glacial roughening is particularly evident in the coastal belt of western Sutherland and western Ross-shire, especially in the considerable areas where the Lewisian Gneiss forms the surface (Plate VIIIB). The principal faults, dykes, igneous sheets and shear planes trending southeast-northwest guided the excavation of the fjords and larger rock basins already mentioned, but numerous lesser basins, with their intervening ridges, also follow these lines. The great complexity of the Lewisian rocks, however, provided numerous lines of weakness trending in other directions for the ice to exploit with the result that, away from the main structure-guided valleys, the sea of rocky knolls often appears from ground level to lack any pattern. Yet there is often a strong correlation with the geological structures as may be seen from the distribution of rock-basin lakes in relation to faults and dykes as shown in Fig. 20. Many rock basins have also been cut in the Torridon Sandstone although they are not as numerous or as complex in shape as those in the Lewisian Gneiss. The landforms of the northwestern coastal belt are repeated in more subdued form on the Lewisian Gneiss in many parts of the Outer Hebrides where they are typified by narrow coastal inlets and hundreds of lakes with irregular outlines (Plate VIIIA). This scenery is partly obscured on the west coasts of the

PLATE VII. A. Loch Gorm, a rock-basin lake in western Sutherland. *Photograph by Tom Weir.* B. Rock bar holding up Loch Monar. *Ministry of Defence (Air Force Department) photograph. Crown Copyright reserved.*

PLATE VIII. Glaciated lowlands of Lewisian Gneiss. A. Lochmaddy, North Uist. B. North of Lochinver, Sutherland. *Photographs by Aerofilms.*

islands by sand deposited by wind and sea but elsewhere rocky knolls pass gradually beneath sea-level as islands, islets and shoals. Rock-bound hollows caused by glacial erosion also occur abundantly in Shetland, as on the rocky plateau of Roeness, in the districts of Walls and Sandsting, and on the peninsula of Lunnasting.

The roughening action of ice-sheets was often severe at considerable altitudes in the uplands (Plate VIIA). In the region of the Great Glen the northeastward-moving ice mass that gouged out the basin of Loch Ness produced scores of small basins on the bordering uplands to a distance of many miles on either side. Between Loch Ness and Strath Glass such lake-filled basins abound up to an altitude of about 1700 feet, while south of Loch Ness in Glendoe Forest they are common up to 2400 feet above sea-level. The volcanic uplands between Loch Creran and the vicinity of Loch Awe have a highly-irregular form and are spattered with rock-basin lakes. Similar scenery prevails on the metamorphic rocks towards Loch Awe and also between Loch Awe and Loch Fyne,

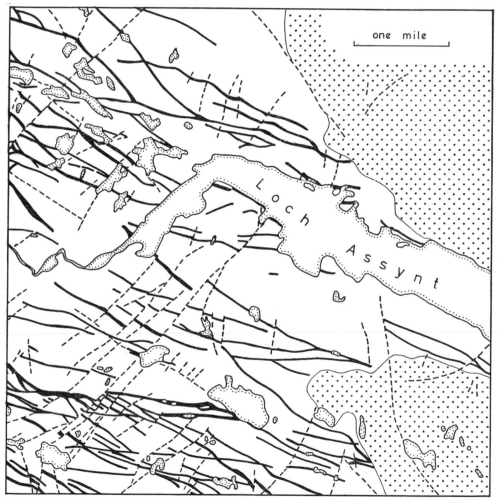

FIG. 20. Lakes in relation to faults (broken lines) and dykes (solid lines) around Loch Assynt in western Sutherland. The dotted area represents Torridon Sandstone and the unshaded area Lewisian Gneiss. Based on Geological Survey One-Inch sheet.

where small rock-bound lakes, often elongated with the strike of the rocks, are frequent to altitudes of 1500 feet. The roughening of the higher ground by the passage of ice is also evident in the craggy igneous hills (particularly the volcanic ones) of the Central Lowlands.

The contrast between the ice-roughened areas, which have suffered modest glacial erosion, and the glacial troughs, where downcutting by the ice was excessive, is nowhere better seen than in Morar. On the uplands on either side of Loch Morar rock basins are found up to an altitude of 2000 feet and from the highest of these one may look down on the loch with its deepest point 3000 feet below. Not far away the evidence on mountains reaching 3000 feet above sea-level shows that the ice surface must at times have stood at least at this altitude. Hence the uplands bordering Loch Morar have certainly been covered by at least 1000 feet of ice, so the presence of clear erosional forms here need occasion no surprise. Neither is it surprising, however, that the Morar trench displays so much more strikingly the erosive action of the ice for, by the same reasoning, this was covered (at its deepest point) by at least 4000 feet of ice. In the western Highlands generally rock basin lakes are only occasionally found above an altitude of 2500 feet. Above this altitude there is still erosional evidence of the passage of ice in the form of small-scale roughening to altitudes exceeding 3000 feet. On the higher parts of the Scottish mountains, however, the most important features fashioned by ice are the corries.

Corries

These large semi-circular recesses scooped out by ice are a distinctive element of the upper slopes of many western mountains and are found in small groups elsewhere. Well-developed corries may be 500 to 1500 feet deep and a half to three-quarters of a mile across, and their steep, often vertical, backwalls frequently lead rock-climbers directly to the summits. The ideal text-book corrie contains a lochan on its floor, but no more than a quarter of the Scottish corries conform with this ideal, although in some instances small lakes have been infilled by the accumulation of sediment. When the lakelet is present it sometimes occupies a small rock basin, is sometimes held up by a morainic dam, and quite frequently owes its existence to both glacial erosion and deposition.

Many corries form the heads of glacial troughs and their steep backwall marks the abrupt ending of such valleys. Many other corries occur isolated on the upper slopes of mountains (Plate XIA). Some of these may have developed on the sites of preglacial valleys or gullies or in shallow concavities on the mountain sides where snow was able to accumulate. In such locations snow patches would persist longest in spring and summer. Melting of the snow in the daytime would soak the ground beneath and downslope from it, while freezing at night would result in disintegration of the water-soaked ground surface. Repetition of this slow process, day after day, year after year, would, it has been suggested, gradually enlarge the snow-patch hollows, with the consequence that snow would persist longer each year and the freeze-thaw process become more effective. This cumulative process, coupled with deteriorating climate, would ultimately result in permanent snow patches and, where these were of sufficient depth, compaction and recrystallisation would eventually be associated with movement of the whole mass of ice and snow as a glacier. Not all corries away from valley heads need have been initiated in this way, however. Landslipping is an important process on many steep slopes in the Highlands and could well have produced some hollows ready-made for ice to occupy and enlarge. This process is well illustrated near Fort William in the mountains on either side of Glen Nevis (Bailey *et al.* 1916). For example, on the high ridge separating Allt Coire Rath from Allt Coire an Eoin are numerous slipped masses of rock, and vertical cracks that extend deep down into the solid rock show that other great masses will fall in the future. These and other landslips are largely due to the oversteepening associated with ice erosion and are therefore unlikely to have helped in the initiation of the earliest corries, but could well have added to their number later.

The rock cliffs of corries emphasise the importance of glacier ice as a transporting agent, for their steepness results from the ability of glacier ice to carry away material in large quantities even at its very source. At the present time frost-shattering of the rock faces gives rise in many corries to screes that partly mask the basal slopes, whereas when glaciers occupied the corries they carried this debris away. The glaciers also steepened the rock walls by plucking away blocks to which they were frozen, a process helped by water that ran down into the gap between rock wall and glacier and joined the two together on freezing. The debris collected by the ice resulted in the abrasion of the corrie floors so that here ice-smoothed rocks are common and striations record the directions in which the ice moved.

Where major lines of weakness occur in the rocks or very different types of rock are juxtaposed the form of corries may reflect these differences. In northwestern Sutherland many of the corries are floored with gneiss, which has not readily lent itself to excavation, whereas the adjacent quartzite is much more susceptible to break-up by freezing and thawing. The shallow rock basins occur along shatter planes and especially at places where these planes intersect (Thompson 1950). On the other hand, many corries have a marked simplicity of shape, forming regular curves in profile and plan. Seen from the air the edge of such corries, as in the Cuillins, Cairngorms and Tweedsmuir Hills, may form almost perfect semi-circles. In each of these three areas the development of this regularity has not been hampered by marked contrasts in rock type. Yet neither does it appear to have been assisted by the major lines of weakness inherent in the rocks. A tendency to approach this simple form seems to be a feature of corrie development and a possible clue to its cause is given by the work of M. H. Battey (1960). He has found that in two corries in Norway the principal vertical joint planes are aligned parallel with the corrie walls. This suggests that release of pressure caused by excavation of the corrie has allowed the rock to expand. Such expansion should assist in the development of a semi-circular form and should perpetuate it once it is established.

The reduction of the divides between corries to sharp-crested arêtes is well illustrated in the Cuillins and the Ben Nevis group of mountains along with those of the Mamore Forest. In these areas also some of the summits have been so encroached upon that they are pointed peaks. Often, however, the summits are very steep on one or two sides only. This results from the much greater frequency of corries on slopes facing directions between north-northwest and east-southeast. As shown in Fig. 21, the vast majority are orientated in these directions while hardly any face towards directions between south and west. This marked preference is caused partly by the prevailing winds blowing snow off summits and plateaux on to sheltered lee slopes and partly by differential exposure to the sun's rays. Especially important is the contrast between the morning sun when air temperatures are low and the afternoon sun when they are high. Fig. 21 shows that the most common direction of all is northeast, but that due north is also very frequent. This double peak results from northeast being most favoured so far as climatic factors are concerned, while a northerly aspect is partly related to the west-east trend of many of the divides. The latter factor is especially effective in the mountains west of the Great

Glen and has produced a marked asymmetry in the relief. North-facing slopes are often steep and rocky and deeply gashed by corries, whereas south-facing slopes sweep down in one continuous descent from watershed to valley floor. This asymmetry is very noticeable in Glen Shiel west of Loch Cluanie as well as in adjacent glens and is also strikingly seen in the mountains on either side of Glen Coe.

The distribution of corries in Scotland as a whole emphasises the importance of climatic factors. In Fig. 22 the overwhelming importance of the west is clear, for the western Highlands along with the mountains of the islands contain almost 90 per cent of the corries. Most of them, including some of the densest groupings, are found where precipitation at the present time exceeds 90 inches a year. In the northern part of the mainland, in Sutherland, important groups of corries occur even though the precipitation is below 90 inches, and this probably reflects the decrease in temperature associated with increase in latitude. In these northern areas lower summer temperatures in particular helped to compensate for the lower total snowfall. There is also a strong tendency in the Grampians for corries to be associated with lower precipitation towards the east. In the Cairngorms and the mountains south of the Dee they occur where the present precipitation is as low as 60 inches a year. In part this reflects increasing distance from the

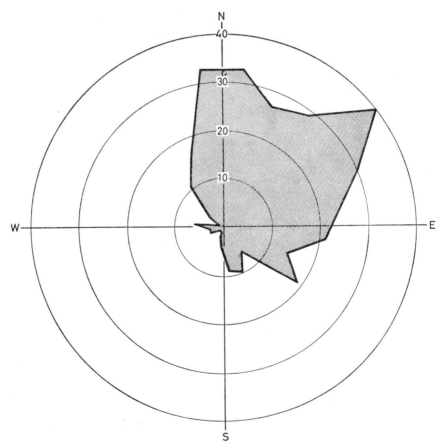

FIG. 21. Orientations of Scottish corries. The scale relates to the number of corries in each 15-degree sector.

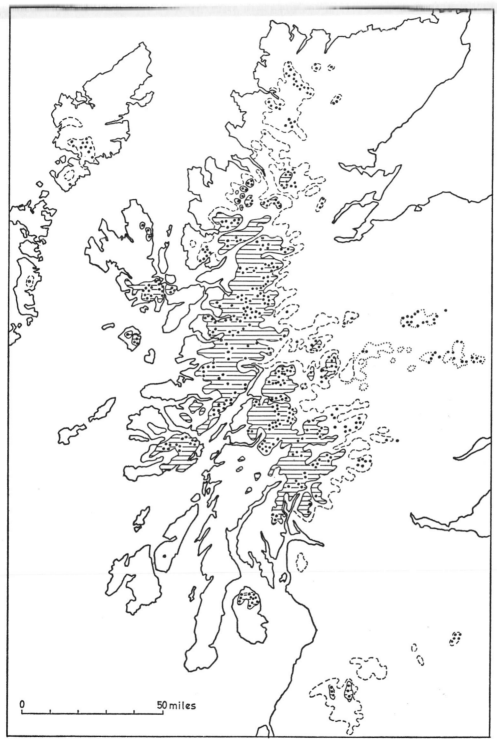

FIG. 22. Location of Scottish corries, after D. L. Linton 1959. Each dot represents one corrie. The shaded area now receives over 90 inches of precipitation a year. The broken line shows the 70-inch isohyet and the 60-inch is added in part of the central Grampians.

ameliorating influence of the Atlantic Ocean. It is also related, however, to the altitudes of the corries themselves.

The Scottish corries show a striking increase in altitude eastwards, as illustrated for successive west-east belts across the country in Fig. 23, where the dots represent the altitudes of corrie floors so far as these can be determined from Ordnance Survey maps. The low average altitude in the west indicates the importance of the abundant snowfall from air masses that had passed over the Atlantic. Eastwards, however, in the shelter of the western mountains, snow could not accumulate in sufficient quantities except at higher and higher altitudes. The protective influence of the western mountains is also to some extent brought out in Fig. 23 by the broken lines, which roughly represent the average altitudes of the corries, for it will be noted that in the two central belts the eastward rise is much more marked than in the other two belts. In part this difference results from the absence in the central and eastern Southern Uplands and Sutherland (as well as in Caithness) of ground high enough for the full altitudinal range of corrie development to be represented. It also probably reflects, however, the greater ease with

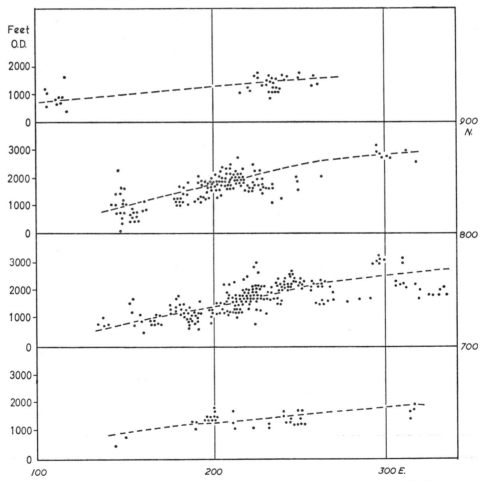

FIG. 23. Altitudes of Scottish corries plotted in successive west-east belts (whose limits are indicated by the grid references on the right). After D. L. Linton 1959.

which westerly winds could carry snowfall inland owing to the discontinuous nature and lower altitude of the western mountains in the Southern Uplands and Sutherland.

The climatic differences between west and east were emphasised in glacial times, especially in the Grampians along with the area west of the Great Glen. The North Sea, reduced in area owing to lowering of world sea-level, would be frozen over for much or all of the year (to the extent that it was not occupied by glacier ice). Hence Britain would, climatically, be one with the Continent and air streams from the east would not be warmed through passing over the North Sea. Neither would they be able to pick up much moisture, so that the considerable winter snowfalls that are now brought to eastern Scotland by showery winds from an easterly point could not occur. These air streams would thus bring dry and bitterly cold weather, especially to the eastern side of the country in winter. Furthermore, especially at times when the country was only partly covered by glacier ice, the differences that now exist when westerly air streams prevail would be emphasised. The accumulation of ice on the western mountains with their heavy snow-fall would, by its very presence, raise the average altitude of the mountain barrier and thus tend to increase the snowfall. The western precipitation would be still further increased relative to that of the east by the accumulation of rime, as mild air from the Atlantic was rapidly cooled at its base by contact with the ice and snow. The differences produced by these various factors would be most marked in the large upland block represented by the Grampians and the mountains west of the Great Glen, and it is here that the eastward increase in corrie altitudes is most marked. In the islands off the west coast corrie floors average less than 1000 feet above sea-level, but in the eastern Grampians the average is 2500 to 3000 feet. There are, in fact, large areas of plateau country in the east at altitudes of around 3000 feet where corries are rare or absent. It should not be assumed, however, that this means ice did not accumulate in these areas, for it probably built up on the plateaux themselves.

The eastward rise in corrie altitudes thus reflects the glacial snowlines. It is not possible to make reliable estimates of snowline altitudes (although the contrary has been claimed), for corries often vary greatly in altitude even in a small area. This is not sur-prising for, in addition to the effects of geology and aspect, the corries we see today are the end product of long periods of glacial conditions when snowlines must have varied widely. The situation is further complicated because of the different conditions that prevailed when a great ice-sheet existed. We have mentioned already that in the western Highlands there is clear evidence that the surface of the ice-sheet stood at more than 3000 feet above present sea-level, and we shall see later that in many other parts of Scotland the ice-sheet surface attained or exceeded 3000 feet. This must mean that the great majority of the Scottish corries (and probably all the mainland ones) have been submerged beneath an ice-sheet, and this probably on a number of occasions. In some instances this invading ice has reduced the gradient of the backwall or has cut a breach in the divide behind the corrie, partly destroying its backwall in the process. Doubtless in other instances the backwall has gone completely to produce a glacial breach and what was once a corrie is now no longer recognisable as such.

In Fig. 24 an attempt has been made to eliminate some of these complications by plot-ting only the altitudes of corrie lakes, excluding those where significant modification by external ice seems likely to have occurred. The diagram is based mainly on map data, so is subject to imperfections, but this does not affect the broad pattern. The highest group of lochans is obviously in the Cairngorms, with 7 out of 9 at 3000 feet or more, and Loch Coire an Lochain by Braeriach highest of all at 3250 feet. In the northern part of the mainland the great majority are below 2000 feet with some as low as 1200 or 1300 feet. Southwards from the belt of high corrie lakes in the central Grampians there is a marked fall in altitude, with lochs Brandy and Whorral overlooking Glen Clova at 2100 feet especially low. Corrie lakes are rare in the southern parts of Scotland, which are therefore omitted from Fig. 24, but it is noteworthy that Loch Skene in the centre of the Southern Uplands is at a mere 1600 feet while Loch Chorein Lochain in Arran lies at only 1100 feet. These altitudes, along with those shown in Fig. 24, suggest that, while the influence of latitude is seen in the northern part of the mainland, the degree of protection from snow-bearing winds exerted by high ground is everywhere very important.

While the corries and their lochans show some interesting variations in their distributional patterns, we must not lose sight of the predominant western occurrence of corries,

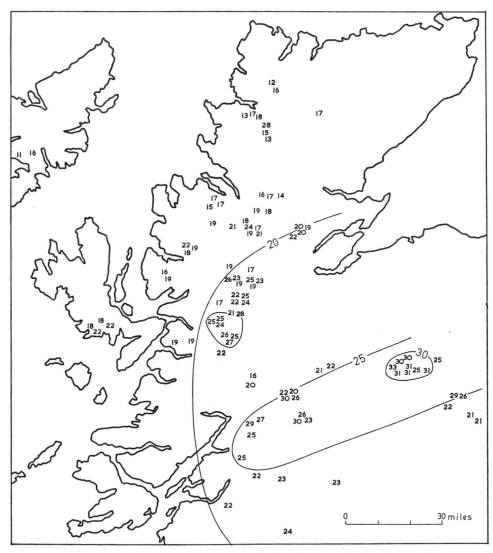

FIG. 24. Altitudes of corrie lakes, in hundreds of feet. The broken lines enclose areas where most of the lakes exceed 2000, 2500 and 3000 feet respectively.

with the area from Loch Broom to Loch Lomond supreme. Controlled by the high western snowfall the corries nurtured glaciers that moved down to lower ground and merged together to build up the great ice-sheets that from time to time spread outwards to cover the whole country. Lesser western centres of high precipitation in the larger islands and Southern Uplands nourished their own masses of ice, but these remained subordinate to the west Highland ice and in some instances were overwhelmed by it. Even less important, in view of their often considerable altitude, were the eastern centres of ice accumulation. Consequently not only corries, but also glacial troughs, rock basins, bars and breaches are predominantly western phenomena. A result is the widespread destruction of the Tertiary landscape in the west but its extensive survival in the east. The western emphasis on glacial action is inevitably reflected in the patterns of ice movement, and in the limits of the ice cover at different stages in its history. Conversely, the evidence of permanently-frozen glacier-free ground, of glacial deposits and of the work of glacial rivers is most clearly seen outside the areas of intense ice erosion. It is to some of these topics that we now turn, dealing first with the deposits laid down by the ice itself.

4

Glacial deposits:
their origin and significance

THE impressive erosion wrought by the ice in many parts of Scotland must inevitably be balanced by an equivalent amount of deposition. This did not all take place on the land, however, for a very considerable part of the material picked up by the glaciers was carried beyond the present coastline and now floors the surrounding seas. These sea-bed deposits have been scarcely investigated as yet, but are known to extend far out on the continental shelf. Some of this material was carried by the ice itself, for at times this extended beyond the Outer Hebrides in the west and beyond the Orkneys in the north. Bergs breaking off the ice mass must have transported some of the debris much farther afield, dropping it on the sea floor as they gradually melted, just as the ice-bergs from Greenland and Antarctica do today. Even at times of modest ice cover, debris was still carried away from the land area as glacial rivers laden with rock flour discharged their contents into the sea. Nevertheless, despite the large loss that must have occurred, there remain in many parts of Scotland extensive deposits of debris laid down by glaciers and by glacial rivers.

The material laid down by the ice itself – the glacial till – is especially abundant in many (but by no means all) lowlands and may completely blanket the solid rocks over wide areas. In some places its surface form merely reflects that of the buried surface of the solid rocks beneath, but in others it has its own distinctive forms such as drumlins and moraines. Apart from their importance as elements of the scenery, these landforms are also of much value in showing the directions in which the glaciers moved and in helping to delimit the extent of the ice cover at various times in the past. Much additional evidence relating to glacier movements and limits has been obtained from a study of the deposits themselves, especially of the types of material of which they are composed.

Lodgement till

The deposits laid down by glaciers can be divided into two main categories, namely lodgement till and ablation till. The former was deposited on the ground beneath moving glaciers. It is typically a tough tenacious deposit containing materials of all sizes, ranging from clay to boulders, and often *appears* to consist of a chaotic assemblage of debris lacking any pattern. The deposit is difficult to excavate since the materials are tightly packed together, a result of compression by the overlying ice and the mode of accumulation. The stones in the till are sometimes angular, especially close to the bedrock from which they were plucked by the ice, but typically they are better described as subangular or sub-rounded. The corners have been smoothed by rubbing against other stones or against bedrock during transit, and often one or more faces of a stone have been rubbed down to a flat or gently curved surface. On such a smoothed surface faint scratches or striae are common and are often readily visible. Hugh Miller, the younger (1884), observed that pieces of coal or shale as small as a finger-nail may bear striae, these being as minute as the lines on a finger-nail itself. He noted too that even particles a hundredth of an inch or so long were delicately scratched with lines about 1/2000 of an inch in width.

The striae on stones may run in various directions but, as was observed in 1850 by Hugh Miller, the elder, the majority of the scratches on a stone are usually parallel with the long axis (he said in 4 cases out of 5), and this is especially true of stones that are long in proportion to their width. Evidently, stones were usually transported with their long axis parallel with the direction of flow of the ice. This being so, we must expect the stones in lodgement till to record by their orientation the direction of ice flow and like-wise we may expect this orientation to be approximately the same as that of the striae on the bedrock surface immediately beneath. The point was made by T. F. Jamieson in 1866 when discussing lodgement till in Caithness. He wrote: 'The scratches on the boulders, as usual, run lengthways along the stones when they are of an elongated form; and the position of these stones, as they lie imbedded in the drift, is, as a rule, such that their longer axes point in the same direction as do the scratches on the solid rocks beneath, showing that the same agency that scored the rocks also ground and pushed along the drift.' Recent studies involving measurement of stone orientations in lodgement till confirm these early observations. It has been found also that the stones in lodgement till often (but by no means always) dip towards the direction from which the ice came.

Another feature of the till, noted particularly in and around Edinburgh, is the occasional occurrence of boulder pavements, first described by C. Maclaren in *The Scotsman* in 1828. These are horizontal or gently-inclined beds of boulders lying within the body of the till, with their glacially-smoothed upper surfaces resembling a pavement. The boulders may have minor scratches in various directions but the dominant direction of the striae is approximately the same as that on the solid rocks in the vicinity. Thus the pavements formerly visible on the shores of the Forth between Leith and Musselburgh recorded a movement of ice towards east-northeast. Such pavements are most commonly seen on the sea shore where the overlying till has been stripped off by the waves, and have been observed at Thorntonloch between Dunbar and Cockburnspath, on the shore of the Gare Loch and on the Solway shore about one mile south of Carsethorn.

The variations in size of the constituents of till reflect in large measure the two domi-nant types of glacial erosion. Rocks with well-marked lines of weakness were often plucked by the ice and gave rise to the innumerable stones that the till contains. On the other hand, abrasion of the bedrock, as the ice with its contained debris passed over it, produced sand, silt and clay. In addition the stones in transit in the ice themselves con-tributed to the finer constituents of the till as they were worn down. Just as the process of abrasion is demonstrated by the smoothed and striated rock surfaces that in places underlie the till, so also is the process of plucking often demonstrated by the basal layers of the till and the rock beneath. When boreholes are put down through lodgement till into the underlying rock it is often not possible to say precisely where the till ends and the rock starts. If sandstone or a similar well-jointed rock underlies the till the upper few feet (sometimes as much as ten feet) of the rock is greatly fragmented and is recorded by the borers as 'broken rock'. Where softer rocks such as shales or fireclays underlie the till, both bedrock and drift are often mixed together through a thickness of several feet.

Since these characteristics are present even in boreholes where rock is not encountered beneath the till until far below sea-level, it is clear that the break-up and distortion of the bedrock has nothing to do with atmospheric weathering. Rather does it record the manner in which the bedrock was eroded and incorporated in the till as the ice moved over it, and this is clearly shown by detailed descriptions and drawings of sections made last century by various workers.

J. Geikie (1878) described how in Harris, where the ice-sheet moved northwestwards, 'the truncated ends of the gneiss were bruised and bent over towards the northwest, and the fragments dislodged from them and enclosed in the superincumbent till streamed away in the same direction' (Fig. 25b). Similar bending over and removal of the strata

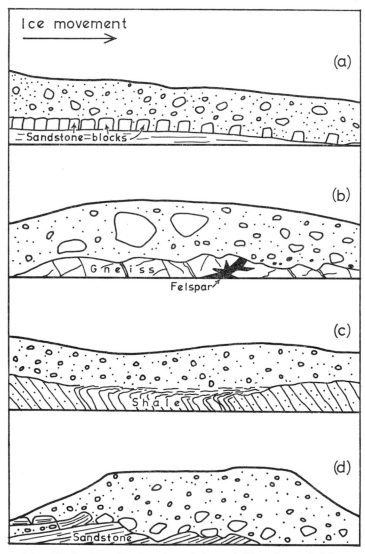

FIG. 25. Sections showing the relations of till to the underlying rocks. After J. Geikie 1878 and 1894, and J. Smith 1893.

in the Tweed valley are illustrated in Fig. 25c, while in Fig. 25d the incorporation of blocks of sandstone in the till is shown. J. Smith (1893) described sections in northern Ayrshire that showed till forced beneath soft shales, which were themselves crushed and drawn out into long black strings. Soft sandstones were crushed into brecciated material that trailed away from their source with the direction of ice movement. Where the sandstone was stronger and its dip favourable, Smith wrote: 'We first see a block started from its parent bed, with a portion of fine clay about the thickness of a knife blade occupying the joint. The block before it will perhaps have moved half-an-inch, the one before that still a little further, till we have a whole fleet of them, all at varying distances apart, and whose onward progress was only stopped by the breaking down of the machine that set them in motion' (Fig. 25a).

Such descriptions, coupled with the sections in Fig. 25 and the evidence of stone orientations and dip mentioned above, suggest that the lodgement till represents material that at one time was itself in motion beneath the moving ice. We may perhaps visualise at the base of the ice a layer of debris lubricated by water and ice particles being dragged along by the ice-mass above. It would appear that this material was itself at least partly responsible for the removal of the bedrock beneath. The thickness of the layer of flowing debris is unknown. It seems unlikely, however, that where the till is thick the whole of it was in motion at one time, and the boulder pavements we have described suggest that to some extent the till was built up layer by layer beneath the ice. Perhaps, therefore, we should envisage a layer of flowing subglacial debris whose thickness is dependent on such factors as the size of the particles and the thickness and velocity of the ice. When the ice is thick and active this moving layer may be in contact with the rock beneath, which is itself being eroded. With the waning of an ice-mass the reduction in its thickness and velocity may lead to the replacement of erosion by accumulation, the lower part of the till becoming stationary and the zone of flowing till gradually moving upwards as more and more material accumulates beneath the ice.

Ablation till

With the continued thinning of an ice-mass, which may result ultimately in its becoming stagnant, ablation till is deposited. Consequently it is often found that lodgement till is covered by the ablation material laid down during the later stages of ice decay.

Ablation till differs in various ways from the lodgement type. Although it contains debris of all sizes, silt and clay appear to be much less abundant than in lodgement till. Consequently the ablation material may often be described as sandy grit with stones, or sandy clay and stones. The stones may have striae and polished surfaces but these are less common than in lodgement till, while angular blocks seem more numerous. The deposit as a whole is less compacted than lodgement till, a fact well known from first-hand experience to labourers on building sites who will readily indicate the two types of material. This difference is borne out by tests of the bearing capacity of the deposits made in connection with construction works. These show that the ablation till will usually not safely bear a weight greater than about $1\frac{1}{2}$ tons a square foot, whereas lodgement till will carry a weight of many tons a square foot and the foundations of many large buildings rest safely on it.

Ablation till is typically a few feet thick, but sometimes attains a thickness of 10 or even 20 feet. It is sometimes separated from the underlying lodgement till by a thin band of water-sorted sand and gravel. The ablation till may contain wisps, lenticles and beds of sand and gravel or laminated silt and clay, and any or all of these deposits may be contorted. Ablation till is not present everywhere, of course, and on many hills the only signs of it are the boulders scattered over the land surface.

As its name implies, ablation till results from the wasting of glaciers due to melting, evaporation and other processes collectively referred to as ablation. Contrary to widespread opinion, it is not simply material that lay on the surface of the ice and was lowered on to the ground as the ice disappeared. Surface debris is rare on ice-sheets and even on valley glaciers it normally covers only a very small part of the surface. Rather is ablation till composed largely of the debris that was being carried in the basal layers of the ice. In some instances the preferred orientation of the stones in the ablation till is approximately parallel with that of the stones in adjacent lodgement till, implying that the structure developed in the material when it was being transported by the ice has been preserved. In other instances the preferred orientation is down the slope of the ground on which the material lies, suggesting that the structure was modified either as the material was let down from the ice or at a later time (Burke 1966).

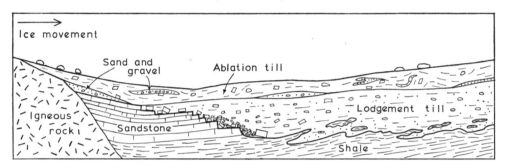

Fig. 26. Diagrammatic section showing relations of lodgement till to rock beneath and ablation till above.

The inclusion of water-sorted layers in the ablation till, and especially the presence in some places of such a layer at the base of the deposit, suggests that the change from the deposition of lodgement till to the deposition of ablation till coincides with the time when meltwaters began to penetrate freely to the base of the decaying ice. The two types of till together represent a unit of deposition that is depicted diagrammatically in Fig. 26, where the broken and disturbed rock at the base relates to a time when the ice was actively moving and the blocks on the ground surface represent the final material left by the decaying ice.

Distribution of till

Lodgement till is characteristic of many lowland areas. It is widespread and thick in parts of the Central Lowlands, the Solway lowlands, the lower part of the Tweed basin, Northeast Scotland and Caithness. On the other hand, in some lowlands, such as those of the Outer Hebrides, it is of very patchy occurrence and is often altogether absent. Clearly, therefore, it is not merely the presence of low ground that is responsible for the abundant development of lodgement till. Rather does it seem that an important factor is rock type. Whereas the metamorphic and igneous rocks of the Outer Hebrides tend to give rise to stones, grit and sand when subjected to glacial erosion, the sedimentary rocks of the other areas mentioned produce considerable amounts of clay and silt in addition to the coarser grades of material. Of particular importance here are the shales and clays, and it may well be that this fine material facilitated subglacial flowage of the till and is thus largely responsible for the abundant development of lodgement till in many lowlands.*

Lodgement till does occur, however, in areas of igneous and metamorphic rock. For example, although poorly developed in much of the Highlands, it locally attains a thickness of a hundred feet in valleys, as may be seen in bluffs cut in it by streams. Much more typical of most of the Highlands and of many of the islands, however, is the less consolidated ablation till. This may form an irregularly-distributed mantle partly concealing the solid rocks or it may produce a hummocky topography comprising vast numbers of individual knolls and depressions. (One such area in Glen Torridon is well named Coir' a' Cheud-chnoic, that is, Corrie of the Hundred Hills (Plate XIB).) In the lowlands characterised by lodgement till the ablation till overlies it as a layer of variable thickness but rarely has any distinct relief of its own.

The distribution of the two types of till taken together shows a strong relation to glacial erosion and to the limits of the ice cover at various times in the past. It is necessary to emphasise the erosional significance of till since there is a common tendency, which is encouraged by text-books, to think of areas of glacial erosion as distinct from areas of glacial deposition. We have already seen in the last chapter, however, that even in the Central Lowlands with its widespread till deposits the ice eroded far below sea-level in places. Erosion is also demonstrated by the content of the till itself, for in both uplands and lowlands it is usually composed mainly of fragments derived from the bedrock close at hand. Thus the very abundance of till in many lowlands implies very considerable erosion by the ice of the bedrock of these same lowlands.

It appears that each major advance of the ice was associated with renewed erosion, although towards the margin of the ice at any given time deposition was more important. One reason for adopting this view is that over much of Scotland there is evidence in any particular area of only one widespread till sheet, this being the layer of lodgement and ablation till laid down by the last ice mass to cover that area. Since it is known that Scotland has been covered by a great ice-sheet on several occasions, this means that the deposits of earlier glaciations were completely (or almost completely) swept away by the last ice-sheet from much of the area it covered. The last glaciation was not, however, a simple event with a single advance of ice to its maximal extent followed by a continuous waning, but comprised several lesser oscillations. The oscillations since the last ice-sheet reached its maximal extent are partly known (Fig. 59) and enable us to envisage periods when the ice was wasting away followed by periods when it began to build up and advance again. The final readvance was represented by valley glaciers in various mountain areas.

Reflecting the pattern of glacial advances and readvances, we find that in Northeast Scotland, far removed from the main centres of ice accumulation and sheltered from them in part by high ground, till is widely developed on low ground. In this area the ice appears to have reached its maximal extent on more than one occasion. Similarly in the Tweed basin and Southwest Scotland abundant deposition of till occurred towards the limits of the readvances shown in Fig. 59, while the same is true of the Clyde coalfield basin. In the Highlands innumerable mounds often characterise the lower ground covered by the last limited advance of valley glaciers.

By the time the last ice-sheet began to waste away from its farthest limit we may therefore envisage the deposits of earlier glaciations as having been largely removed from

* In eastern Caithness much of the fine material in the till may have been derived from the adjacent sea bed (p. 81).

much of the ground it had covered. Towards the margin of the ice-sheet deposition prevailed and, as the ice decayed, so this zone of deposition (first of lodgement till and then of ablation till) moved inwards to replace the erosion that had been previously occurring. When the climate deteriorated and the ice temporarily advanced again, so the zones of erosion and deposition moved outwards with it. Consequently, till deposited not long before was often eroded, except in the peripheral belt towards the limit of the readvance. The relationships to one another of such till sheets are shown diagrammatically in Fig. 27.

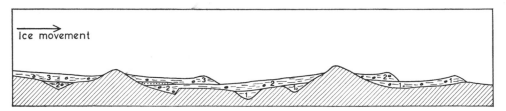

Fig. 27. Diagram showing the relation to each other of till sheets associated with different glacial advances or readvances.

Contents of till

An important aspect of till (and of related deposits, such as those laid down by glacial rivers) is the type of rock debris of which it is composed for, in addition to local materials, there occur other rock fragments that may have travelled considerable distances and that tell us a great deal about the directions in which the ice moved.

The fact that till is usually for the most part of local origin is shown by its colour, for this is very often the same as that of the solid rocks beneath. Thus on the Old and New Red sandstones the till takes on the red colour of these rocks, as may be seen in Lauderdale, parts of Nithsdale and Annandale, southern Arran, the Highland border belt from Loch Lomond to Strathmore, and the Moray Firth area. The Old Red Sandstone is not always true to its name, however, and in parts of Caithness is associated with a leaden-coloured till. The grey shales and the coal seams of the coalfields impart to the till a colour that is variously described as grey, bluish or bluish-black, while the metamorphic rocks of the Highlands and Outer Hebrides often give rise to tills that are fawn or grey in colour.

Where solid rocks of contrasting colour are juxtaposed the corresponding change in till colour may take place in hundreds (sometimes even in tens) of yards from the line of junction, thus revealing the general direction of the ice movement and the local character of the main constituents of the till. Few reliable figures for the composition of till have been published but such as are available show that most of the stones have not travelled very far. James Smith (1838) found that in Glasgow the stones in the till comprise about 60 per cent local sandstone, between 9 and 10 per cent metamorphic rocks from the Highlands, and less than 1 per cent granite from the Highlands. R. Craig (1874) counted thousands of stones over 3 inches in length in till in northern Ayrshire and Renfrewshire and found that 95 per cent of them could have come from the bedrock within five miles of where they were found. It needs to be emphasised, however, that studies of till have been almost entirely concerned with the stone content and it may be that analysis of the finer particles might produce different results, at least in some areas.

PLATE IX. A. Grained landscape in metamorphic rocks, margin of Cairns-more of Fleet granite. B. Drumlins near New Galloway, Kircud-brightshire. *Ministry of Defence (Air Force Department) photographs. Crown Copyright reserved.*

PLATE X. A. Crag-and-tail of Duncryne Hill, by Loch Lomond. *Geological Survey photograph. Crown Copyright reserved.* B. Hummocky moraines and former lake site, Glen Strathfarrar, Inverness-shire. *Ministry of Defence (Air Force Department) photograph. Crown Copyright reserved.*

While the distribution of fragments of sedimentary rocks in the till often indicates the general direction of ice movement, the distribution of igneous rock fragments is often of much greater value. This arises partly because most igneous rocks are more durable and are therefore better able to withstand transport by ice; partly because some igneous rocks have distinctive characteristics that enable the fragments distributed by the ice to be confidently related to the parent source; and partly because certain igneous rocks crop out over small areas. In some instances the movement of the ice is clearly marked by the trail of debris streaming from a mass of igneous rock, the most striking example of this being the narrow belt of boulders that leads eastwards from a small outcrop of essexite near Lennoxtown. This outcrop measures only 700 yards by 100 yards, yet the boulders were traced by A. M. Peach (1909) along the southern slopes of the Kilsyth Hills and then (after a gap of a few miles where later deposits conceal the glacial ones) along the shores of the Firth of Forth to a distance of 40 miles from the parent source (Fig. 28). For the first two or three miles from the essexite outcrop the boulders are numerous, especially in the central part of the boulder train. Farther away the boulders are much less abundant but they remain restricted to a narrow belt which is no more than $2\frac{1}{2}$ miles wide at a distance of 15 miles from their source and only 4 miles across even 35 miles away. This implies a consistent direction of ice movement in this part of the Central Lowlands when these boulders were being deposited.

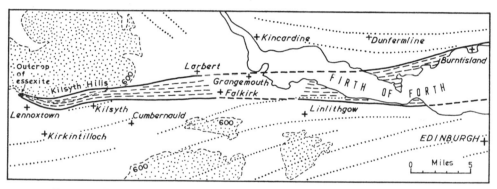

FIG. 28. The Lennoxtown boulder train, based on A. M. Peach 1909. Dotted lines record the trends of the ice-moulded relief.

Unlike the Lennoxtown boulders, most Scottish erratics to which attention has been directed have a wide field of distribution. In some instances, in fact, they appear to have been carried to all points of the compass. In Figs 29-32 some of the better-known distributions have been plotted on the basis of statements in many publications, especially the memoirs of the Geological Survey. It must be emphasised that these maps are incomplete, for no really thorough studies have yet been made of the distribution of any of the erratics. It is also possible that in some instances erratics have been allocated to the wrong source, for only rarely have thin sections been made of them for comparison under the microscope with sections of the presumed parent rock. Despite these limitations, however, the erratics help considerably in understanding the patterns of ice movement in certain parts of the country.

In the western part of the Southern Uplands the various granite masses are the most useful sources of erratics (Charlesworth 1926a). Boulders of the Loch Doon granite are distributed in all directions (except, apparently, eastwards) and thus emphasise the importance of the Loch Doon area as a centre of ice radiation. This spread is indicated diagrammatically in Fig. 29 by the radiating arrows, which are drawn to extend over the ground in which these erratics are said to occur. These lines do not indicate the routes followed by the ice, which were often far less direct. It must also be remembered that this area, in common with the rest of Scotland, has been covered by ice on a number of occasions. Hence some of the erratics may have reached their present resting places by devious routes, having been transported in different directions by the glaciers at different times.

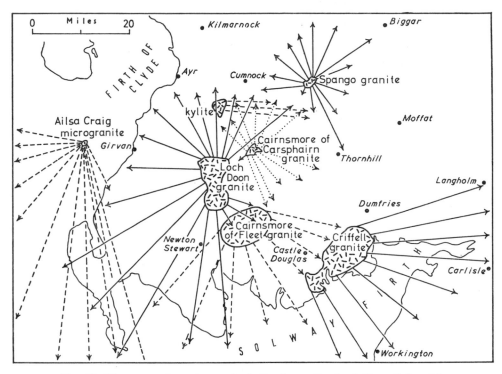

FIG. 29. Transport of certain erratics in Southwest Scotland. Compiled mainly from information in J. K. Charlesworth 1926a and J. B. Simpson *et al.* 1936.

The Cairnsmore of Fleet erratics were spread out less widely than those of the Loch Doon granite and were carried in directions varying between southwest and east-south-east. The erratics of Criffell granite reveal a more easterly component in their distribution and have been traced across northern England through the Tyne gap. Southwards some of the granite erratics from the Southern Uplands were carried across the site of the Irish Sea and have been found as far away as North Wales and the Midlands. On the other hand, they were carried a very much shorter distance towards the north. This reflects the importance of the powerful Highland ice which, for long periods, occupied much or all of the Central Lowlands and the Firth of Clyde and forced the Southern Upland ice to move southwards and eastwards.

The influence of the Highland ice is also seen in the eastward transport into the upper Nith valley around New Cumnock and Sanquhar of boulders of kylite, whose only source lies between Dalmellington and Ochiltree in Ayrshire (Simpson *et al.* 1936). The Highland ice that filled the Firth of Clyde also covered much of central Ayrshire, where erratics of Highland schist are common, but farther south, where high ground comes close to the sea, it affected only a narrow strip along the coast. From Bennane Head southwards its former presence is recorded by boulders of Ailsa Craig microgranite, which increase in numbers to become abundant in the neighbourhood of Stranraer. These readily-identifiable stones, derived from the small round-topped island that rises steeply to 1100 feet in the middle of the Firth of Clyde, have been found over a wide area extending from the Mull of Kintyre to Antrim, southern Lancashire, South Wales and southern Ireland. To reach the farthest point at which they have been discovered they must have travelled at least 300 miles.

In the Highlands south of the Great Glen four areas of igneous rock – three of granite

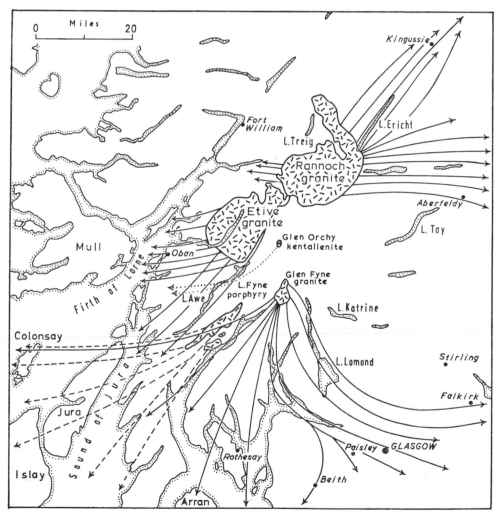

Fig. 30. Transport of some erratics in the western Grampians and adjacent ground. Compiled mainly from information in Geological Survey publications.

and one of porphyry – are particularly useful in tracing the paths followed by the ice (Fig. 30). These erratics portray clearly the radial flow of the ice that prevailed for long periods from the major area of accumulation in the Southwest Grampians. Unfortunately the pattern is incomplete since a suitably-placed mass of igneous rock was not available to supply readily-identifiable erratics for the sector between east and south. The landforms, striae and local transport of some of the metamorphic rocks do show, however, that a movement of the ice-sheet towards east and southeast prevailed in this sector.

Among the erratic stones from the Highlands that early aroused interest were those of granite found in the Glasgow area. At first it was thought that these stones had come from the Ben Cruachan mass, but in 1852 W. Hopkins traced them into the Highlands along the shores of lochs Lomond, Goil and Long and part of Loch Fyne. Towards the heads of lochs Lomond and Fyne he realised he was approaching the source of the boulders for they became larger, more angular and much more abundant, and he found the rock in place roughly midway between the heads of the two lochs in the uplands between Glen Fyne and Loch Sloy. This Glen Fyne granite, despite the limited area of its outcrop, has since been traced far afield and has been found at places as widely scattered as Colonsay, northern Arran, Airdrie and Edinburgh. Its distribution in Fig. 30 is shown by curving lines since there is sufficient evidence in places to enable the routes of transport to be indicated in a general way. For example, the boulders are common along the shores of Loch Lomond and are scattered over the Kilpatrick Hills and the Strathblane gap. They have been followed also along the shores of the Clyde estuary through Glasgow into the coalfield basin, while a distributary stream has been traced down the eastern side of the Garnock valley towards Kilwinning. From the Strathblane gap eastwards the path of the ice is recorded by the Lennoxtown boulder train, and from this and the Glen Fyne erratics we may infer that part at least of the ice-stream that flowed slightly north of east across the Lothians had previously travelled along the Loch Lomond valley and across the Kilpatrick Hills. It may also be observed that the recorded distribution of the Glen Fyne granite seems incomplete. For example, ice from the Loch Lomond valley flowed into the Forth basin through the glacial breach occupied by Loch Arklet and also through the gap between Drymen and Buchlyvie, so that erratics of the Glen Fyne granite should be scattered over a larger part of the Central Lowlands than is indicated in Fig. 30.

The transport of erratics of the Loch Fyne porphyry adds to the radial pattern, the stones fanning out to between west and southwest across Knapdale and Jura and as far as Colonsay. In the neighbourhood of Loch Craignish the distribution of these stones overlaps with that of the erratics from the Loch Etive granite complex. It may be that these granite erratics, which are rather scarce here, relate to a southwestward movement of ice preceding the last movement directed more towards the west. Apart from the features produced by glacial erosion referred to on p. 49, this approximately westward flow of ice is strongly suggested by the great abundance of granite erratics around Oban, as well as around lower Loch Etive and in Benderloch (Kynaston et al. 1908). A general westward movement in this area is also suggested by the transport of Glen Strae augite-diorite (not shown in Fig. 30) and Glen Orchy kentallenite to the hills south of Loch Scamadale.

The main transport of Rannoch granite was towards the east and northeast. Large blocks of this rock are strewn along both sides of Loch Ericht and lie stranded in the shallow water at the head of the loch (Hinxman et al. 1923). They continue into Glen Truim where they are joined by another stream of the same granite blocks that can be followed past Loch Garry and through the Pass of Drumochter. A third trail of these erratics can be traced past Loch an Duin into Glen Tromie. These various routes lead through the main west-east watershed of the Grampians and the transport of the Rannoch granite thus accords with the evidence of glacial breaching of this divide. The granite erratics also show that the ice spread over high ground between the deep breaches, although they are apparently absent from some of the most elevated tracts, such as the summit of Ben Alder and the highest parts of the Gaick plateau. The glacial breaches lead to the Spey valley and the granite erratics have been followed down this valley in diminishing size and numbers to Kingussie and perhaps even as far as Aviemore. They were also spread over the basin of the Garry and carried eastwards down the Tummel valley. Their southern limit of distribution seems to be well defined, for while they occur high up on the divide between the Tummel and the Lyon they appear to be quite absent from Glen Lyon itself.

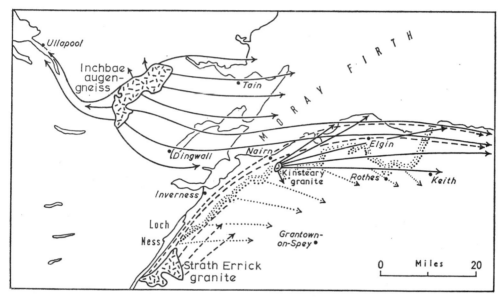

FIG. 31. Transport of some erratics in the neighbourhood of the Moray Firth. Compiled mainly from information in W. Mackie 1905 and Geological Survey publications. The southern limit of the Old Red Sandstone to the south of the Moray Firth is indicated. The outcrop of the Inchbae augengneiss has been extended to include the conglomerate in which pieces of this rock occur.

The northeastward movement of ice that gouged out the basin of Loch Ness and roughened the high ground on either side is recorded by the northeastward carry of erratics from the granite outcrop in Strath Errick (Fig. 31). Towards the Moray Firth, however, the ice-stream began to turn towards the east and some of the erratics were carried along the Moray coastlands at least as far as the mouth of the Spey (Mackie 1905). This movement is also recorded by the similar distribution of boulders of the distinctive conglomerate of Strath Errick and Strath Nairn, which are numerous in the coastlands of the south side of the Moray Firth and often of large size. Further evidence is provided by the distribution of pieces of the Kinsteary granite, which appears at the surface over only a small area close to Nairn (Fig. 31). The flow of ice along the coastlands of the Moray Firth suggests deflection by a powerful ice-mass from some other source. That such a mass was nourished, at least in part, in the interior of Ross-shire is shown by the distribution of erratics of the Inchbae augen-gneiss, which have long attracted attention. These erratics have been found over the whole of Easter Ross, excepting only the highest ground of Ben Wyvis and a narrow strip by the Beauly Firth, and point to a general eastward movement of ice in this area. They have been discovered also at various points on or near the coasts of Morayshire and Banffshire. This may mean that the ice from Ross-shire actually impinged on this coastal zone or that the erratics reached their present resting places as a result of transport by different ice-streams at more than one time. In either event, however, it is evident that ice from Ross-shire (doubtless along with ice from the mountains farther south) was responsible for the deflection of the ice that streamed out of the Great Glen.

The erratics of the Inchbae augen-gneiss are also of considerable significance in that B. N. Peach and J. Horne (1892) inferred from their distribution that, at the time of maximal glaciation, the ice-shed in this part of the Northern Highlands was situated at least six miles to the east of the existing water-shed at Loch Droma. They adopted this view as a result of finding that the Inchbae erratics can be followed westwards from the parent rock outcrop through the glacial breach at Loch Droma and thence along the shores of Loch Broom almost to Ullapool. This interpretation needs to be modified, however, for as can be seen in Fig. 31, the meagre carry of these rocks towards the west coast does not bear comparison with the widespread carry towards the east. Rather does it appear that the ice-shed during much of the last glaciation lay to the west of the augen-gneiss outcrop, and that the transport of boulders of this rock to the west and northwest occurred at a late stage of the glaciation when a large valley glacier flowed through the Loch Droma breach to Loch Broom.

The position of the ice-shed at times of extensive ice cover in the Northwest Highlands as a whole is not accurately known, although the available evidence is suggestive. A short distance east of the watershed in the Fannich Mountains striae at an altitude of about 3000 feet point west-northwest, while striae at lower levels also show a movement of ice westwards across the watershed. Similar evidence is provided by the striae in the extreme western part of the basin of Loch Monar. Much farther north, in the Ben More Assynt range, striae and the transport of blocks of thrust Lewisian Gneiss and Moine Schist show that ice moving towards the west must have crossed this high ground that now forms the divide between eastward- and westward-flowing streams (Peach and Horne 1892). On the other hand, a very short distance to the east of the several localities mentioned there is clear evidence of a prevailing eastward movement of ice. It thus appears that at times of extensive ice-cover the ice-shed was situated, at least in places, a short distance to the east of the present drainage divide. As the ice moved across the original divide erosion of the glacial breaches described in the last chapter occurred, and doubtless this excavation was continued at times of more modest ice-cover, as suggested by the westward carry of augen-gneiss shown in Fig. 31.

Returning to the Moray coastlands, Fig. 31 shows that, in addition to the movement of ice towards the east and east-northeast, there is evidence of a movement towards a direction south of east. This is indicated by the distribution of erratics of Old Red sandstone and conglomerate, but since these rocks together cover a wide area only the general direction of transport is suggested by the lines shown in Fig. 31. Much clearer evidence of a movement towards directions south of east is provided in the ground extending eastwards from the vicinity of the River Spey. In this area several distinctive igneous rocks come to the surface over quite small areas. As shown in Fig. 32, the Netherly diorite, Bin Hill gabbro, Blairshinnoch amphibolite and Barra Hill dolerite have all been carried towards the southeast (and even south), implying that the vast ice-mass that emanated from the Great Glen and the western mountains gradually changed course to grind

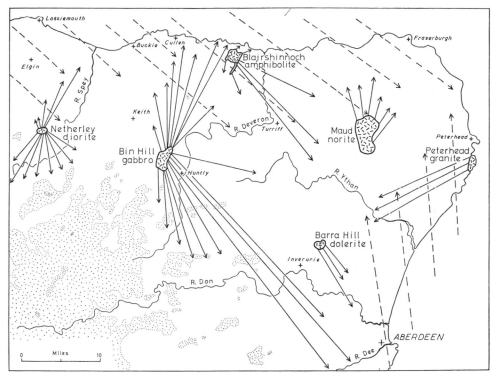

FIG. 32. Transport of some erratics in Northeast Scotland. Based mainly on H. H. Read 1923, A. Bremner 1932, and F. M. Synge 1956. The broken lines represent the landward transport of shelly drift with Mesozoic erratics (north coast) and red drift (east coast). Ground above 1200 and 2400 feet shaded.

across Northeast Scotland. The Netherly and Bin Hill rocks, however, as well as the Maud norite, have also been transported towards northerly points, thus showing that on at least one occasion a very different direction of ice movement prevailed. Yet further complication is introduced by the distribution of the Peterhead granite, which has been transported inland towards the southwest from its coastal outcrop. The variable patterns of ice movement revealed by these erratics have fortunately been discussed by a number of workers and we will return to the consideration of them in Chapter 7.

The Northeast is also of particular interest because of the Scandinavian erratics that have been found. Such erratics, which must have travelled at least 300 miles, are rare in Scotland and have been found only along the east coast. A Scandinavian boulder has been discovered in Shetland and another in Orkney, while single boulders have been found on the shore at Portsoy in Banffshire and by Tantallon Castle in East Lothian. The boulders

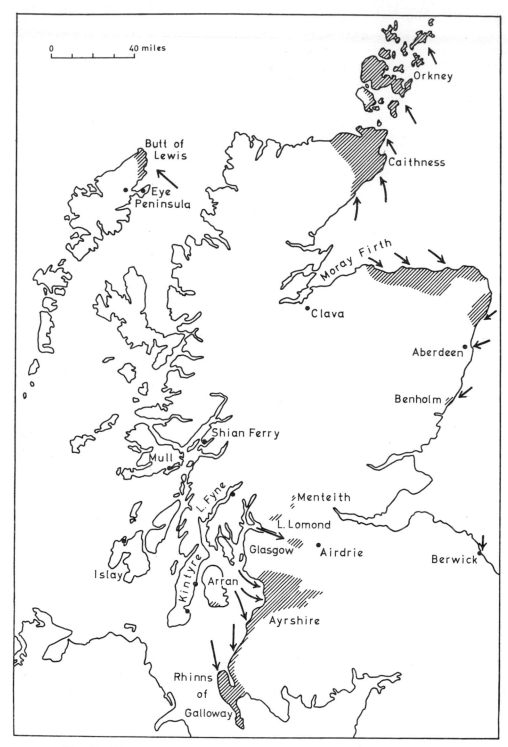

Fig. 33. Distribution of glacial till containing marine shells and/or other marine organisms. The related directions of ice movement are suggested by arrows. Based on numerous sources.

are most numerous around Aberdeen, several having been found near Ellon and a considerable number having been seen in a cliff section and on the adjacent shore at the Bay of Nigg immediately south of the city (p. 133).

One aspect of the drift that has long attracted interest is the presence in it of marine organisms in many places. The distribution of this type of deposit so far as it is known at present is shown in Fig. 33 and it can be readily appreciated why some geologists, such as John Smith in Ayrshire, argued strongly for a marine origin of the till long after most other workers had rejected this idea. In almost all the locations shown in Fig. 33 the drift contains marine shells, usually in till but sometimes in associated sands and gravels. The shells are usually in fragments and sometimes only their strongest parts are preserved, although occasionally a complete shell may be found. The shell fragments are often rubbed at their edges and sometimes striated and the original markings on their outer surfaces may be obliterated. T. F. Jamieson (1866), describing the Caithness shelly drift, said that where the shell fragments are elongated the striae run lengthways along them, and stated that even the minute foraminifers when viewed under the microscope have a rubbed and worn appearance.

One way in which shells became incorporated in the glacial deposits was through ice from the land moving into the sea (or over ground formerly covered by the sea). Such deposits have been found in the Forth valley near Lake of Menteith, around the southern end of Loch Lomond, at Shian Ferry by Loch Creran, between lochs Spelve and Uisg in Mull and possibly on the shores of Loch Fyne. Except by Loch Fyne these shelly deposits are incorporated in moraines that mark the limit of a late readvance of glaciers from adjacent mountains. They show, for example, that Loch Lomond (or at least part of it) was an arm of the sea before, and perhaps during, the time glacier ice last advanced into it.

In all the other places shown in Fig. 33 the marine deposits were carried by ice that moved from the land across areas now covered by the sea and then on to a land area again. The great Highland ice-stream that flowed down the Firth of Clyde spread till with marine organisms widely over the lowlands of central Ayrshire and up to considerable heights on the surrounding hills. Shells have certainly been found at an altitude of over 1000 feet and, it has been claimed, even as high as 1330 feet a few miles from Muirkirk (Smith 1898, 1902). The most inland point at which they have been obtained is about midway between Muirkirk and Douglas. This deep penetration of the Highland ice accords with the carry of kylite erratics into the Nith valley (Fig. 29) and also hints strongly at the influence of the Highland ice in the glacial breaching of the original Southern Upland watershed between Sanquhar and Thornhill. The strip of shelly drift along the coast of southern Ayrshire and in the Rhinns of Galloway accords with the distribution of Ailsa Craig erratics and indicates the ability of the Southern Upland ice, helped by the relief, to fend off the Highland ice from the western hills at the time the shelly drift was deposited.

In the coalfield basin of the Clyde shells have been found in or beneath the glacial deposits at only two points, namely Chapelhall near Airdrie, and Blairdardie about five miles northwest of the centre of Glasgow. Both finds were made last century and their validity has been questioned, but there seems no reason to doubt these old records. More significant, however, is an analysis made of the glacial deposits at various points in and close to Glasgow. J. Wright (1896) took samples of till at ten different places and in every instance it was found to contain foraminifers. The presence of these minute marine organisms is not surprising in view of the ice movement up the Clyde valley past Glasgow recorded, for example, by the Glen Fyne granite (Fig. 30). This study of more than seventy years ago does lead one to suspect, however, that a resumption of this type of investigation might considerably extend the distributions shown in Fig. 33 and might prove of considerable value in defining the limits of till sheets laid down by ice that had moved over the sea bed.

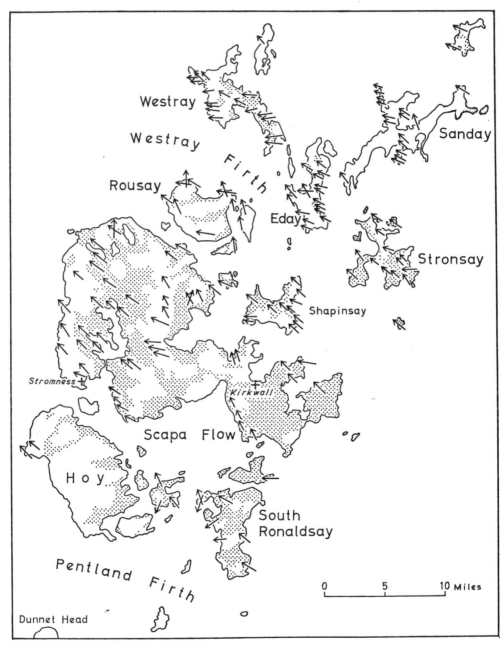

FIG. 34. Striae and distribution of glacial drift in the Orkney Islands. Based on B. N. Peach and J. Horne 1880, and G. V. Wilson *et al.* 1935.

Although there is widespread evidence that most of the Outer Hebrides was covered by the mainland ice-sheet moving northwestwards and westwards, shelly tills have not been observed except in northern Lewis. Neither have they been found in many other western islands. J. Geikie's (1894) suggestion that the fairly gentle sea-bed slope on the eastern side of northern Lewis (as opposed to the steep slope that exists offshore elsewhere along the eastern side of the Outer Hebrides) may have facilitated transport of sea-floor material on to the adjacent land, may provide a partial explanation of this anomaly in the Outer Hebrides, although it needs to be remembered that in these and other islands very few detailed studies have been made.

On the eastern side of Scotland shelly drift is of widespread occurrence in the coastal belt from Lossiemouth and Elgin to beyond Fraserburgh and has been carried inland as much as ten miles. This movement accords with the general southeastward transport of certain erratics referred to already. On the other side of the Moray Firth a movement of ice on to the land is demonstrated by the widespread distribution of shelly till in Caithness and the Orkney Islands. Striae, boulder orientations and other evidence show that in the southern part of Caithness the movement was northwards, but inland and towards John o' Groat's, as well as in the Orkneys, the prevailing direction was northwestwards (Figs 34 and 39). This direction of ice-flow implies that the Scottish ice pouring into the Moray Firth area was unable to spread freely to the east owing to the presence of the Scandinavian ice-sheet and was deflected across Caithness and the Orkneys. Such deflection also seems to be needed to account for the transport of shelly drift from the bed of the North Sea into various parts of the coastal belt between Peterhead and Montrose (Fig. 33).

Considering the glacial drifts with marine organisms in Scotland as a whole, it appears that almost all of them relate to the last ice movements in the areas in which they are found, for they usually form the uppermost layer of glacial drift. The principal exceptions are the shelly drifts of the coastal zone between Peterhead and the mouth of the Tweed and those around Elgin and the mouth of the Spey. The shells themselves, of which one of the most common is *Cyprina islandica*, usually suggest a cold climate although not an extremely cold one (the 'subarctic' type of Chapter 8). It needs to be emphasised, however, that the shells have not usually been studied systematically, that assemblages relating to different environments were probably mixed together during transport by the ice, and that often only the stronger shells are readily identifiable so that published faunal lists do not necessarily represent the true character of the deposits picked up by the ice. One deposit that has been investigated in some detail – in northern Lewis – shows distinct evidence of climatic changes and includes evidence of a climate at least as warm as the present one (p. 195).

One very significant group of erratics found especially in parts of eastern Scotland comprises various sedimentary rocks belonging to the Mesozoic era, particularly Jurassic and Cretaceous ones. These erratics are included in the deposits containing marine shells and it appears that their distribution in eastern Scotland is exactly the same as that of the shelly drifts. The Mesozoic erratics are especially abundant in Caithness and the coastal belt eastwards from Elgin and are sometimes of very large size. Here they include limestones, sandstones, fossil wood, jet, chalk and chalk flints. On the east coast of Aberdeenshire the shelly drifts occur with chalk and chalk flints, around Benholm they are associated with pieces of jet, and at the mouth of the Tweed they are found along with fragments of Belemnites. These erratics are important because chalk or other Cretaceous rocks do not occur anywhere on the land area of the east of Scotland *in situ*,

while Jurassic rocks are restricted to a narrow coastal strip between Helmsdale and Golspie, a few very tiny patches on the coast near the entrance to the Cromarty Firth and a
small area by Lossiemouth. Chalk and chalk flints are intimately associated with the
shelly drifts in southern Ayrshire and the Rhinns of Galloway beginning at about
Ballantrae and increasing in abundance southwards and suggest that chalk forms the
adjacent sea floor in places. This evidence, apart from its relevance to ice movements,
is of considerable importance in relation to the Tertiary evolution of Scotland, as
discussed in Chapter 1.

Another interesting aspect of the Mesozoic erratics in Caithness, Morayshire and
Banffshire is the remarkable size of some of them. Large ice-transported boulders are
widely distributed in Scotland generally and in populated areas were much more numerous in past times than they are now, many having been broken up to be incorporated in
walls or buildings or used as road metal. Some of the largest ones are so conspicuous that
they have been introduced into local folk-lore, their presence being attributed, for
example, to giants who tossed them across lochs or from one island to another. Consequently one finds boulders are known by such names as Rob Roy's Putting Stone
(near Taynuilt by Loch Etive), Samson's Putting Stone (near Callander) and Fingal's
Putting Stone (near Kingussie). Boulders have also long attracted scientific attention
and a Boulder Committee was set up last century by the Royal Society of Edinburgh
under the energetic leadership of D. Milne-Home. Between 1872 and 1884 this committee published ten reports relating to the location, size, origin and many other aspects
of Scottish boulders, although unfortunately the value of the conclusions expressed was
somewhat marred by the unorthodox views of Milne-Home himself.

Transported boulders weighing tens of tons are common in the Highlands where
valley sides are steep, especially as one approaches the corries, although some are found
in lower ground. Among some of the largest Scottish examples are a boulder about 30
feet square at the base, 15 feet high and probably weighing 400 tons that lies near the
coast south of the Corrie Burn in Arran; one near Ormsary House by Loch Caolisport
in Knapdale that originally had dimensions of 52 by 36 by 20 feet; and one near North
Harbour in Barra roughly estimated to contain 24 000 cubic feet of rock. These conspicuous masses lying on the surface are small, however, compared with some transported masses revealed by quarrying operations or geological investigations. At Leavad
in Caithness a mass of Cretaceous sandstone measures about 240 yards by 150 yards
by 26 feet thick. It rests on green shelly clay that is 25 feet thick at one point and extends
at least 120 yards farther than the sandstone in one direction. The sandstone and shelly
clay together form one huge erratic that can only have come from the present sea floor
at least 9 or 10 miles away (Carruthers 1911). Between Elgin and Lossiemouth a transported mass of Jurassic rock was shown by quarrying operations to measure at least 300
yards by 120 yards by 40 feet thick. Farther east in Banffshire several large erratics of
clay with Jurassic fossils have been located, some of them big enough to have contained
clay pits worked for many years. In Edinburgh at Comiston a sheet of volcanic rock about
8 to 10 feet thick and measuring perhaps 400 feet by about 60 feet was encountered on
top of water-laid sand in a sand pit. This sheet of rock is thought to have been carried
from a part of the Pentland Hills about two miles away (Campbell and Anderson 1910).
Finally we may mention a vast block of limestone at the foot of the Lammermuir Hills
in East Lothian that measures about a third of a mile long and a quarter of a mile broad,
contains an old limestone quarry, and must have been carried by the ice at least three or
four miles.

Another interesting aspect of glacial transport revealed by many of the erratics to which we have just referred is the ability of ice to carry material uphill on a considerable scale. The deposits transferred from the present sea bed to the adjacent land areas clearly demonstrate such uphill movement, amounting to a thousand feet or more in Ayrshire. More remarkable than this is the great Leavad erratic which, to reach its present resting place on the Caithness plateau, must have been carried inland by the ice from the sea floor up the cliffs and over hills at least 500 feet high before being deposited on their farther side. Less obvious but equally significant is the widespread evidence of uphill transport of erratics in many inland areas. Thus near the Loch Doon granite area, whose highest point is 2270 feet, granite boulders are found on the summit of Merrick (2764 feet), which is composed of metamorphic rocks. A similar upward carry of at least 500 feet is shown by boulders of Glen Fyne granite found by the summit of Beinn an Fhidleir at over 2600 feet, the highest point of the rock outcrop being 2115 feet. The Lennoxtown essexite was carried obliquely up the southern slopes of the Kilsyth Hills to 700 feet above its outcrop in a distance of two miles.

There is abundant evidence of the uphill carry of the Rannoch granite. The outcrop of this granite, apart from one small area, is below an altitude of 2000 feet and most of it forms ground at altitudes of 1000 to 1500 feet. Yet blocks carried westwards by the ice may be seen on the mountains on either side of Glen Coe at an altitude of 3000 feet. Northeastwards they exceed 3000 feet on the mountains between Loch Ericht and Loch Garry, reaching 3300 feet on the summit of Beinn Udlamainn, and they occur up to a similar altitude in the mountains west of Ben Alder (Hinxman et al. 1923). Eastwards of the outcrop the granite erratics occur high up on the watershed between the Tummel valley and Glen Lyon, attaining 3400 feet close to the summit of Schiehallion. Some of these erratics may well have been carried upwards through 2000 feet. In the Northwest Highlands between Little Loch Broom and Loch Maree other striking evidence is available. On An Teallach blocks of thrust Torridon Sandstone have been found at close to 3000 feet, although this rock does not exceed 1500 feet in altitude at its outcrop in the area from which the erratic blocks must have been derived. On Slioch (3217 feet) boulders of Moine Schist, thrust Lewisian Gneiss and Cambrian pipe rock have been found not far from the summit cairn. The blocks of thrust Lewisian Gneiss indicate a minimal uplift of 1000 feet in a horizontal distance of $2\frac{1}{2}$ miles, while the boulders of pipe rock point to a still greater ascent (Peach et al. 1913a).

These proofs of uphill carry of erratics must mean that at times of extensive ice cover the basal layers of the ice-sheet moved uphill and over some of the highest mountains. In the western Highlands this agrees with the evidence of glacial erosion extending to high levels on many of the mountains (Chapter 3). The striae and roches moutonnées often show that this overriding was accompanied by a partial deflection of the ice around the mountain masses, so that we may imagine the main flow of the ice taking place along the valleys where, as we have seen, erosion was often excessive. It also seems very probable that, for the basal layers of the ice to move upwards to high altitudes, the surface of the ice-sheet must have been situated at a considerably higher elevation than the highest erratics. In fact, it seems difficult to avoid the conclusion that, when these erratics were transported, the mountains on which they now occur were completely buried beneath a considerable thickness of glacier ice.

5

Glacial deposits and associated landforms

THE principal consequence of the deposition of lodgement till (with or without a veneer of ablation till) in most lowlands was a smoothing of the landscape. Even in lowlands where the till forms distinctive features such as drumlins, the dominant impression is one of rounding. The same is true of upland valleys and hill slopes where a considerable amount of lodgement till has been laid down, for the innumerable irregularities of the rock surface are hidden beneath a smooth mantle. In lowlands the glacial drift is usually thickest along valleys and other depressions and thins out up hill sides, the higher slopes and summits being drift-free. In many valleys in the Highlands, however, the drift is thickest on the lower slopes of the valley sides, having been removed from the central tract of the valley by glacial and postglacial streams. It may often be seen in narrow tributary valleys where streams have cut down into it to produce steep but rather unstable bluffs.

The consequence of this distribution is that on the higher slopes where the drift is thin its surface form often reflects that of the rock surface beneath except for the very minor irregularities. On low ground, however, the surface of the till may be quite different from that of the buried rock and small valleys in particular may be completely hidden. Such valleys are known to be common in the Clyde basin east and southeast of Glasgow, where they are filled with till and other deposits. A buried valley 150 feet deep underlies part of Motherwell. Another follows a winding north-south course for four miles from Kirk o' Shotts to Wishaw, its general direction being quite different from that of the present drainage. Deep buried valleys also record former courses of the Mouse Water and Avon Water, tributaries of the Clyde, while an old course of the Clyde itself is marked by a steep-sided narrow valley that is known to be over 300 feet deep at one point.

Where old valleys are concealed by drift the streams now often flow in rock gorges. Near Lanark the Clyde occupies a vertical slot a hundred feet deep that merges northwards into a much deeper though less steep-sided gorge, the river tumbling successively over the falls of Bonnington, Corra and Stonebyres.* The Mouse and Avon waters also occupy deep rock gorges in their lower courses. Quite often gorges alternate with rather more open valley sections. This may result from the river re-occupying an old course in one place and cutting a new one in another, as exemplified by some of the valleys in Midlothian south of Edinburgh and in Caithness around Lybster and Dunbeath (Crampton *et al.* 1914).

* This now happens only when the river is high, for at other times much or all of the water goes through the tunnel to the power station.

84

Ice-moulded landforms

Over large areas of central and southern Scotland the ice has converted the land surface into a series of linear swells and depressions that trend parallel with the last dominant direction of its movement. Similar forms are found in some other parts of the country as, for example, in the lower ground of Caithness. Sometimes the positive features are composed entirely of till, sometimes they are entirely rock, and often they are a combination of both rock and drift. All have in common, however, an alignment that shows they were fashioned by the actively-moving ice and we may refer to them as ice-moulded landforms. They include drumlins and crag-and-tail features as well as related landforms for which no specific term is available.

The best-known drumlins are the ones on and between which Glasgow is built. All the hills in the city fall into this category except Necropolis Hill, which is a crag-and-tail associated with the outcrop of an igneous sill. The Glasgow drumlins are mostly about half a mile long and a hundred feet or so high and form smooth streamlined hills. They show the usual asymmetry of drumlins, being steeper on the side from which the ice came, in this area the western side. The highest point normally lies nearer the western end, while eastwards the ground falls away gently in a long tapering tail. Sometimes two or three drumlins merge together to form a composite feature and occasionally, as in the northeastern part of Fig. 35, many combine to produce an undulating drumlin upland. The drumlins shown in Fig. 35 are part of a much larger system that splays out towards the east and southeast. Within the city the drumlins on the north side of the Clyde point approximately eastwards. Beyond Bishopbriggs and near Kirkintilloch they trend slightly north of east, while towards Coatbridge they are south of east. On the south side of the river between Paisley and Pollokshaws east-southeast is favoured and even southeast. The drumlins thus show how the ice-stream gradually spread out as it moved up the

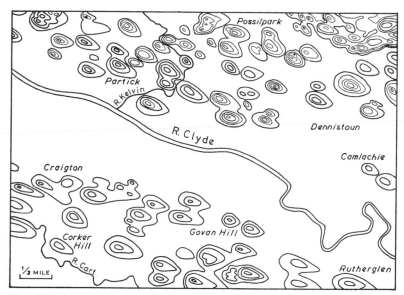

FIG. 35. The Glasgow drumlins. The shapes of the drumlins are brought out by form-lines. The belt of drumlin-free ground bordering the Clyde is composed mainly of marine and fluvial deposits accumulated against and around the drumlins. After S. Elder *et al.* 1935.

Clyde valley, distributing as it did so Glen Fyne and other Highland erratics (Figs 30 and 38).

Many of the Glasgow drumlins contain a core of rock around which the till accumulated. Some, however, are composed of very thick till, 70 feet having been found at Gilmorehill and over 100 feet at Hamilton Hill. Quarrying operations at the former showed that the sandstone surface beneath the thick till was finely striated towards a direction slightly north of east. Like these striae, most others in the Glasgow area agree with the directions of ice movement recorded by the drumlins, and remind us that, even in this area of abundant glacial deposition, the ice has also eroded the rock. Furthermore, as we noted in Chapter 3, there is evidence of very considerable erosion in this same area represented by the deep gouges cut in the rock far below sea-level and now thickly covered with drift of various types. It seems probable, as D. L. Linton (1963) has suggested, that the visible expression of this important glacial erosion is to be seen in the deep straight trench of the Clyde between Hamilton and Crossford cut down several hundred feet into the gently-sloping till-covered ground on either side. The erosional features that now exist represent, of course, the cumulative result of ice action during the various glaciations to which the area has been subjected. The drumlins, however, were fashioned during the last ice movement into the area and appear to have been formed in the zone bordering the ice margin in which deposition prevailed.

The drumlins have inevitably affected the drainage pattern to a marked degree. In the country east of Glasgow the small streams wander rather indeterminately between the various streamlined mounds. A number of small lochs such as Bishop, Lochend, Woodend and Johnston lochs exist and the sites of former shallow lochs are marked by flat spreads of peat, lake and river deposits. In Glasgow the winding course of the incised River Kelvin is determined by the drumlins between and around which it flows (Fig. 35). The drumlins also affect many man-made features of the landscape. Housing estates are often planned in relation to their curving slopes, and main roads, such as Sauchiehall Street in the heart of the city, often make use of the low cols between drumlins.

Ice-moulded landforms are common in much of lowland Ayrshire, the volcanic plugs in particular favouring the development of crag-and-tail features. In some of the low ground near Kilmarnock the land surface is moulded into a series of drumlins usually a quarter to half a mile long and trending almost exactly west-east. On the higher ground between Beith and Neilston, however, crag-and-tail features, as well as striae, point to directions between southwest and south. Moulding is again seen in the southern and western parts of Arran, and near Auchencar on the west coast crag-and-tail forms point towards a direction west of south. The same trend is seen in the ice-moulded ridges of rock and drift on the western side of the Kintyre peninsula between Killean and Kilchenzie. In the low ground of Galloway, systems of smooth rounded drumlins, the different groups aligned in various directions, are excellently developed near Newton Stewart and Castle Douglas (Plate IXB). By no means all the Galloway lowlands are of this character, however, for in many places instead of smoothing the ground the ice roughened it to produce innumerable rocky knolls and ridges.

In the Tweed basin the graining of the landscape by the ice is particularly pronounced and a whole series of features is present extending from the high ground west of Selkirk and Hawick to the coast around Berwick. On the plateaux between the Yarrow and Teviot at elevations of around 800 to 1200 feet glacial erosion was assisted by the fact that the ice moved approximately southwest-northeast with the grain of the bedrock,

PLATE XI. A. Moraine-dammed lake, Loch Coire an Lochain, Braeriach, Cairngorms. B. Hummocky moraines by Lochan an Iasgaich, Glen Torridon, Ross-shire. *Geological Survey photographs. Crown Copyright reserved.*

PLATE XII. A. Meltwater channel cut in granite, near Lairig Ghru, Cairn-gorms. B. Fluvioglacial terraces in Glen Einich, Cairngorms. *Geological Survey photographs. Crown Copyright reserved.*

and a series of rock ridges and partly-drift-filled hollows follows this trend. Glacial deposition took place mainly in the valleys, especially in those aligned across the direction of ice movement, as in the hill country south of Hawick and Jedburgh where most of the streams flow northwards. Here the till is often widespread on slopes facing east and north-east, becoming thick towards the valley floors. The slopes facing in the opposite direction, which felt the full force of the ice-sheets, are often rougher and steeper, and towards and on their upper parts ribs of ice-scraped bare rock stick out where the ice ground up and over the summits. In the area between Melrose, Jedburgh and Hawick the roughened plateau country gradually gives way to a much smoother landscape as the ground becomes lower towards the Tweed and glacial deposits increase in importance. Thereafter the low ground on either side of the Tweed is dominated by a great number of swells and depressions that at first trend northeastwards but then gradually curve round to point due east by the time the coast is reached at Berwick. As in other areas, this ice-moulded landscape has a marked effect on the drainage pattern, for almost all the minor streams follow the peaty or alluvial hollows between the ice-moulded ridges and a map of these streams alone is sufficient to show clearly the course of the ice. The pattern of minor roads is equally striking: these roads form an imperfect grid system the more numerous elements of which trend with the ice-moulding in a southwest and northeast direction around Kelso, swinging round gently to a west and east direction in northernmost Northumberland between Berwick, Cornhill and Beal.

Around and between the firths of Forth and Tay the scenery is dominated by two types of landform. On the one hand are the smooth features developed on the sedimentary rocks of the Carboniferous and Old Red periods. Occasionally these are drumlins composed of thick till (as around Bannockburn) but more often the sedimentary rocks are

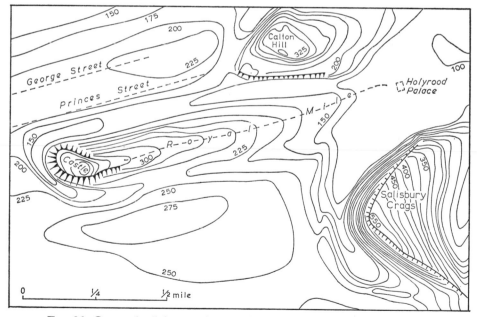

FIG. 36. Crag and tail features in central Edinburgh. Where the thickness of deposits overlying the till or rock is known the contours have been adjusted in order to represent the ice-moulded surface of the till or rock beneath these deposits.

E.S.S.—G

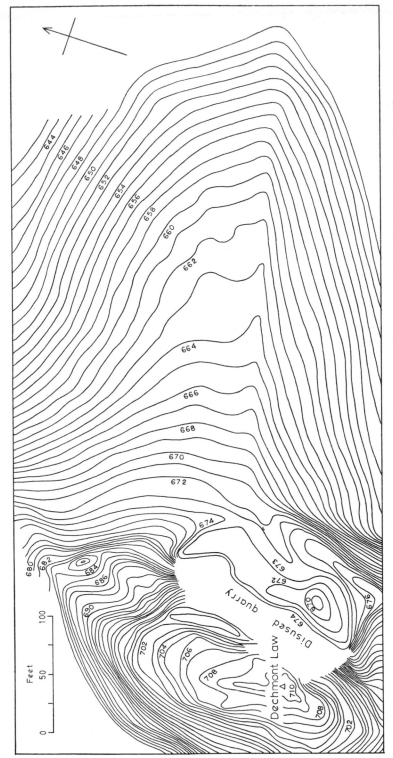

FIG. 37. Contour map (one-foot interval) of part of the Dechmont Law crag-and-tail in West Lothian. Reproduced by permission of the West Lothian Water Board.

covered with a mantle of drift that, along with the rock beneath, is frequently moulded into broad swells and depressions. On the other hand, there are the numerous outcrops of igneous rock that often form hill groups or conspicuous isolated hills. Usually these are almost free of drift, at least on their upper slopes and summits, and their irregular craggy forms present a striking contrast with the smoothness of the form developed on the surrounding sediments.

The two types of landscape are juxtaposed in the well-known crag-and-tail features of which the classic Edinburgh example is the crag of the Castle Rock with the tail whose crest is followed by the Royal Mile. Other good examples in Edinburgh include Calton, Blackford and Craiglockhart hills, while farther afield we may cite North Berwick Law and Traprain Law in East Lothian and Dundee Law and Downie Hill near the Tay. The side of the crag facing the direction from which the ice came is usually steep – sometimes precipitous – and its base may be partly or entirely surrounded by a smooth curving depression. Such depressions are to be seen on the western side of Salisbury Crags (Fig. 36) and Blackford Hill in Edinburgh as well as at various places in the volcanic uplands that border the southern side of the Firth of Tay. A similar feature occurs at the western base of the Castle Rock in Edinburgh although here its full depth (40 feet below present ground level in one part) is hidden by lake deposits, peat and an accumulation of rubbish. This depression is continued along both sides of the tail for its full length of a mile (Fig. 36). The divergence of the basal layers of the ice-sheet around the resistant basaltic mass of the Castle Rock is thus clearly recorded, as is the resultant local overdeepening (amounting to at least 200 feet) and the protection of the tail of relatively weak material on the sheltered side of the basaltic mass.

There is a rather widespread belief that the tail of crag-and-tail features is composed of drift. As A. Geikie pointed out as far back as 1863, however, the tail is usually composed largely or entirely of solid rock. Drift may veneer the tail and tends to thicken as the low ground is approached towards the end of the tail. The part of the tail of Dechmont Law in West Lothian shown in Fig. 37 has been investigated in more than 40 boreholes. These reveal that till is present only in very small patches and even then is no more than a few feet thick. Much the greater part of the tail has bedrock up to the ground surface. It is thus clear that the tail is here an erosional feature, the relatively soft shales and mudstones of which it is composed having been shaped by the ice in relation to the amount of protection afforded by the igneous crag.

The importance of erosion by the ice can also be demonstrated in areas where almost the whole ground surface is covered by till. The ground to the south and southwest of Falkirk forms a series of parallel swells and depressions aligned west-southwest to east-northeast, these linear features gradually declining in altitude in the latter direction. The slopes are usually gentle or moderate and have the regular smooth form typical of till-covered ground. The interesting point about this area (and it is by no means unique) is that boreholes show that the till is usually only 5 to 20 feet thick, except where small valleys have been obscured by it. The till, in fact, has done little more than smooth out the very minor inequalities in the rock surface, so that the buried rock surface is itself almost as smooth and regular as the visible till surface. In other words, depite its veneers of till, the landscape is essentially an erosional one shaped by the ice into tapering streamlined ridges. One gains the impression that the main work carried out by the ice in this area, and in others like it, was erosion, the present till cover having been laid down towards the end of the period that the area was last covered by ice.

We have mentioned already in Chapter 3 the much more emphatic erosion by the

ice in the deep trenches beneath the River Carron, part of the Firth of Forth and elsewhere, and the impression may be gained that erosion predominated everywhere in the
Forth and Tay region. It must therefore be made clear that the till attains a considerable
thickness in places. For example, immediately to the southeast of Falkirk a few of the
ice-moulded ridges have a great thickness of drift, 160 feet having been found at one
point. On the other side of the Forth a boring in a drumlin near Alloa revealed a similar
thickness of till. Glacial deposits are also thick in some of the areas where erosion by the
ice was most intense. Thus the deep gracially-eroded trench of the Forth valley by
Grangemouth and Bo'ness contains a variety of deposits, but often includes thick till
that in one borehole was found to form a layer 200 feet thick out of a total drift thickness
of 453 feet.*

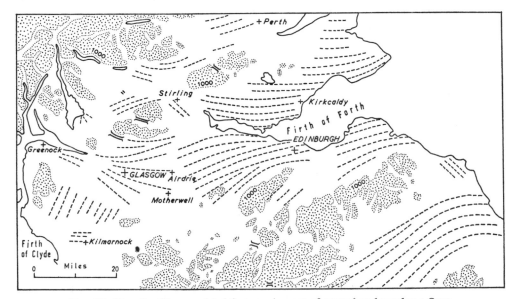

FIG. 38. Trends of ice-moulded features in part of central and southern Scotland. Some glacial breaches are also indicated. Land above 1000 feet shaded.

Whether erosional or depositional or both, the landforms fashioned by the ice in the
Forth and Tay region combine to form a system of ridges and depressions whose regular
alignment produces a distinctive pattern over a great part of the land surface (Fig. 38).
Here and there the igneous hill masses locally disrupt the continuity of the pattern but
even they show in greater or lesser degree the alignments imposed by the overriding
ice. Thus many of the hills in the volcanic upland south of the Firth of Tay have an
asymmetrical profile with their gentler slope inclined towards the east. The volcanic
Garleton Hills in East Lothian show a similar asymmetry, while some of the low igneous
hills not far away are scored by numerous parallel grooves as much as fifty feet deep that
frequently run across their highest parts. In Edinburgh the volcanic Braid Hills at first
sight appear to form a chaotic jumble of rough knolls and smooth hollows but closer

* The greatest thickness of superficial deposits known in Scotland occurs in this trench, attaining
655 feet at one point near Bo'ness. To what extent the deposits consist of till at this point is not
established, since they have not been bored through, only the base of them having been encountered
in underground coal workings.

inspection soon reveals a prevailing alignment towards the east, a trend differing slightly from that of the crag-and-tail features farther north in the city owing to the slight spreading of the ice as it began to escape from the constricting influence of the Pentland Hills. Even Salisbury Crags, whose vertical face may seem to reflect merely the resistance of the igneous sill of which it is composed, show clearly the effects of the ice-stream. Although affected by faults and by the fact that the sill is inclined with the prevailing direction of ice movement, the westward-facing point of the Crags, together with the moulding of the underlying sedimentary rock (now scree-covered) and the curving basal trough all reflect the work of the ice (Fig. 36).

Inevitably the drainage pattern has been greatly affected by these profound alterations of the relief and the details of the preglacial river system are unknown. Even where buried river valleys exist we cannot assume that these were formed in preglacial times, for many may well have been produced in the intervals between the various glaciations while some appear to have been cut by glacial meltwaters. The drainage pattern we see today therefore consists largely of streams that follow the gutters provided by the ice ready-made for them to occupy. Here and there these streams, especially the larger ones, change course and break through the intervening ice-moulded ridges to reach the sea or to resume their former direction of flow along a parallel gutter.*

In the extreme north of the mainland, on the low plateau of Caithness, ice-moulding is again widely developed, but the effects are much less striking than in the Forth–Tay region owing to the widespread occurrence of Old Red Sandstone and the scarcity of igneous rocks. No upstanding igneous hills disrupt the continuity of the smooth ice-moulded forms and the prevailing impression away from the magnificent coastal cliffs is one of monotony that is emphasised by the extensive peat bogs. Over a wide area of northern Caithness the swells and depressions are aligned from southeast to northwest parallel with the movement of the ice-sheet that deposited the shelly drift (Fig. 39). These features appear to be mainly formed of bedrock but are usually swathed with till. In the linear depressions occur lochs such as Calder, Scarmclate, Watten and Heilen, which are elongated more or less parallel with the direction of ice movement. Towards the south in the more hilly parts of Caithness inland of Dunbeath, Lybster and Ulbster the results of ice action are much more impressive. Here the ice-sheet from the Moray Firth moved onto the land and had to surmount the hills, which rise to altitudes of 700 or 800 feet. In doing so it often bit deeply into the land and, assisted by the strike of the rocks and the numerous bands of crushed rock, produced innumerable sharp ridges and grooves (some of the latter now being partly occupied by small rock-basin lakes) along lines trending towards the north and north-northwest (Crampton et al. 1914).

We have referred already to the Outer Hebrides as an area where glacial erosion predominated, although considerable accumulations of till occur in parts of northern Lewis. Elsewhere till may become locally important as may be illustrated by North Uist, where the landforms have been described and mapped by G. L. Davies (1956). The ice-sheet moved across the island towards a direction north of west, its principal action being erosive, with the production of an irregular rocky landscape on the lowlands that is now masked by peat over most of the interior or by sand along the northern and western coasts (Fig. 40). On the lee side of some of the ice-scraped eastern hills, however, tails of rock and till with slightly-concave slopes occur, that associated with Eaval being half a mile long. The scattered hills away from the east coast have a different form and long, usually-convex slopes on which rock outcrops are rare prevail. Finally, in the southwestern part

---

* In certain localities streams occupy valleys cut by glacial meltwaters (Chapter 6).

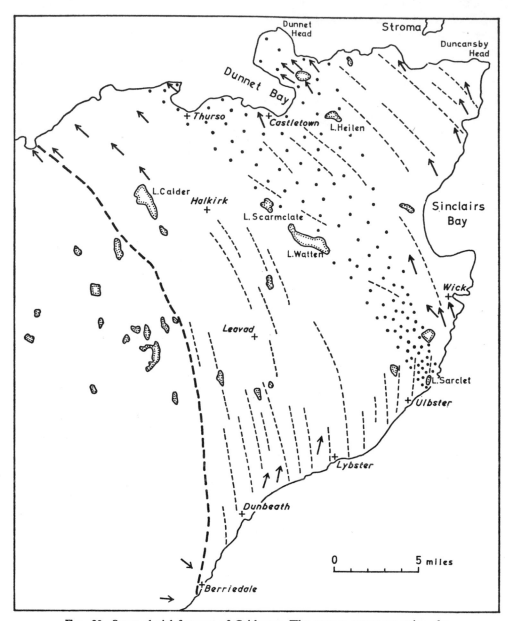

FIG. 39. Some glacial features of Caithness. The arrows represent striae, the
thick broken line the western limit of shelly drift, and the thin broken lines
the landforms trending with the direction of ice movement. The area in
which erratics of Sarclet conglomerate (outcropping 4 miles south of Wick)
have been found is indicated by dots. Based mainly on T. F. Jamieson
1866, B. N. Peach and J. Horne 1881, and C. B. Crampton *et al.* 1914.

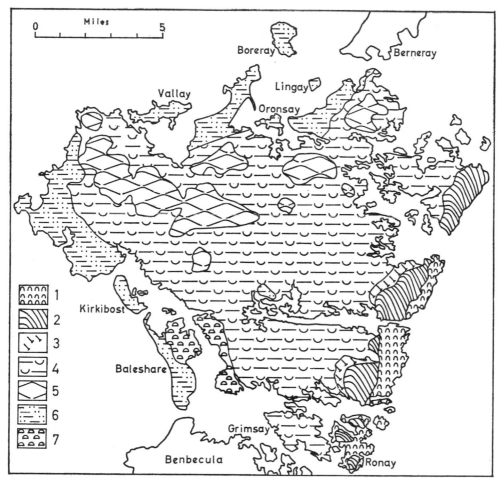

FIG. 40. Glacial landforms of North Uist, after G. L. Davies 1956. 1. Heavily glaciated lowland of east coast. 2 and 3. Crags and tails. 4. Glaciated central lowland with lakes and widespread peat. 5. Smooth glaciated hills 6. Machair (blown sand). 7. Drumlin belt.

of the main island and on part of the adjacent island of Baleshare is a belt of very small drumlins, most of which are about 25 feet high and 50 yards long and between which the ground is usually marshy. Some of the drumlins now form small islands at high tide, while the remains of others that have been almost destroyed by the sea are represented by low mounds of boulders visible at low water.

Moraines

While the ice-moulded landforms attain their optimal development in lowlands, especially in those composed of sedimentary rocks, moraines are most commonly found in the valleys and corries of the uplands. They are particularly common in the valleys cut into the higher mountain areas, especially in the west. Hence they are most charac-teristic of the western Highlands and the mountainous western islands, but they are also found in the valleys of the highest parts of the Southern Uplands.

The moraines often form extremely hummocky terrain comprising hundreds or

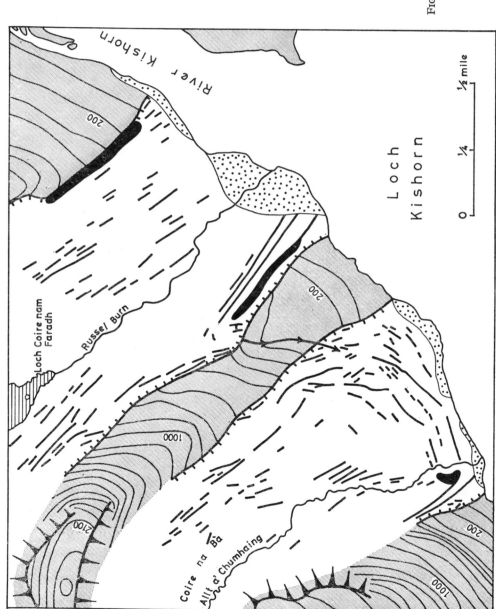

Fig. 41. Morainic ridges, and the limits of the glaciers that deposited them, by Loch Kishorn. The postglacial raised beach and related deposits are also shown.

River Kishorn

Loch Kishorn

0   ¼   ½ mile

200

200

1000

Loch Coire nam Faradh

Russel Burn

2100

Coire na Bà

Allt a' Chumhaing

200

1000

thousands of individual mounds (Plates XB and XIB). Many of the mounds are no more than 20 or 30 feet high but some attain heights of more than 100 feet. They are largest and most abundant on and near the valley floors but often also extend hundreds of feet up the valley slopes. Between the mounds small lochans may occur but more often there are thick accumulations of peat, while narrow strips of alluvial material intermittently follow the streams that wander between the mounds. The surfaces of the mounds are often littered with angular boulders and similar boulders are plentiful in the mounds themselves, as may be seen in the many road cuts available at the present time in connection with road improvement schemes. The boulders are usually mixed with an assortment of stones of all sizes, as well as with finer material. This debris is mostly ablation till and was deposited by valley and corrie glaciers, often during the final phase of the last glaciation.

On ascending a valley in the mountains one frequently finds that the morainic landscape starts quite suddenly. Often the margin of the moundy area is not marked by any distinctive feature. In other instances, however, the margin is sharply defined by a clear end moraine that marks a downvalley limit of the glacier that deposited the mounds. The moraine may form a sweeping curve across the valley floor and climb obliquely up the valley slopes on either side as a lateral feature. Within it may occur other moraines of similar form. Such moraines are beautifully displayed in many of the upland valleys of Sutherland and Ross-shire. One in the valley of Abhuinn a' Gharbrain may be seen from the Garve–Ullapool road as a conspicuous rampart over 100 feet high and behind it a small loch has been impounded. On the east side of Beinn Dearg Mhòr (between Little Loch Broom and Loch Maree) three successive arcuate end moraines form striking ridges of which the outermost is well over 100 feet high. Often the former margin of a valley glacier is accurately marked by a moraine within which glacial drift is plentiful and outside which on the valley slopes bare rock is common. Such contrasts are often seen and are particularly clear in the ground covered by Figs 41 and 42. The mountain slopes rising from the shore of Loch Kishorn are characterised by ice-scraped bare ribs of Torridon Sandstone aligned parallel with the shore. Crossing the rock ribs almost at right-angles are two pairs of lateral moraines that define the limits of two valley glaciers that descended steeply from the mountains to terminate in Loch Kishorn. The ground formerly covered by the two glaciers is strewn with boulders and morainic debris and in the valley of Allt a' Chumhaing successive positions of the intermittently-retreating ice-margin are recorded by the series of arcuate ridges shown in Fig. 41. In the adjacent area shown in Fig. 42 small glaciers nourished in the east-facing corries of Ben Bhan merged together to form a mass of ice that moved down towards adjacent lower ground. The limit of the confluent glaciers in the south is clearly defined by the sudden ending of the dominantly-drift-covered ground, while in the east various positions of the ice-margin may be recorded by the various morainic mounds aligned in a general north and south direction.

End moraines are well developed in some of the valleys of the Southern Uplands close to the highest hills. Series of them marking successive positions of the margins of glaciers nurtured in the hills of the Merrick range can be seen in the Water of Minnoch valley. Others formed by glaciers nourished in the Cairnsmore of Fleet uplands occur on the gentle slopes of the broad basin drained by the Big Water of Fleet and its headstreams. Towards the source of the Meggett Water in the Tweedsmuir Hills lateral moraines littered with angular blocks form successive parallel steps and ridges along the lower slopes of the valley side. Higher up on the valley side are smooth banks of till laid down earlier when the area was covered by an ice-sheet and subsequently truncated by the

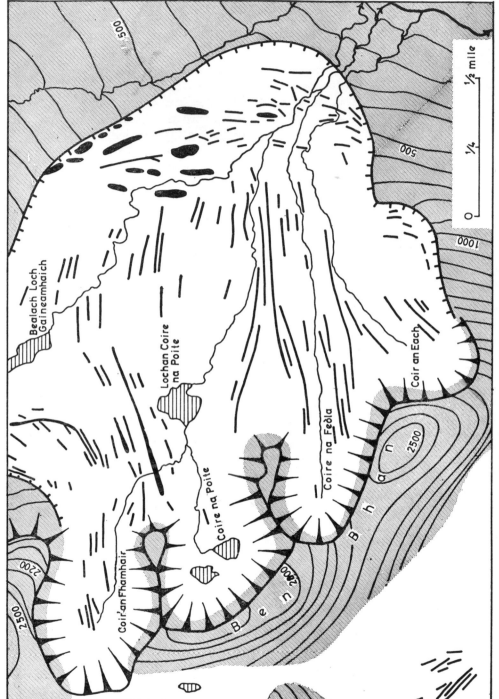

Fig. 42. Corries, moraines and associated glacier limits on the eastern side of Ben Bhan, between lochs Kishorn and Torridon.

valley glacier that laid down the moraines. At the very head of the Meggett valley and spreading over the broad col that leads to the corrie containing Loch Skene morainic mounds again appear in force. They are limited in part by a small but clear end moraine some 10 to 20 feet high that forms a smooth mound that can be followed through the thick peat wastes on either side and is appropriately named 'The Causey'.

Although end moraines are locally conspicuous and often of considerable importance in defining former glacier limits, they comprise but a tiny proportion of the morainic mounds that occur in the valleys of the Scottish uplands. In many of these valleys the moraines appear to form a sea of chaotic mounds lacking any systematic arrangement. It may be that in some valleys there is in fact little pattern, the deposits representing the debris let down onto the ground as the glaciers finally decayed, probably associated with considerable redistribution of the material by meltwater streams. In other instances knobbly bedrock outcrops appear to have exerted a considerable control on the distribution of the morainic material, for locally many of the mounds may be seen to have a core of solid rock. Often, however, the mounds occur in lines and when viewed from the vantage point of an adjacent mountain slope or when mapped in detail quite distinct patterns may become apparent. On the floors of some valleys the moraines comprise straight or almost straight ridges or lines of mounds with quite steep sides. These linear features descend obliquely towards the stream running along the valley floor, often at an angle of between 30 and 45 degrees to it, but the ridges from the opposing sides of the valley do not actually meet since the stream itself and its deposits occupy this critical zone. Moraines of this type may be seen in the valley of Allt a' Chùirn Deirg in Applecross Forest and an example from the Talla valley in the centre of the Southern Uplands is shown in Fig. 43. The origin of these features is not established, but their straightness and V-shaped pattern in plan, along with their regularity, make formation along an ice

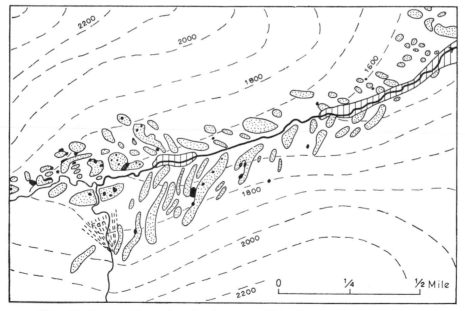

FIG. 43. Pattern of moraines in the upper Talla valley, Tweedsmuir Hills. Moraines shown by dotted areas, kettle holes by solid black and flood plain of Talla Water by vertical shading.

margin rather unlikely and suggest the possibility of subglacial accumulation in relation to crevasse systems in the ice at a time when the ice had become stagnant.

Another type of morainic feature was certainly produced subglacially and equally clearly owes its formation to active ice. This type of feature, which is not uncommon on corrie and valley floors in the higher mountains, consists of ridges of debris aligned parallel with the former directions of movement of the glaciers. The ridges may be anything from a foot or two to 10 or 20 feet high. Sometimes only two or three appear together but more often they occur in considerable numbers and the landscape resembles a ploughed field on a greatly exaggerated scale. Such an analogy is by no means inappropriate, for the linear mounds and intervening depressions suggest a grooving and ridging of the ground by the ice as it ploughed over the land surface. The individual ridges may be only 20 or 30 yards in length but the larger ones form continuous features for more than half a mile. As shown in Figs 41 and 42, they may be approximately parallel with each other or form gently-curving systems that faithfully record the courses of the former glaciers. In Fig. 42, for example, it is evident that the glaciers fed by the snows that accumulated in Coire na Poite and Coire ne Feòla spread out as they emerged from the confining corrie walls, while the glacier issuing from Coir' an Each caused a deflection of the ice from Coire na Feòla. Some of the largest and most continuous ridges trail away downslope from the base of the steep rocky bastions that separate the corries and are especially prominent in the zone in which adjacent glaciers merged. They are thus in some respects of the nature of medial moraines, although this is not meant to imply that the debris of which they are composed originally accumulated on the ice surface in the way that visible medial moraines on glaciers in other countries accumulate today. Rather do these moraines reflect the abundance of debris obtained by the glaciers from the side walls of the corries as they flowed past them. Doubtless some of this debris was eroded by the ice itself and some was supplied by frost action on the rocky slopes above the glaciers. One particular source of this debris was the gullies that gash the walls of many corries, not only in the mountains north of Loch Kishorn, but in many other parts of Scotland. This is shown by the fact that quite frequently linear moraine ridges commence on the less steeply sloping ground beneath a gully. It thus appears that, while glaciers occupied the corries, debris descending the gullies went down beneath the ice to contribute to the moraines. Other morainic ridges commence in the lee of rocky outcrops and even in the shelter of individual boulders, although the latter ridges are quite small. Whatever the reason for the location of the morainic ridges they all combine to produce a small-scale but nevertheless distinct graining of the land surface that may be referred to as a fluted moraine landscape.

One small but important group of moraines that we have not so far mentioned and which deserves special consideration is the group formed by glaciers that extended beyond the limits of the mountain areas into the lowlands. Moraines of this type form distinctive features in Scotland only close to the mountains. The two best examples are the large end moraines around the southern end of Loch Lomond and in the western part of the Forth valley. On the western side of Loch Lomond a moraine forms a distinct feature on the slopes of Shantron Hill, four miles south of Luss, reaching 800 feet above sea-level (Simpson 1933). From here it descends westwards into Glen Fruin, which it crosses at 300 feet, almost on the watershed between Loch Lomond and the Gare Loch. It then swings back eastwards along the southern side of Glen Fruin and rises to 600 feet before declining to below 100 feet in the Leven valley south of Balloch. Thereafter the outermost morainic deposits can be followed almost continuously along the lower slopes of the

Kilpatrick Hills, where they reach an altitude of just over 500 feet. After declining again in the low ground around Drymen, the morainic limit rises quite rapidly and can be traced intermittently to an altitude of 1000 feet on the eastern side of Loch Lomond (Fig. 44). The moraine can thus be followed over a distance of more than 25 miles. Inevitably over such a distance it varies considerably in form and composition and is best

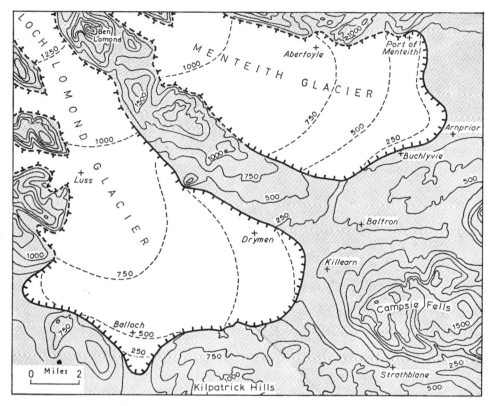

Fig. 44. Glacier limits and glacier form as inferred from the Loch Lomond and and Menteith end-moraine complexes. Continuous lines represent glacier margins where moraines are continuously or intermittently present, and broken lines suggest glacier limits elsewhere. Contours are continued across the glaciers to suggest their surface form.

described as an end-moraine complex. In places, as in Glen Fruin and near Drymen, it contains a great deal of water-laid sand and gravel; between Drymen and Balloch it is in part composed of transported marine clay with shells; while in many other places it consists of angular debris. Its form varies from a single small ridge, as in Glen Fruin, to a complex assortment of large mounds and hollows. Between the moraine limit and the southern shore of Loch Lomond drumlins and the crag-and-tail of Duncryne Hill point radially outwards (Plate XA).

The other large end-moraine complex, in the adjacent part of the Forth valley, was followed by J. B. Simpson for more than a dozen miles. It forms a broad arcuate loop passing through Buchlyvie and Port of Menteith and enclosing the western part of the Forth lowlands. Starting as a low ridge at an altitude of 800 feet on the moors some half-dozen miles west of Buchlyvie, the feature declines in altitude so that at Buchlyvie it is only about 200 feet above sea-level. Here it comprises a series of mounds and terraces formed mainly of sand and gravel. Near Arnprior, where the moraine complex turns northwards, it is composed mainly of glacier-transported marine clay with shells. The main ridge system here rises 60 feet above the low ground on either side and runs parallel with the general trend of the morainic belt. In addition minor ridges approximately at right-angles to the principal ones ascend the inner slope of the moraine and appear to represent moulding of its inner flank by the basal layers of the ice as they rode up it. Northwards, on the eastern side of Lake of Menteith, the feature forms a conspicuous system of ridges up to 100 feet high, which are composed of marine clay and sand and gravel. The morainic system turns sharply westwards near Port of Menteith and thereafter follows the steep hill slopes towards Aberfoyle.

One aspect of these moraines that is worthy of remark is the evidence they provide of the gradient and size of the former glaciers. In Fig. 44 the altitudes of the morainic limits have been used to construct a tentative contour map showing the surface form of the Loch Lomond and Menteith glaciers when they were at their maximal extent in late-glacial times. The rapid increase in thickness of the ice close to its margin, followed by a more gentle surface gradient, is comparable with the situation on many present-day active glaciers. The piedmont lobe of ice in the Forth valley probably attained a thickness of 800 feet or so in its central part (for example, over the site of Aberfoyle). The Loch Lomond ice was much thicker and over the deep basin in the upper part of the loch, which descends to nearly 600 feet below sea-level, must have approached or attained a thickness of 2000 feet even though its terminus was only 15 to 20 miles away.

In describing these two morainic complexes reference has been made to the water-laid sands and gravels that locally constitute a large part of them. Similar deposits are interspersed with many of the other morainic accumulations in the valleys of the Scottish uplands, and in some valleys are so abundant as to be entirely predominant. These stream-laid deposits along with the channels cut by glacial rivers form an important group of landforms in their own right and it is to these that we now turn our attention.

6

Landforms produced by glacial rivers

THE ice-masses that covered Scotland were associated with innumerable rivers that produced their own distinctive landforms in many parts of the country, while in some places lakes were impounded by the ice. Much of the water was provided by the melting of the ice-masses themselves, but in addition water was contributed by the melting of snow and the temporary surface thawing of frozen ground. This production of meltwater must have been largely confined to the late spring and summer seasons. Consequently, at times when the ice-masses were decaying rapidly, not only had the precipitation of a whole year to be discharged in a few months, but to this was added the stored-up precipitation of many years released by glacier wastage. Inevitably the resultant melt-water rivers were often of great size and locally had a pronounced effect on the landscape, in some places cutting deep channels in solid rock and in others distributing debris over many square miles of country.

The deposits laid down by meltwater rivers and in ice-dammed lakes during times of glacial advance were usually redistributed by the ice as it moved over them. Likewise the channels cut by the glacial rivers were modified by the ice or buried beneath till and other deposits. Hence very little is known of the work carried on by meltwaters during such times. On the other hand, during periods of glacier decay meltwaters produced a great variety of erosional and depositional features, and many of those formed during the decay of the last ice-masses still survive as important elements of the landscape. The pro-duction of these landforms in Scotland was greatly facilitated by the numerous valleys and basins amidst uplands of considerable altitude. In order to appreciate the effects of this relief on meltwater activity we may imagine an area of varied relief covered by an ice-sheet with a surface gradient (away from its margin) of the order of 1 in 100 to 1 in 200. When the climate ameliorated the surface of the ice-sheet would be gradually lowered as it was attacked by warm air masses, insolation, and perhaps by rain, and we may therefore envisage the ice surface as a very gently inclined plane that was lowered onto the irregular land surface buried beneath. In due course the highest hills would begin to project through the ice surface as nunataks and, as downwasting continued, so the area of ice-free upland would become larger and the ice itself would become increas-ingly restricted to the floors of the valleys and basins. One consequence of such down-wasting was that the ice became increasingly cut off from external sources of nourishment and hence its motion became more and more sluggish until finally, in many areas, it became stagnant or dead. Another consequence was that meltwaters from the ice and

the streams draining from the ice-free uplands were impeded or diverted by the ice
decaying in the lower ground. Sometimes lakes were held up at the ice-margin, but more
often the decayed condition of the ice with its numerous crevasses and tunnels enabled
the streams to flow down under or into the ice, there to continue their erosional and
depositional activities. Owing to the ice often being stagnant the features produced under
such conditions often exist as distinctive landforms today.

Similar features were produced by streams flowing into and beneath the valley glaciers
that occupied many Highland valleys, for often these glaciers, like the ice-sheets, became
slow-moving and finally stagnant as they decayed. Once free of the ice the meltwater
rivers from both ice-sheets and valley glaciers continued to erode and deposit, in some
places cutting deep gorges and in others, particularly close to the ice margin, laying down
spreads of sand and gravel.

Meltwater channels

Many meltwater channels are readily identifiable as such, for they form deep gashes in
spur crests in locations where under present conditions no large river could possibly
flow (Plate XIIA). Many others descend hill slopes obliquely and are equally anomalous
in relation to the present drainage. Yet others run straight down slopes but may be distinguished from normal stream valleys by their size or by their relations to other meltwater
channels that run along the slopes.

The sides of many meltwater channels have been considerably modified by weathering
and mass wastage since they were formed. Only where they are in particularly resistant rock

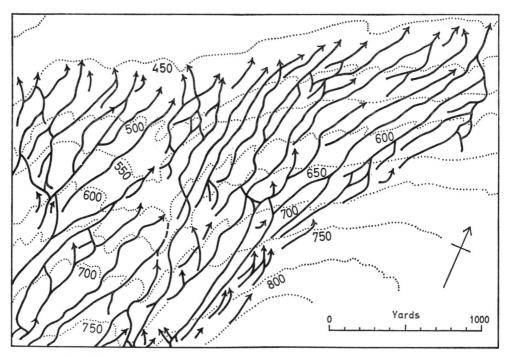

FIG. 45. Part of a system of meltwater channels on the southern slopes of Strath
Allan. After J. B. Sissons 1961a.

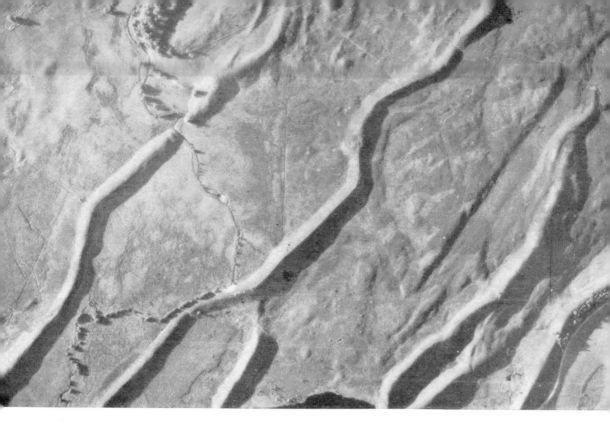

PLATE XIII. A. Eskers in Strath Nairn. *Ministry of Defence (Air Force Department) photograph. Crown Copyright reserved.* B. Parallel roads of Glen Roy. *Photograph by W. A. Sharp.*

PLATE XIV. Frost-shattered ridge of Liathach, Wester Ross. Ben Eighe beyond and Fannich Mountains in distance. *Photograph by Tom Weir.*

or where a considerable stream flows along them have they remained relatively fresh and sharp. Their floors have often been raised by material from their slopes, by the accumulation of peat or by later river deposits. Quite frequently alluvial fans have been built out across the floors of channels by streams entering from their sides. These fans are sometimes referred to as 'corroms' from the Gaelic word literally meaning a 'balance', for the streams that built them (and, in some instances, that are still building them) may flow either way along the meltwater channel.

Many meltwater channels are quite small features, often only 10 to 40 feet deep, and they record the courses of small streams whose waters were derived locally. Where they follow approximately the contours of the hill sides these channels may have been formed along the ice-margin, but were more probably formed beneath the ice. Quite often after following the contour for a few hundred yards channels turn abruptly downslope and here they were clearly formed by waters that coursed down under the ice. These subglacial chutes may descend a slope for several hundred feet but may then come to an end quite suddenly, implying that the streams that cut them here flowed into the ice to become englacial streams. Especially on till-covered slopes of gentle or moderate gradient small channels may occur in great numbers and form complex interconnected systems. Such systems occur along various stretches of the Highland border belt northeast from Callander and are especially well developed on the lower hill slopes bordering both sides of Strath Allan. A small part of one of these systems comprising channels mostly less than 20 feet deep, is illustrated in Fig. 45. The bends in these channels show that meltwaters flowed obliquely down the hill side beneath the ice for a short distance, then turned sharply to flow straight downslope, only to resume their oblique descent again after a few tens of yards, a pattern of flow that suggests partial control by structures in the ice (Sissons 1961a). A different type of evidence showing how meltwaters ran down under the ice occurs on the face of Meall Cumhann a little beyond the upper end of the Glen Nevis gorge (Bailey *et al.* 1916). Here the rocks of the precipitous valley side have been waterworn into hollow surfaces and gigantic semi-potholes over a vertical distance of some 200 to 300 feet, and it appears that a torrent plunged down between valley wall and glacier eroding potholes partly in the rock and partly in the ice.

Meltwater channels are very common on the crests of spurs and occur up to high levels in the uplands, in places exceeding 2000 feet in the Southern Uplands and 3000 feet in the Highlands. Although quite often these channels have utilised pre-existing cols, in many instances they disregard local details of the relief, for they cross the crests and flanks of spurs indiscriminately and even go over the very summits of hills. Channels of this type are of frequent occurrence in the south of Scotland as, for example, in the hills bordering the upper Tweed valley, where they have been described by R. J. Price (1960). Over considerable areas such channels show a similar orientation to each other and clearly carried water in the same general direction. They appear to be best explained by superimposition of englacial streams onto the ground buried beneath the ice. We may imagine numerous streams flowing through the ice above the level of the hill tops at a time when the uplands were locally completely ice-covered. As the ice wasted down these streams would be lowered onto the buried land surface beneath, impinging first on the tops of hills and spur crests, which they consequently notched. With continued downwasting of the ice these channels would be extended downslope and new ones would be cut, the meltwater drainage often becoming increasingly concentrated (as the dry channels themselves now show) in the valleys between the spurs. By the time the spur crests had emerged through the downwasting ice the original simple drainage system had become completely dismembered and, in many instances, had been replaced by a much more complex one controlled by the valley slopes.

Many of the largest meltwater channels occur in the floors of pre-existing cols. Some of the most impressive ones, 200 feet or more deep, are in rather remote locations as, for example, those cut in granite in the upper part of the Findhorn valley and the deep gash that crosses the divide between the Yarrow and Tweed drainage in the hills south of Innerleithen. A particularly striking meltwater gorge is followed by the water of Caiplich which now no longer uses its former route along Glen Loin but turns sharply away to flow through its former valley side into the Ailnick Water (Fig. 15). A conspicuous col channel may be seen beautifully silhouetted in the northward view from the highest point of the Cairn o' Mount road in Kincardine, while a short distance east of the road (although not visible from it) the peat-covered plateau is suddenly interrupted by a deep trench that carried meltwaters southwards from the Dee drainage basin towards the Howe of the Mearns. A number of quite large channels cut in pre-existing cols or valleys are readily accessible, however, for they have been utilised by roads and railways. Among these are the channel extending from Granthouse towards Eyemouth in Berwickshire; the channel near the head of the Douglas Water between Douglas and Muirkirk; Glen Farg, which crosses the Ochils a few miles south of Bridge of Earn; the Slòchd Mor near Carrbridge, that carried meltwaters from Strath Dearn to the Spey basin; and the long channel that leads from near Dufftown in Glen Fiddich past Keith, where it is joined by another long channel that carried waters eastwards from the Spey valley.

In some instances the erosion of large channels in cols was assisted by lines of weakness in the rocks. For example, the channel cut in the floor of Strath Finella in Kincardine in parts follows the Highland Boundary fault, while in the Cairngorms between Glen Lui and Glen Quoich the excavation of the Little Glen with its precipitous walls 300 feet high was assisted by the presence of a major shatter belt. Frequently, however, geological factors were not particularly helpful and that, despite this, the channels are often of great size, testifies to the immense power of some of the meltwater rivers.

Some col channels were cut by the overflowing waters of ice-dammed lakes. The best-known examples in this category are those associated with the former lakes of Glen Roy and adjacent glens, although these channels are quite small compared with the ones just mentioned. Most col channels were probably initiated subglacially, however. This may be demonstrated by eskers leading into or out of them (as on the nothern flanks of the Cairn-gorms) or sometimes by their up-and-down long profiles cut in solid rock that imply that the meltwater rivers were flowing under considerable hydrostatic pressure beneath the ice. Quite often the main channel in the bottom of a col is flanked by smaller ones cut into the slopes on either side (as shown in the southwestern part of Fig. 51) and the dis-cordant junctions of the tributary channels with the main one show that the latter was the last to be excavated. The relationships of such channels to one another and to the cols in which they are situated seem most satisfactorily accounted for by superimposition of englacial streams. Such streams, working their way down through the ice as it wasted away, would be retarded where they encountered spur crests buried beneath the ice, whereas streams over the site of a col would be in a relatively advantageous position and would work down more rapidly. Some of the streams would encounter the slopes of the col, but deep erosion would not be favoured in such locations, for such streams would tend to move along the ice-rock contact towards the lowest part of the col or would be tapped by streams that had already gained this position. Thus the constant tendency was for the waters in and beneath the ice to move towards the lowest part of a col, where the largest

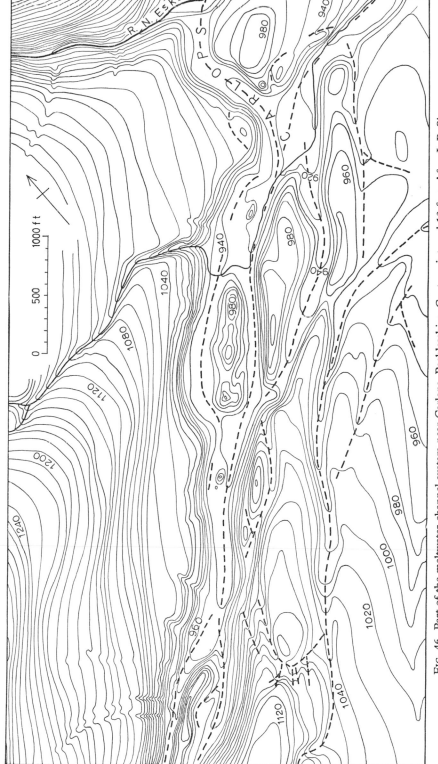

FIG. 46. Part of the meltwater channel system near Carlops, Peeblesshire. Contour interval 10 feet. After J. B. Sissons 1963b.

channel now exists. We may imagine that, with continued lowering of the ice surface, the roof of the subglacial tunnel would eventually become so thin that it would collapse, and for a time the col channel would be bordered by walls of ice. Some col channels functioned still later, for terraces of sand and gravel sloping gently down into their entrances and spreads of such deposits sloping away from their exits show that they became free of ice while water still poured through them between ice masses on either side.

Large channel systems are sometimes quite complex and a part of one such system is shown in detail in Fig. 46. In this locality a whole series of closely-spaced interconnected rivers flowing northeastwards appears to have been lowered onto the ground beneath the ice. The rivers cut down into the rocks to varying depths, reducing the ground between to steep-sided ridges. The most favoured rivers were those that followed various branches of the Pentland fault system and they excavated the deepest channels and the ones that were used longest. This and many other groups of large channels occur, as one might expect, where large meltwater rivers carrying the drainage from a considerable area existed. One of the most impressive systems, comprising numerous channels 50 to 200 feet deep, extends for 20 miles along the foot of the Lammermuirs from near Gifford almost to St Abb's Head. Another system occupies a corresponding position on the opposite side of the Central Lowlands following the basal slopes of the Highland edge past Edzell and Fordoun to Stonehaven. Many channels, both large and small, show a similar general trend over large areas of country and this trend is usually more or less the same as the direction of the last ice movement. For example, in the South-

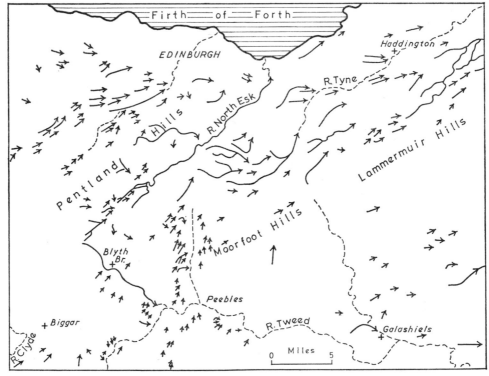

FIG. 47. Principal meltwater channels in part of Southeast Scotland.

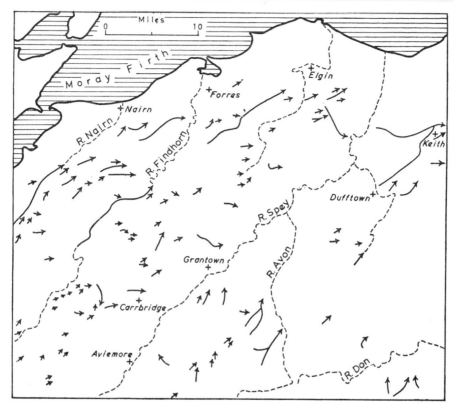

FIG. 48. Principal meltwater channels in the area between the Cairngorms and the Moray Firth. Based mainly on publications of the Geological Survey and A. Bremner.

ern Uplands from the east coast to beyond the Clyde the great majority of the channels carried meltwaters towards directions between east and north in accordance with the flow pattern of the ice-sheet nourished on these uplands. Part of this glacial drainage system is shown in Fig. 47 together with that of the adjacent part of the Central Lowlands. The regional changes in direction of the channels are evident and reflect the spreading of the Southern Upland ice-sheet and the movement of the Highland ice-stream down the Forth valley. On the southern flanks of the Southern Uplands in Dumfriesshire, Kirkcudbrightshire and Wigtownshire most of the channels carried meltwaters towards directions between south and east in accord with the movement of the ice towards the Solway and the Tyne gap. Similar relationships are evident in other parts of the country where the meltwater drainage has been mapped in sufficient detail. Thus over a large area extending from the Monadhliath Mountains across the Spey basin to that of the Don the great majority of the meltwater rivers flowed towards the northeast (Fig. 48).

It must be emphasised that the meltwater channels shown in Figs 47 and 48 do not record the glacial drainage at any particular point in time. Rather do they record (so far as scale and available evidence permit) the cumulative results of meltwater erosion in the areas shown. As the ice downwasted, the original simple drainage systems, only to a limited degree controlled by the form of the ground, were disrupted and the glacial rivers became increasingly influenced by details of the local relief. The final courses of the meltwater rivers were usually along the floors of the present valleys where, in some places, they continued to erode. This aspect of meltwater erosion is often forgotten and the gorges in which the present rivers flow are frequently referred to as 'postglacial'. Yet in view of the fact that in the past many Scottish rivers were immensely swollen with meltwaters it seems very probable that most, if not all, of these gorges were largely or entirely excavated in glacial times. Some of the gorges have now been partly obscured owing to the construction of hydro-electric dams as at Kilmorack in the Beauly valley and at the eastern end of Loch Tummel. Many are frequently visited by tourists, among them the gorges of Corrieshalloch by the main road to Ullapool, of Killiecrankie, of the North Esk near Edzell, and of the Black Rock of Novar at Evanton by the Cromarty Firth. That glacial meltwaters flowed through such gorges is often shown by the abundant deposits of sand and gravel they laid down on the adjacent valley floors.

In some instances streams occupy valleys that were largely or entirely cut by meltwaters. For example, the Midlothian North Esk flows in a trench 100 to 200 feet deep for a dozen miles. The origin of this trench is shown by the deep almost-streamless meltwater channels that lead directly into it between Penicuik and West Linton. In fact, the whole valley is itself a meltwater channel and, as can be seen in Fig. 46, the present stream enters the channel from the side and merely utilises the valley already made for it in glacial times. This situation is repeated many times in the Lothians. In East Lothian, for example, the streams often flow for miles along meltwater channels parallel with the Lammermuir scarp. Only rarely have they deepened these channels and much more often they meander over the deposits they have accumulated on the channel floors.

Kames and kettles

Much of the material eroded by the meltwater rivers was very soon deposited again, this deposition often taking place on, in and especially beneath the decaying ice. Debris was accumulated in subglacial tunnels, crevasses were filled in, and blocks of ice were surrounded by or buried beneath the stream deposits. When the ice finally melted, the crevasse and tunnel fillings were left as upstanding ridges and mounds, often with undulating crest lines and irregular shapes, while the sites of the ice blocks were marked by depressions. The term 'kame', applied to the former, is quite commonly used in Scottish place-names for an elongated steep-sided mound. The dead-ice hollows between the kames often form completely-closed depressions or kettle holes. Sometimes water drains away through the floors of kettle holes leaving them dry, sometimes they contain intermittent or permanent pools or lakes, but usually they are occupied by peat.

The kame and kettle landscapes are often composed of materials whose coarseness and abundance testifies to the power of the meltwater rivers. Typically they consist of sand and gravel and frequently some of the stones are six inches to a foot or even more across. Where the material is very coarse little sign of stratification may be evident, but normally the material is clearly stratified, with rapidly-alternating layers of sand and gravel of various grades reflecting the constantly-changing conditions of flow of the glacial rivers. Faulting and bending of the beds are common and occasionally the beds lie vertically or are even slightly overturned, a consequence of the melting away of the masses of ice against, beneath and over which the materials accumulated. The bedding of the flanks of the kames often accords approximately with their slopes, while the angle of slope tends to vary with the size of the material. Mounds of coarse debris are usually sharp with slopes as great as 30 or 40 degrees, while those composed largely of sand are often quite smooth and rounded with less abrupt slopes. Lying discordantly amidst the deposits, or sometimes scattered over the surface of the kames, boulders may occur. Such boulders fell into or onto the deposits from the ice above, the incorporated ones probably having been released from the roofs of subglacial tunnels as the meltwater rivers were forced against them by the accumulation of their own deposits.

The numerous mounds and hollows of kame and kettle landscapes occur in many valleys and lowlands and often litter the adjacent slopes, occasionally to considerable altitudes. They are particularly abundant around the base of hill slopes scored by numerous channels, as witness the large accumulations along the Highland edge (especially northeastwards from Blairgowrie), along the margin of the Southern Uplands at many places between Dunbar and Girvan, and around the borders of the Clyde coalfield basin. The deposits consist mainly of rock types from the hill slopes above and it is evident

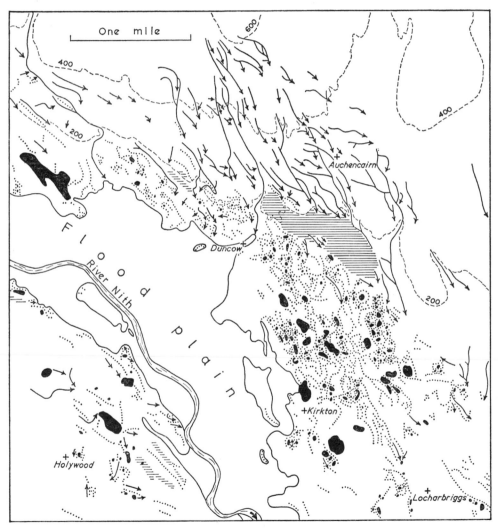

FIG. 49. Fluvioglacial landforms in the Nith valley north of Dumfries, after
J. C. Stone 1959. Meltwater channels are represented by arrows, kames by
lines of dots, kame terraces by horizontal shading, and dead-ice hollows
by solid black.

that the submarginal rivers eroded the higher slopes and carried the materials thus obtained down to lower levels in the ice. Often the kames and kettles are themselves channelled and one may picture the zone of submarginal meltwater erosion moving downslope as the ice wasted away, the coarse deposits constantly being redistributed until many of them attained their final resting place amidst the dead ice at the foot of the slope. Such events are well illustrated along the southern slopes of the Kilsyth Hills between Kilsyth and Denny, while a vast accumulation of sand and gravel, partly formed in this manner, borders the floodplain of the Nith near Dumfries. As can be seen in Fig. 49, this accumulation comprises scores of kames (up to 50 feet or so high) interspersed with numerous dead-ice hollows and would doubtless have been much more extensive but for destruction by the Nith.

Kames are common in many valleys in the Highlands and, especially in the west, are often intricately intermixed with the hummocky moraines described in Chapter 5. Rigid distinction between the two types of landscape is frequently not possible and a section through a single mound may show that it is in part composed of unsorted morainic debris and in part of water-laid deposits. In some valleys, however, there are great accumulations of moundy sand and gravel, as in Glen Dochart from Killin past Crianlarich to Tyndrum. Many kames occur on the broad floor of the Spey valley and here there are various kettle lakes such as lochs Vaa, Roid, Garten and Mallachie. Not far away, on the northwestern slopes of the Cairngorms, the moundy fluvioglacial deposits reach altitudes as great as 2000 feet and stream sections show that locally their thickness attains 200 feet. Generally little is known about the depth of such deposits in the Highlands. In Glen Tromie, to the west of the Cairngorms, however, excavations associated with the hydro-electric scheme showed that the morainic and fluvioglacial deposits are as much as 250 feet thick. Tunnelling operations revealed cavities in the drift 12 feet or more across at depths of 50 to 90 feet. These cavities appear to mark the positions of buried blocks of ice and have been preserved owing to the coarse nature of the deposits, the boulders interlocking like an arch as the ice melted out. As J. G. C. Anderson (1951) suggested, such chambers might well be called 'enclosed kettle holes'.

While the kame and kettle landscapes often appear to comprise a chaotic mass of mounds and hollows, it is doubtful if total disorder ever prevails. Sometimes the mounds tend to lie in two main directions aligned approximately at right-angles to each other as if their orientations were determined by a crevasse pattern in the ice. Very often a significant proportion of the mounds display a rough parallelism, as in Fig. 49, where many are aligned towards southeast and south-southeast. Where there is good reason for believing that the mounds were built up by rivers flowing along their length they may be distinguished as eskers. Many short eskers were built by streams running downslope beneath the ice and such eskers sometimes begin at the lower ends of subglacial chutes. Highland valleys often provided ideal situations for the development of such features and they abound in the deep valleys in the heart of the Cairngorms, where they have been mapped in detail by D. E. Sugden (1965). Eastwards from Loch Avon, for example, the lower slopes of the northern side of the glacial trough are covered by a remarkable series of mounds that trend downslope (Fig. 50). Most of the ridges are 10 to 30 feet high, but some rise 70 feet above the valley floor. They are composed of sand and gravel, sometimes including considerable quantities of boulders, while their surfaces are scattered with boulders lowered onto them from the decaying ice.

Eskers are most prominent on lowlands and valley floors where they sometimes record the courses of the subglacial rivers for several miles (Plate XIIIA). They are well developed

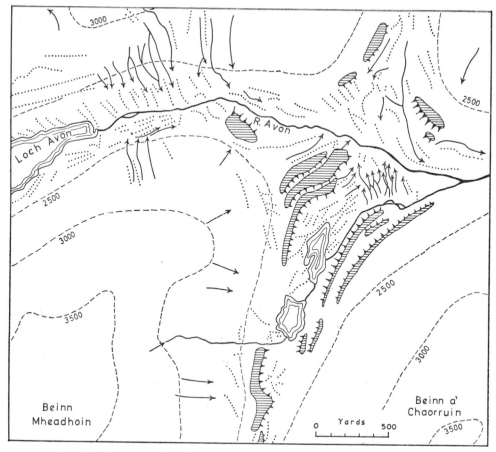

FIG. 50. Fluvioglacial landforms in Glen Avon in the Cairngorms, after D. E.
Sugden 1965. Meltwater channels are represented by arrows, kames
(including eskers) by lines of dots, and kame terraces by horizontal shading.

in the Moray Firth coastlands between Croy and Nairn, near Dornoch, and between
Golspie and Brora where, like many other large lowland eskers, they trend in approximately the same directions as the last ice movements. Large eskers occur among the
extensive sand and gravel accumulations in the basin of the Water of Feugh near
Strachan and small ones, perhaps the highest in Scotland, have been mapped by Sugden
at an altitude of over 3000 feet in the Cairngorms near the head of Glen Einich. Small
eskers often have steep sides, undulating crest-lines and sinuous courses. Occasionally
the sinuosity is pronounced and one very small esker in a col by the Allt Laire (tributary
to the Spean) forms an almost complete circle that was on the point of being cut off to
produce an abandoned esker meander at the time the glacial stream ceased to flow
through the col. Eskers are often intimately associated with meltwater channels and in
ideal situations enable one to reconstruct the courses of some of the glacial rivers as they
flowed along beneath the ice, eroding in some places and depositing in others. Such a
river system by the Tinto Hills in Lanarkshire is shown in Fig. 51. Here the meltwaters
that poured northwards through the col in the western part of the map area at first cut
channels beneath the ice, but lower down the slope they began to deposit the materials

they had eroded as small gently-winding esker ridges. Eastwards erosion again became dominant and the rather complex system of small channels, none of them more than 25 feet deep, was produced. Still farther east, towards the Clyde, deposition again prevailed and some of the meltwater channels are continued by a small esker. Near the Clyde this is joined by an esker leading out of a small valley and by another one that wanders down the Clyde valley. Where the three rivers came together they combined to produce a

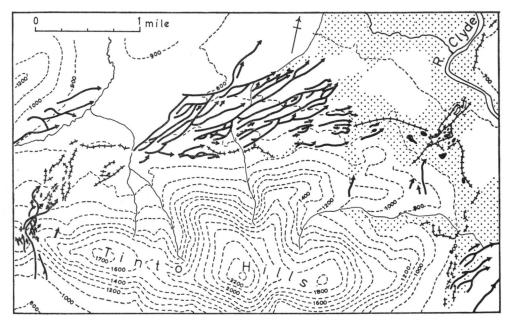

FIG. 51. A glacial drainage system comprising meltwater channels and eskers situated by the Tinto Hills, Lanarkshire. Kettle holes are shown in solid black. Dots represent fluvioglacial deposits not forming eskers or kettle holes. After J. B. Sissons 1961b.

larger esker that crosses the Clyde valley and leads away northwards. This drainage system shows clearly how the meltwaters took advantage of a col and favoured the lower hill slopes as they sought to reach the valley floors. It also shows that the decaying ice-sheet must have locally become stagnant by the time the meltwater features were formed, for otherwise the delicate esker ridges trending in various directions could not have survived.

Some eskers form parts of complex belts of fluvioglacial sand and gravel that extend for many miles. One such system borders the lower Teviot valley as far as Eckford, where the river swings northwards to join the Tweed, and then continues past More-battle to lead into the meltwater-modified valley in which Kirk Yetholm lies. By far the best known system of this type, however, is the one that extends for 20 miles down the Douglas valley, alongside the Clyde, and into the Medwin valley. This vast accumulation of fluvioglacial materials has been (and still is) explained in various ways, interest being centred especially on the part around Carstairs where the features are particularly impressive. The village lies at the base of a system of steep-sided ridges 50 to 80 feet high that constantly separate and rejoin but on the whole maintain a rough parallelism. Between the ridges are deep elongated kettle holes, most of which are floored with peat but a few of which contain pools or small lakes. The deposits have been studied in detail by G. A. Goodlet (1964) and, as can be seen from Fig. 52, comprise various types of material. The main deposit, of which some of the ridges are entirely composed, is remarkable for the great quantity of large boulders that it contains. Although some of these are as much as 3 or 4 feet across, most of them are nevertheless partly rounded, and they demonstrate the great power of the meltwater rivers. Overlying the boulder deposits in the mound illustrated in Fig. 52 are other, less coarse gravels, and on top of these come bedded sands, the faulting and contortion of these deposits having resulted from the melting of ice that was buried beneath the boulder deposits. Taken as a whole the ridge system trends towards the northeast and east and, like other important meltwater routes in the hills to the south (e.g. Fig. 51), accords with the direction of movement of the last ice-sheet.

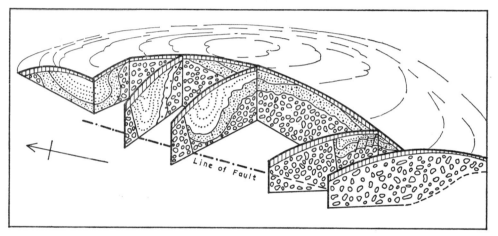

FIG. 52. A section in the Carstairs esker system, showing boulder deposit overlain by less coarse material. Length of section (in direction of fault) about 130 yards. After G. A. Goodlet 1964.

Kame terraces and outwash

While moundy forms characterise the fluvioglacial deposits accumulated beneath, within and on the ice, flat or gently-sloping spreads and terraces typify those laid down against and beyond the ice-margin (Plate XIIB). On many hill slopes and valley sides impersistent gently-inclined terraces can be detected, and are often especially clear on suitably-oriented slopes when brought out by low-angle sunlight. Sometimes such kame terraces, built up between the ice margin and an ice-free slope, are much more pronounced and may form massive accumulations. In other instances the terraces form distinct steps one above the other, as on the hill slopes south of Nairn where individual steps sloping down gently northeastwards can be traced for several miles. Occasionally a terrace runs into a meltwater channel cut through a small spur, to be resumed again farther along where the channel dies away, the action of the marginal meltwater stream thus having been closely analogous to the cut and fill method of railway or modern highway construction.

Kame terraces often occur at the entrances or exits of meltwater channels, an example of the latter being provided by the Burn o' Vat channel near Dinnet in Deeside. This channel, cut in granite, includes in its course a vast, almost perfectly circular pothole (the Vat itself) some 60 feet in diameter and 40 to 60 feet deep. Shortly below the pothole the channel ends above the level of the adjacent low ground but is continued along the hill slopes on either side by kame terraces that decline away from its exit and were probably deposited during the final stages of the excavation of the channel. Debris that was poured out of the channel amidst the stagnant ice litters the ground beyond and the site of one large detached block of ice is marked by the kettle hole occupied by Loch Kinord (Bremner 1916).

Kettle holes are common in kame terraces and sometimes the dead ice masses were so numerous that a terrace might equally well be described as a series of flat-topped kames at an accordant level. Such is the nature of the highest of the large terraces near Eaglesham about ten miles south of Glasgow. This and some of the lower terraces here, the largest of which is a mile long and more than a quarter of a mile broad, are fronted by steep, rather irregular ice-contact slopes each of which marks the position of the main ice margin at the time a particular terrace ceased to be formed. It has been suggested (Richey *et al.* 1930) that the Eaglesham terraces in part accumulated in a narrow marginal lake, for in places they contain much horizontally-bedded sand and have little surface gradient. This origin is by no means uncommon and as a further example we may cite the terraces that extend intermittently along the lower slopes of the Tummel–Tay valley around Pitlochry and down to Dunkeld. Where these terraces were laid down by marginal streams they are composed of sand and gravel and slope gently down the valley, but where they were accumulated in narrow marginal lakes silt and sand predominate and the terrace surfaces are almost horizontal (Bremner 1939).

Much larger than most of the kame terraces, however, and including some of the greatest masses of material laid down by the meltwater rivers in Scotland, are the outwash deposits poured out beyond the glacier margins. In some of the larger Highland valleys these deposits form fans of debris sloping outwards in all directions from the mouths of tributary valleys. In form they thus resemble alluvial fans built up by streams in more recent times, but in size and coarseness of material they show that they were produced by streams far bigger than those that currently occupy the valleys, and their glacial origin may sometimes be verified by tracing the debris upstream when it will be found to terminate amidst a sea of hummocky moraines. A large fan in the Don valley close to Kintore was produced by meltwaters that poured through a col that leads from the Kemnay basin. This fan, formed during the decay of the ice-sheet, was partly dissected by the meltwaters into two main levels and has been considerably eroded by the Don to produce a scarp a mile long and up to 50 feet high (Bremner 1921).

The sand and gravel plain that occupies several square miles of Strathmore south of Blairgowrie represents another outwash deposit and, except where its surface is interrupted by kettle holes containing lochs such as Fingask and Stormonth, it rises gently northwards from the vicinity of the Tay and Isla towards the point where the River Ericht emerges from the Highlands. Farther along Strathmore another great sheet of outwash was spread out far across the low ground by the glacial ancestors of the North Esk and West Water. Well away from the Highland edge this deposit consists mainly of sand and quite small gravel but towards the uplands it increases in coarseness until at their base it consists largely of cobbles and boulders up to a foot or more in diameter. Here, in the mouths of Glen Esk and the West Water glen, the outwash is replaced by kame and kettle landscapes that mark the terminal zones of large valley glaciers from which the outwash rivers issued. These outwash deposits, like many other similar ones, were eroded by the meltwater rivers into a series of terraces, some of which are shown in Fig. 53. On the highest terrace linear depressions a few feet deep can be made out in places and may represent some of the final courses of the braided streams that built it up. On the lower terraces more definite river channels can be located here and there, some of them forming ill-drained gently-curving depressions along the bases of the erosional bluffs that limit the successive terraces.

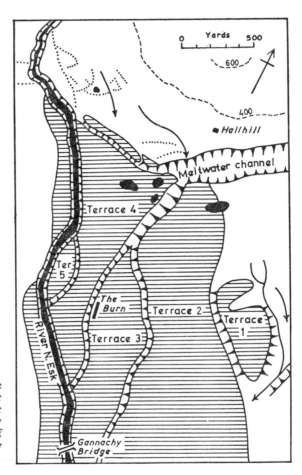

FIG. 53. Outwash terraces by the River North Esk, near Edzell. Small meltwater channels represented by arrows, kames by lines of dots, and kettle holes by solid black.

Although fluvioglacial deposits are in general much less abundant in the westward-draining valleys of the Highlands and in the western islands than in many other parts of Scotland, there are some very notable exceptions. Several large accumulations occur around the coasts of central and eastern Mull and massive outwash deposits almost block the entrance to Loch Etive and form the greater part of the conspicuous promontory at Corran Ferry midway along Loch Linnhe (p. 154 and Fig. 65). Another great outwash mass borders the southern side of the entrance to Loch Carron and, when viewed from the northern side (where a similar but smaller accumulation exists) its regular smooth top stands out in striking contrast against the rough rocky slopes behind. At the head of the loch and extending several miles up Strath Carron fluvioglacial deposits, among them a score or so of kettle lakes, again become abundant. Thus the main road along the margin of the strath takes advantage of the gentle gradient of a kame terrace that, declining down-valley from 170 to 80 feet above sea-level in a couple of miles, merges imperceptibly into a peat-covered outwash plain that occupies the full width of the valley floor and continues the gentle down-valley slope from 80 to 25 or 30 feet above sea-level.

Fluvioglacial features are plentiful in the small valleys that lead down to the coast between Oban and Lochgilphead. A neat example of valley infilling by outwash occurs along the course of the Euchar river between Loch Scamadale and Kilninver. It is clear that at the time this outwash was accumulated a tongue of ice covered the present site of Loch Scamadale, for the outwash train begins some 30 feet above the western end of the loch (among a small group of kames). The surface of the deposit slopes gently down the Euchar valley for several miles and towards its lower end has been dissected into small but conspicuous terraces that overlook the narrow incision occupied by the present river. A similar set of features in the next valley to the south commences at the western end of Loch Tralaig. In the adjacent valley occupied by Loch Avich the situation is slightly different, for this loch drains to the east. Kame terraces on the valley slopes above the western end of the loch lead westwards into a meltwater channel that carried the drainage across the present watershed when the site of the loch was occupied by an ice tongue. Farther south, at the seaward end of Loch Awe, this situation is repeated and greatly embellished. This loch is peculiar in that its present outlet through the Pass of Brander to Loch Etive lies close to its inland end. The glacial drainage, however, escaped for a considerable time through two meltwater channels at its southwestern end and one of these fails by a mere 30 feet or so to carry the present discharge of the loch. The higher of the two channels leads southwards to Kilmichael Glassary while the other (which has a huge pothole in its floor at Gurach) runs first westwards and then turns south to Kilmartin. Between the heads of the channels and Loch Awe the low ground is covered with fluvioglacial deposits, among which is the kettle hole containing Loch Ederline. The flat tops of some of the kames are accordant in altitude with kames terraces that border the low ground and the latter lead into the Kilmartin channel where they are continued by outwash terraces that are very prominent around Kilmartin itself (Hill *et al.* 1905).

Terraces composed of outwash are a characteristic feature of many Highland valleys, especially in the central and eastern parts of these uplands. They abound in the Dee and Don valleys and are particularly clear between Dinnet and Aboyne where the coarse deposits contain many granite boulders. Large terraced outwash plains up to a mile across are included among the vast fluvioglacial accumulations that litter the floor of the Spey valley for tens of miles and are especially well developed around Aviemore and Nethy Bridge. More local but equally prominent features occupy the narrow valley of the Findhorn around and upstream of Dulsie Bridge, border Glen Glass below the loch, and occur at five or six different levels around Achnasheen in central Ross-shire. In some of these localities aggradation took place because the meltwaters emerged from the ice at one place only to find their down-valley escape route barred at another. More often meltwaters were able to escape freely down-valley but aggradation nevertheless occurred on the floors of the larger valleys, for their slope was insufficient to allow the streams discharging from the ice to carry away their heavy loads of debris. Repeatedly as the ice wasted back up the valleys outwash aprons of coarse gravel were built up but, even as this was happening, others, deposited shortly before, were being dissected into terraces. Erosion was sometimes so severe that the terraces became restricted to intermittent patches fringing the valley floor, perhaps now giving a hint of their original complexity where a resistant rock outcrop locally retarded their destruction.

It is necessary to emphasise this pattern of outwash deposition rapidly followed by erosion, for the great majority of the Scottish river terraces originated in this manner. This means that, while the highest terrace at a particular place is usually a true depositional feature, the lower ones are often steps cut out of the original deposit. It also means that the English custom of attempting to correlate surviving fragments of river terraces over long stretches of a valley in order to reconstruct former gently-sloping river profiles related to past higher sea-levels has little or no application in Scotland. Only in the immediate vicinity of present or former coastlines are Scottish terraces related to sea-level changes. Elsewhere their slopes are related to the volume, velocity and load of the glacial rivers. Terrace gradients are usually between 20 and 100 feet a mile, and slopes of 60 to 80 feet a mile are common for the terraces composed of coarse debris. Consequently a given terrace can often be traced down-valley for only a short distance from the kame and kettle topography in which it originates before it is lost in the deposits of the valley floor. The repetition of such features means that many of the major Scottish valleys contain a large number of short steeply-sloping river terraces. As an example we may cite the Tweed valley. Along its lower course from Berwick to beyond Kelso the river is bordered by an almost continuous belt of fluvioglacial deposits that forms numerous terraces close to the river itself. A given terrace may be traced upstream from the level of the floodplain to a height of 30 to 50 feet above the river before it dies out. Meanwhile another terrace has often appeared at a lower level and this may in turn be followed in a similar manner. Farther upstream, where the Lyne joins the Tweed, the valley is almost choked with a flat-topped mass of fluvioglacial deposits whose flanks are cut into several lesser terraces. The sharp upstream termination of this mass of material may record a position occupied by the ice margin for some time. In the upper part of the Tweed valley a quite different system of terraces appears. Near Drummelzier these terraces barely rise above the floodplain of the river, but after some miles they reach 30 to 40 feet above. They appear to be composed partly of outwash laid down by streams draining from small glaciers that occupied tributary valleys in the Tweedsmuir Hills and partly of debris that flowed down the steep hill slopes under cold climatic conditions.

Englacial water-tables and ice-dammed lakes

So far in this chapter we have emphasised the work of rivers during glacier decay and have made only brief reference to ice-dammed lakes. It was inevitable, however, that during the decay of the ice-masses lakes were held up in many places where the free flow of rivers from the hills was impeded, although these were by no means as large or as numerous as has sometimes been suggested. Their former existence is demonstrated by laminated silts, clays and sands, and by the steeply-dipping fore-set beds of gravel deltas. Where such deposits occur they are usually of limited extent, while the kettle holes that often pit their surfaces and the ice-contact slopes that bound them also show that most of the lakes were small bodies of water at the edge of the ice that were rapidly filled up with debris almost as soon as they came into existence.

In view of the innumerable tunnels and cavities that were present in the decaying ice it may seem somewhat surprising that lakes should have existed at all. To explain this apparent anomaly we must look more closely at the nature of the ice decay. We have seen already how in many places meltwaters flowed down under the ice-marginal zone to erode subglacial chutes or complex systems of channels. These features quite often show that the meltwaters penetrated between 300 and 400 feet beneath the ice surface, but no instance is known as yet in Scotland where more than 400 feet of penetration can be demonstrated. This suggests that during times of widespread glacier decay the meltwater rivers were largely or entirely restricted to the uppermost 400 feet or so of the ice and were probably unable to penetrate deeper owing to the pressures in the ice. It would seem, therefore, that we may imagine this zone of meltwater flow, probably with the principal englacial rivers in its basal part, being lowered onto the land surface beneath as the ice wasted down. When these rivers impinged on the buried spurs and hill tops the super-imposed meltwater channels we have described already (p. 103) began to be produced.

As the hills emerged through the downwasting ice surface and the original superimposed drainage system was increasingly disrupted, it was often replaced by streams that flowed along the hill slopes beneath the ice-marginal zone (p. 103). In other areas, however, escape in this manner was not possible. Instead, the drainage was impeded and large-scale deposition took place in the ice-marginal zone. At first such deposition was sub-glacial, but as the ice continued to waste away deposition between its margin and the hill slopes also occurred. In favourable localities, as, for example, where the meltwater outlet was through a channel cut in the floor of a large col, the ice wasted back from the hill slope (probably greatly helped by the melting action of the glacial rivers) to allow a small lake to develop in which rapid sedimentation took place. Such a lake could not be held up by the rotten ice of the marginal zone but was impounded by the firm ice farther back from the margin. This situation is shown in Fig. 54, where it will be seen that the lake surface is prolonged into the ice by a water level that may be referred to as an englacial water-table. Above the level of the water-table meltwaters flowed freely down the hill slopes beneath the ice to cut channels. At the water-table the meltwater flow was checked and deposition began, the numerous openings in the ice beneath the water-table becoming choked with debris.

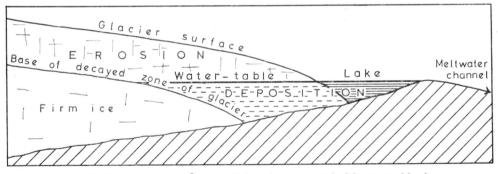

FIG. 54. Diagram showing ideal relations between englacial water-table, ice-dammed lake and fluvioglacial erosion and deposition.

The later stages of such a sequence of events are often clearly recorded in the landscape today. An example is provided by the valley of the Eddleston Water, which stream flows southwards to join the Tweed at Peebles. As can be seen in Fig. 47, the dominant flow of meltwaters in this area was in the opposite direction. Consequently, as the Southern Upland ice-sheet that had covered the area wasted away, there came a time when the drainage was impeded by the emergence of the watershed that now separates the Tweed drainage from that of the Forth. This caused an englacial water-table and very small marginal lakes to develop in the Eddleston valley, the water escaping near the northern end at an altitude of slightly below 900 feet. Scores of meltwater channels descend to this level and numerous kames and kettles lie below it, while the level itself is marked by kame

PLATE XV. Sgorr Dhearg in the Royal Forest looking northwest to Loch Leven. *Photograph by Aerofilms.*

PLATE XVI. A. Frost-shattered summit of Ben Nevis, with glacial troughs and corries beyond. *Photograph by Aerofilms*. B. Subdued relief in the Orkneys, viewed from above Kirkwall. *Ministry of Defence (Air Force Department) photograph. Crown Copyright reserved.*

terraces and the flat tops of a few of the kames. The water-table and lakes ceased to exist when continued decay of the ice allowed drainage to the Tweed valley to take place. That this occurred while a considerable amount of glacier ice still occupied the Eddleston valley is shown by two large ice-controlled meltwater channels that descend as much as 200 feet below the level of the water-table. The meltwaters from these channels flowed southwards beneath the ice to the Tweed valley where they probably joined a subglacial river flowing along the floor of that valley to emerge finally at the margin of the Tweed ice and make their contribution to the outwash deposits (Sissons 1958).

Such reversals of meltwater drainage during the later stages of ice decay, leading to the re-establishment of the normal drainage, occurred in various places. They probably account for the incised courses of the River Irvine near Darvel and the Endrick Water above Fintry, and for the deep gorge of the River Devon at Rumbling Bridge. In each of these localities fluvioglacial deposits show that the meltwater rivers first drained eastwards, while the incised river courses suggest that later they found a way westwards beneath the ice, the present rivers having taken advantage of the routes thus excavated for them. In other instances the meltwaters continued to deposit after the drainage had been reversed. Thus the numerous submarginal channels on the slopes of Strath Allan descend to a constant level (Fig. 45) where they die away to be replaced by a sea of kames and kettles that floors the lowland. The change-over from erosion to deposition reflects the control of an englacial water-table whose level was determined by a meltwater channel that leads out of the eastern end of the strath. At a lower level, however, at the western end, a steep-sided esker leads towards Dunblane and probably marks the course of the meltwater river that re-established drainage down the strath.

While only small lakes were held up by the ice during deglaciation and these were often partly occupied by masses of decaying ice or filled with debris almost as soon as they were formed, large lakes are known to have been dammed up in certain areas during periods of glacier advance (and in some instances these lakes persisted for a time as the ice later began to decay). The difference was partly a result of the much steeper surface gradient of the ice-marginal zone during times of glacier advance and partly of the much firmer condition of the ice itself at such times.

By far the best known of these lakes are those of glens Roy, Gloy and Spean and minor tributary glens. The 'parallel roads' that often mark their former shorelines (Plate XIIIb) have attracted far more speculation than any other set of landforms in Scotland and by 1885 they had been discussed in at least 35 publications. While the traditional view that they were hunting roads constructed by Fingal and his companions for chasing deer did not find favour in scientific circles, many other explanations did, it being variously postulated that the 'roads' had been caused by high sea-levels, a great inundation, ice-marginal deposition, debris-dammed lakes and ice-dammed lakes. This last explanation, for the most part the correct one, was first suggested by L. Agassiz and subsequently convincingly demonstrated by T. F. Jamieson (1863).

Ice advancing from the high precipitation areas west of the Great Glen occupied the southern part of the glen and extended into Glen Spean, where it merged with glaciers nourished in the corries of the Ben Nevis range and with ice that had moved down the valley now occupied by Loch Treig. The approximate limits of this glacial advance and of the lakes that were impounded at that time are shown in Fig. 55. The Glen Spean lake was about 12 miles long but only about 200 feet deep at its deepest point and was little larger than the present Laggan Reservoir. The Glen Roy lake was about 10 miles long and that in Glen Gloy about $4\frac{1}{2}$ miles, their maximal depths close to the ice margin

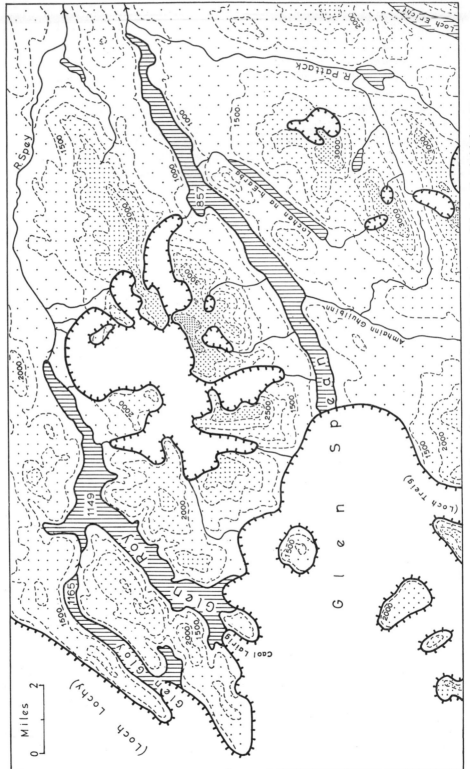

FIG. 55. Ice-dammed lakes in glens Roy, Gloy and Spean at the time of maximal extent of the ice that held them up.

being respectively 650 and 550 feet. With the subsequent decay of the ice the lake levels were lowered. The lake at 1149 feet in Glen Roy was succeeded by one at 1068 feet controlled by a col that leads into Glen Spean. In Caol Lairig these two levels were followed by one at 975 feet when the lake level in this valley was controlled for a time by the col at its head. In both valleys the lake waters thereafter stood at the 857-foot level of the Glen Spean lake, for the latter had persisted throughout the time the lakes in Glen Roy and Caol Lairig had been falling in level.

The altitudes of the 'roads' were established by extensive levelling carried out last century by the Ordnance Survey. This showed them to be essentially horizontal except in certain localities where they were formed in immediate proximity to the ice. The 'roads' usually form obvious lines along the valley sides when viewed from a distance but are often rather disappointing features when one walks along them. They are usually about 10 to 30 yards wide, slope towards the valleys, and are composed of angular debris. They often become wider, however, where streams flowed into the lakes and on the flattish floors of glens Roy and Spean, where debris was able to accumulate, deltas were produced. One of these at the level of the lowest road forms a large flat-topped mass of sand and gravel at the junction of the rivers Turret and Roy, while a similar feature composed of sand causes the marked constriction in the Laggan Reservoir where the Amhainn Ghuilbinn enters it.

Although the Glen Roy area has been repeatedly discussed, certain problems remain to be solved and much basic mapping of the fluvioglacial landforms has yet to be done. One point we may note is that, during the advance of the glaciers, it may well be that there occurred an additional sequence of lake levels occupied in the reverse order to that

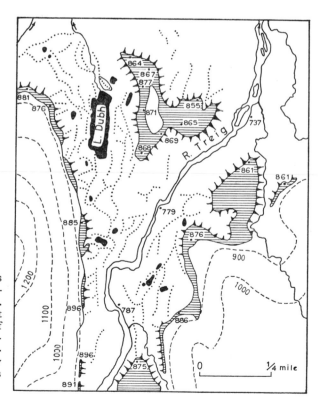

FIG. 56. Fluvioglacial landforms in the Treig valley immediately north of Loch Treig. The 'road' and related flat or gently-sloping spreads of sand (kame terraces) are indicated by horizontal shading. Kames are shown by lines of dots and kettle lakes in solid black.

described above. A second point is that overflow channels have not been found at the levels of some of the 'roads', as, for example, the 'roads' at about 1050 and 965 feet in Glen Gloy. Thirdly, the details of the ice decay and the way in which the lakes were finally drained have not been established. There are, however, within the ice limits shown in Fig. 55, great quantities of fluvioglacial material that were laid down amidst the decaying ice. For example, in the lower part of Glen Roy and in Glen Gloy below its junction with Glen Fintaig numerous ridges run down the valley sides from the 'roads'. Some are formed of bedded sand and gravel, some of angular debris, and some of both types of material. All of them, however, appear to be the result of debris having been carried down the sides of the glens into the decaying ice. Deposits are most abundant in the area around the junction of the rivers Treig and Spean. Here, below the level of the 'road', the valley slopes are almost entirely covered with immense quantities of sand, which forms terraces, kames and kettle holes or mantles the slopes with no distinctive form. Solid rock is rarely seen except along the incised courses of the Spean and Treig. On the other hand, above the level of the 'road', sand is usually quite absent and bare rock common. The landforms of part of this area are shown in Fig. 56. In this locality none of the numerous kames rises above the level of the 'road' (although some rise to the same altitude) and many of them lead out from the 'road' into the adjacent lower ground. It is thus evident that these features were all formed at the same time and that the 'road' is here a series of kame terraces accumulated against the margin of stagnant ice. The terraces are slightly above the usual altitude of the 'road' (857 feet), but as a group they are clearly related to it and show that an englacial water-table existed here in the thoroughly-decayed ice.

Similar evidence exists farther down Glen Spean. In other places in the lower part of the glen the 'road' is absent for a mile or more where glacier tongues from the Ben Nevis range were wasting away. The 'road' continues intermittently, however, as far as the hill slopes above Spean Bridge, some 22 miles distant from the point where the water escaped into the Spey basin. At the final stage of the existence of this water body we may envisage it as a long narrow open lake in its eastern part (perhaps for 14 miles or so), while in the western part were detached masses of dead ice, decaying glacier tongues, and large accumulations of sand as well as areas of open water, a uniform level being possible owing to the free movement of water through the ice. The subglacial route (or routes) by which this water body was subsequently drained away and the later stages of the glacial drainage of this area have not yet been elucidated.

The only other place in Scotland where 'roads' similar to those of the Glen Roy area have been found is in Rannoch Moor, but the lakes that existed here were small. The 'roads' are best developed in the valley of the Water of Tulla where J. Mathieson and E. B. Bailey (1925) identified former lake levels at altitudes of 1041, 1030, 1020 and 816 feet. The outlets of the three higher lakes are not firmly established but the waters of the lowest escaped through the col that leads from Loch Dochard to Glen Kinglass. The advance of a glacier down the Loch Lomond valley in the late stages of the last glaciation caused lakes to be formed in the Endrick and Blane valleys, as will be appreciated from Fig. 44. The thick deposits of silt and clay that floor the latter valley may represent the bottom deposits of this lake. Within the ice limit, between Killearn and Drymen, deposits of sand as much as 100 feet thick were laid down amidst the decaying ice up to the level of an englacial water-table controlled by the floor of a channel through which the meltwaters were discharged into the Forth valley.

In the Spey valley around Rothes and Knockando a large lake was held up between ice that had come down the valley and the Moray Firth ice-stream that had blocked its lower end (Bremner 1934a). The lake was apparently filled up almost as rapidly as it was formed by the great quantities of sand and silt washed into it, these deposits accumulating in horizontal layers to thicknesses as great as 200 feet. With the decay of the Moray Firth ice the lake level fell in stages from its original altitude of slightly over 600 feet to about 400 feet, the waters for a considerable time escaping through the long channels that meet at Keith (Fig. 48). The lowering of the lake level and its final draining resulted in the sediments being cut into a fine series of terraces, as many as eight being visible one above the other.

Doubtless in many places lakes were completely overwhelmed by advancing ice, but the evidence has been obliterated or obscured. In the Clyde basin for some distance above Glasgow, however, evidence of such a lake survives. Here beds of sand, silt and clay that attain a thickness of 100 feet in some of the buried river valleys are overlain by till, showing that the ice-stream that moved up the Clyde valley over the site of Glasgow blocked the river to produce a lake, which was reduced in area as the ice advanced into it. In some places the advancing ice greatly contorted the bedded deposits as it moved over them although in other places they were apparently frozen solid, for they contain fossil frost wedges (p. 219). The lake was extinguished when the ice merged with the Southern Upland ice and with ice moving through the Darvel-Strathaven gap. During the subsequent decay of this ice-mass the lake did not re-form and instead smaller lakes and englacial water-tables developed, as near Eaglesham and east of Lanark. In the latter area, following the formation of the Carstairs esker (p. 112), extensive deposits of sand, now disposed as smooth mounds, were laid down amidst the dead ice in relation to a water level controlled by the long meltwater channel that leads past Blyth Bridge to the Tweed (Fig. 47).

Other aspects of fluvioglacial landforms

So far in this chapter we have tended to assume that the fluvioglacial landforms were produced in association with the last ice-mass to cover a particular area. For most of these landforms this assumption is warranted and certainly the depositional landforms could not have survived from an earlier glaciation. However, it may well be that some of the large meltwater channels were utilised on more than one occasion and some were not used at all during the decay of the last ice-cover. In the Midlothian basin, for example, the direction of some of the buried valleys suggests that they are old meltwater channels (Tulloch and Walton 1958). In the same general area, near Gorebridge, is an exceptionally large channel, up to several hundred yards broad, that carried vast volumes of meltwater eastwards out of the Midlothian basin. Yet, at Borthwick, this channel is almost completely blocked by a massive barrier of fluvioglacial sand and gravel. But for this barrier one might well have assumed that the channel had been formed during the final deglaciation of the area. It may well be that many other large channels where such evidence is not present have had a more complex history than appears.

Emphasis has also been laid in the preceding pages on the importance of glacier stagnation and, often, on meltwater activity beneath the ice. Many fluvioglacial deposits, however, form ill-defined spreads of material whose surface rises and falls gently as vague swells and depressions with no distinctive form. These deposits may have been laid down within or on the ice, or while the ice was still moving, subsequently having been partly redistributed when it finally wasted away. Similar explanations may account for the forms of some large belts of fluvioglacial deposits, such as the one that extends for six miles from Falkirk to Linlithgow and is often referred to as the Polmont kame. These deposits of sand and gravel comprise a steep-sided winding esker ridge, a zone of less clearly defined mounds, and certain massive rounded mounds whose shape is not dissimilar to that of adjacent drumlins. This set of features suggests that a major glacial river flowed through this area for a considerable time, deposition commencing while the ice was still active, when some of the deposits were moulded into the large mounds, and continuing until the ice had become completely stagnant, when the esker was formed.

Such relationships raise the question of the connection between belts of fluvioglacial deposits and the ablation till described in Chapter 4. Only rarely does any significant quantity of ablation till overlie fluvioglacial deposits, the most that is usually found consisting of scattered boulders. Since many fluvioglacial features were formed beneath the ice this suggests that where subglacial rivers existed they incorporated the ablation till in their own deposits. Thus, ideally, we might expect a lateral change from well-sorted material in the centre of a belt of fluvioglacial deposits to unsorted ablation till beyond its margins. Such relationships appear to exist. For example, around Howgate in Midlothian a typical esker of well-sorted debris is bordered by a belt of kames of much less definite form and this in turn is followed by low swells and depressions composed of unsorted angular debris.

Finally, it may be mentioned that in places there occur moundy belts up to several miles long that look like systems of kames except that the mounds are perhaps slightly more rounded. They differ greatly from kames, however, in that they are composed mainly of stiff till along with a lesser proportion of water-laid sand and gravel. One set of such features east of Glasgow extends through Baillieston to Flemington (except where interrupted by the Clyde) and another leads out from the base of the Ochils near Milnathort in Kinross. These features may mark the courses of subglacial streams into whose tunnels till was squeezed owing to the ice pressures on either side, an explanation that has been applied to similar features in some other countries.

7

The glacial sequence

In the course of the last five chapters we have made reference to the fact that Scotland has been partly or wholly covered by glacier ice on more than one occasion. We now turn to the evidence that demonstrates this. Much the greater part of this evidence relates to the last great build-up of glacier ice and the subsequent deglaciation, events that occurred between about 25 000 and 10 000 years ago. During this period the deposits laid down in earlier times were eroded or buried over most of the country, so that the picture we can obtain of earlier glacial events is very incomplete. In fact, deposits accumulated during the earliest glaciations of Quaternary times have not yet been identified in Scotland, although we can infer that such glaciations occurred from evidence in the English Midlands and especially in East Anglia. Here stratified deposits containing plant and animal remains indicative of a climate as warm or warmer than at present are sandwiched between till sheets in various places. The till sheets imply that on several occasions Scotland along with much of the rest of the British Isles was covered by a great ice-sheet, while the organic layers imply that in the intervening interglacials the ice disappeared completely. In Scotland itself only one locality (northernmost Lewis) has so far been discovered where organic remains suggesting a climate as warm as the present one occur beneath glacial till (p. 195).

In trying to decipher the sequence of glacial events in Scotland we are therefore forced to concentrate our attention on the most recent events, especially on those associated with the decay of the last ice-sheet. This decay was not continuous but was interrupted by periods when the climate deteriorated and glacier margins readvanced. The limits of the three principal readvances are tentatively marked in Fig. 59. In parts of eastern Scotland beyond the limit of the outermost readvance and, occasionally, within the limit, there is also evidence of earlier ice movements that sometimes differed greatly in direction from later ones. A further matter to which we may direct our attention is the size of the Scottish ice-sheet when at its maximal extent.

Maximal dimensions of the ice-sheet

In seeking to determine the maximal size of the Scottish ice-sheet we are concerned both with its horizontal and vertical dimensions. The two principal questions that need to be answered are: how far did the mainland ice-sheet extend beyond the present coastline? and, were the highest mountains completely covered by the ice-sheet or did they stand above it as nunataks?

Southwards, the importance of the Scottish ice is demonstrated by its dominance over

125

locally-nourished ice-masses in and around the basin of the Irish Sea. It filled the large area now occupied by this sea and extended on to adjacent land areas, discharging a great lobe between the Pennines and the Welsh mountains, surrounding the mountains of Wales on their northern and western sides, and impinging against the Wicklow Mountains in eastern Ireland. It over-ran the Pembrokeshire peninsula and apparently extended along the southern coast of Ireland at least as far as Cork. Eastwards the Scottish ice encountered the much greater Scandinavian ice-sheet at times of very extensive ice-cover and was therefore unable to expand freely over the North Sea bed at such times. Part of the Scottish ice was deflected southwards along or off the east coast of England, while another part traversed Caithness and the Orkney Islands (Figs 34 and 39). The Shetland Islands, however, appear at times to have been overwhelmed by the Scandinavian ice-sheet itself, although at other times ice nourished on these islands was very important locally.

Along the west coast of Scotland striae, erratics and other evidence show that all the islands of the Inner Hebrides were overwhelmed by the mainland ice-sheet. The only large areas that are said to lack such evidence are the heart areas of the highest mountain groups of Skye and Mull. The long island chain of the Outer Hebrides from the Butt of Lewis to Barra Head was covered by the mainland ice-sheet except for the highest ground which, in northern Harris, nourished its own glaciers that merged with the ice from the mainland. That the small island of North Rona, situated about 45 miles north-northeast of the Butt of Lewis and a similar distance northwest of Cape Wrath, was overwhelmed by the ice-sheet is shown by the presence of Torridonian and Cambrian erratics (Gailey 1959). Almost a dozen miles to the west of North Rona the half-mile-long island of Sula Sgeir has small foreign stones, while small erratics are scattered over most of the Flannan Islands situated 20 miles out into the Atlantic beyond the coast of Harris (Stewart 1933). On the other hand, no evidence of the former presence of the ice-sheet has been found on St Kilda located some 40 miles west of North Uist (Wager 1953). It thus appears that when the ice-sheet was at its maximal extent its margin was situated between the Flannan

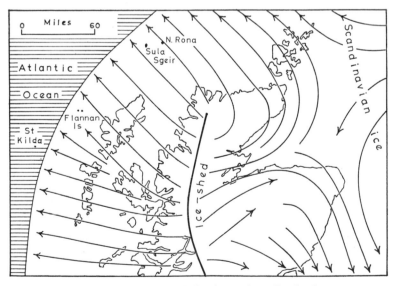

Fig. 57. Maximal glaciation in northern Scotland.

Islands and St Kilda, the latter along with distant Rockall being the only islands that were not affected by the ice-sheet (Fig. 57).

In view of the area covered by the ice-sheet one would expect, from analogies with Greenland and Antarctica and from the calculations of the form of ice-sheets made by physicists, that its thickness would be sufficient to bury even the highest peaks of the mainland. While this cannot be demonstrated with certainty, the evidence is very suggestive. For example, as far away as North Wales, more than 200 miles from the heart area of the ice-sheet in the Southwest Grampians, ice of Scottish derivation was able to carry marine shells from the bed of the Irish Sea to an altitude of 1350 feet on the slopes of Moel Tryfaen, while in eastern Ireland the Scottish ice reached 1800 feet on the slopes of the Wicklow Mountains. In South Uist J. Geikie (1878) found evidence of the passage of the ice-sheet to within 300 or 400 feet of the 2034-foot summit of Beinn Mhor, and in the mountains of Harris he observed plentiful evidence of the former presence of the ice-sheet to an altitude of at least 1600 feet. T. J. Jehu and R. M. Craig (1934) raised the latter figure, for they found the 1829-foot summit of Sgaoth Ard to have been beautifully smoothed by the over-riding ice and on the slopes of Clisham (2622 feet) noted *roches moutonnées* produced by the ice-sheet up to 2000 feet above sea-level.

In Northwest Scotland many mountains have striae, erratics or other evidence near or on their summits that show that they were mostly or entirely buried beneath the ice-sheet. Between Loch Broom and Loch Torridon erratics have been found at about or over 3000 feet on An Teallach, Sgùrr Bàn and Sgùrr an Tuill Bhàin, and on or close to the summits of Beinn an Eòin (2801 feet), Meall Chiubhais (2882 feet) and Slioch (3217 feet). Between Loch Torridon and Loch Carron striae produced by the ice-sheet have been observed at an altitude of almost 2750 feet on Ben Bhan and erratics from the east can be seen above 2600 feet. In the same area the top of An Rhuadh Stac (2919 feet) is finely striated, erratics occur on Sgùrr Ruadh up to 2900 feet, and the bare summit of Maol Cheandearg (3060 feet) is strewn with blocks of Cambrian pipe-rock that have been carried westwards. To the south of Strath Carron striae related to the ice-sheet have been observed at over 2750 feet on Sgùrr na Feartaig (Peach *et al.* 1913a, 1913b).

Similar evidence is available from various points in the Grampians. Striae have been observed at 3600 feet on the summit ridge of Aonach Beag in the Ben Nevis range and granite erratics have been seen at over 3600 feet near Glen Coe. In the mountains between Loch Laggan and Glen Roy systems of meltwater channels directed towards the northeast with the former movement of the ice-sheet extend up to altitudes exceeding 3000 feet, while meltwater features related to ice-sheet conditions attain similar elevations in the Cairngorms. To the east of the Cairngorms boulders of granite from these mountains are scattered over the summit of Morven (2862 feet) north of Ballater. The transport of the Rannoch granite to altitudes exceeding 3000 feet has already been described (p. 83), the highest point at which these erratics have been definitely identified being 3400 feet near the summit of Schiehallion. On the same mountain striae have been observed at over 3000 feet, while Ben Vrackie (2757 feet), near Pitlochry, is striated to its summit. On the mountains of the Highland edge in Perthshire striae again occur at high levels, exceeding 3000 feet on Ben Vorlich.

To the south of the Highlands erratics of mica-schist have been seen on the Ochils at 2000 feet while on top of Ben Cleuch, the highest point of these hills (2363 feet), striated stones have been found. The Lomond Hills of Fifeshire were likewise over-ridden by the ice-sheet and ice-worn erratics of Old Red Sandstone have been found at 1450 feet. Striae occur on the top of Allermuir Hill (1617 feet), the northernmost summit of the

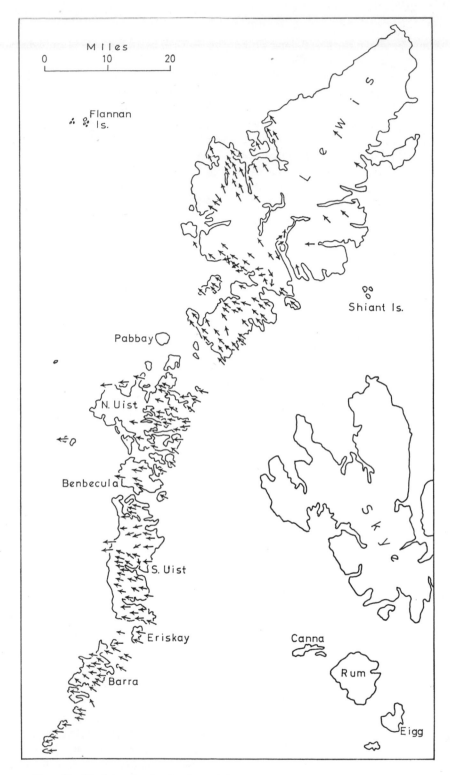

Fig. 58. Glacial striae in the Outer Hebrides. Based on J. Geikie 1894, and
T. J. Jehu and R. M. Craig 1923, 1926.

Pentlands, and erratics have been discovered on the summit of Scald Law (1898 feet), the culminating point of the range. That the Lammermuir Hills were covered by the ice-sheet is shown by the presence of abundant Carboniferous erratics derived presumably from the lower ground of East Lothian. In the middle Clyde area the isolated summit of Tinto (2335 feet) bears evidence of the passage of the ice, while on the other side of the Southern Uplands near the Solway erratics are scattered over Criffell (1866 feet). In the central tract of the Southern Uplands the summit of Merrick (2764 feet), the highest point in the whole of southern Scotland, is littered with erratics from the adjacent Loch Doon granite mass.

It is thus evident that the whole of Scotland south of the Highlands has been entirely covered by the ice-sheet. The fact that in the Highlands themselves there is evidence of the former presence of an ice-sheet up to altitudes of around or above 3000 feet over a wide area extending from southern Perthshire to Aberdeenshire to Wester Ross implies, in view of the gradient that the ice-sheet surface must have possessed, that in at least part of this area the surface of the ice-sheet stood very much above 3000 feet. We must also remember that most of the altitudinal evidence cited above is minimal, for the altitudes mentioned often relate to the mountain summits. Furthermore, the fact that some of the high-level erratics have been carried upwards through many hundred (and occasionally through as much as 1500 or perhaps 2000) feet strongly suggests that the surface of the ice-sheet attained an altitude very much above the points where these erratics have been found (p. 83).

On the other hand, there is no direct evidence to show that some mountains were buried by the ice-sheet and sometimes the evidence that is available *seems* inconsistent with this interpretation. No proof that Ben Nevis has been over-ridden has been found, although it has been sought for. The summit of Ben Alder appears to be devoid of erratics of Rannoch granite although they are plentiful at slightly lower levels. The highest ground of the Gaick plateau appears to be similarly free of these erratics. On the northern, western and southern flanks of the Cairngorms fluvioglacial landforms in particular provide evidence of the former presence of an enveloping ice-sheet to an altitude of about or somewhat above 3000 feet, but there is no direct evidence available (such as erratics) to show that the highest parts of these mountains were covered by ice from an external source. Evidence of the passage of external ice has not been observed within a thousand feet of the summit of the isolated mass of Ben Wyvis, but is widespread below an altitude of 2300 feet on its western flank. In assessing the significance of this evidence various factors need to be borne in mind. For example, detailed studies of erratics, striae or related evidence have been made on very few of the Scottish mountains. Often, too, such evidence is difficult to obtain, for the highest parts of many mountains have been subjected to intense frost-shattering (Plate XIV), while the plateaux are frequently covered with peat as well. In addition, since the last great ice-sheet existed, many uplands have been centres from which valley glaciers radiated, with the consequence that much of the proof of the former presence of an ice-sheet has been modified or destroyed. Furthermore, we cannot necessarily assume that erratics were carried to all areas covered by the ice-sheet, for the upper part of the ice-sheet may have been free of debris.

Considering the evidence as a whole, it would seem reasonable to envisage an ice-sheet with its highest parts situated some 4000 to 5000 feet above present sea-level. In western Sutherland and Wester Ross the axis of the ice-sheet was probably situated slightly to the east of the present watershed in places and continued southwards over the Ben Nevis range to the western part of Rannoch Moor (Fig. 57). In addition to this principal ice-shed local ice-domes probably existed, comparable with those that have been shown to correspond with mountain areas buried beneath the Antarctic ice-sheet at the present time. For example, such domes may have been situated over the Gaick plateau, the Cairngorms and the western and central parts of the Southern Uplands. While the highest parts of the mountains of Harris stood above the ice-sheet and made their own contribution to it, it is not certain that any of the mainland peaks formed nunataks. If such nunataks did exist they were most probably in the extreme northwest as, for example, Foinaven and Ben Hope. At other times, when the ice-sheet was less extensive, the mountain summits stood above its surface. At such times they were subjected to severe frost action and it is probable that much of the frost-shattered rock debris on the mountain tops was produced when the last ice-sheet and the valley glaciers that succeeded it covered the lower ground. The belts of marginal and submarginal phenomena, such as moraines and fluvioglacial features, and the distinct erratic limits that can be traced along the slopes of many uplands also probably relate to the maximal limit of the last ice-sheet and to the limits of the readvances that interrupted its decay.

The radial movement of the ice-sheet across the Outer Hebrides is clearly recorded by striae, which show that the ice flowed almost due west in the southern part of the island chain but more nearly northwest in Harris and Lewis (Fig. 58). A similar radial flow appears to have prevailed over the western part of the mainland between the Sound of Mull and Cape Wrath. Thus between the Sound of Mull and Loch Alsh the ice-sheet moved westwards, but in the coastal belt of the mainland north of Loch Alsh the high-level striae indicate a movement towards west-northwest and northwest (Fig. 57). On the other side of the country, however, a simple radial flow was prevented by the Scandinavian ice-sheet. The southwestward transport of boulders of Peterhead granite (Fig. 32) and the occurrence of Scandinavian erratics in the Aberdeen area suggest that the Scandinavian ice-sheet at one time may have itself crossed the coastline of Northeast Scotland (although this evidence can be interpreted in other ways). The greatest pressure of this ice-sheet appears to have been exerted between Northeast Scotland and Caithness, for it was here that the Scottish ice split into two vast streams, one of which flowed northwestwards across Caithness and the Orkneys and the other southeastwards across Northeast Scotland. The latter ice-stream transported shelly drift with Mesozoic erratics into Banffshire and Aberdeenshire and carried erratics of Bin Hill gabbro and Barra Hill dolerite towards Aberdeen (Fig. 32). The course of this ice-stream (or of a closely associated one) is recorded around Benholm and Inverbervie by shelly till with Mesozoic erratics and Aberdeenshire igneous rocks (Campbell 1934) and by striae pointing south-southeast inland of Montrose (Bremner 1934a). With such an ice movement the ice-mass that would otherwise have streamed eastwards through the Central Lowlands must have been deflected towards the south and southeast. That this ice-stream was forced back across the coast near Berwick is indicated by the shelly till there, while farther south in the coastal zone of Northumberland and Durham there is abundant evidence of ice having moved along the coast. Over central and southern Scotland generally, however, these early ice movements have not been distinguished but instead there is evidence of later readvances of the ice.

The Aberdeen-Lammermuir Readvance

In the lower ground of the Tweed basin the great assemblage of ice-moulded landforms directed towards the northeast and east reflects the last ice movement in this area. The southern limit of these ice-moulded features lies in the vicinity of Cornhill and Beal and is associated with a large area of kames and kettles around Cornhill. To the north of this line the drumlins point eastwards, but to the south of it striae and fluvioglacial features relate to the earlier ice movement towards the southeast and south-southeast. On the opposite side of the Tweed basin the drumlins die away against the rising ground of the Lammermuirs and their limit is in places associated with numerous kames as, for example, near Duns. Higher up the Lammermuir slopes fluvioglacial features are rare or absent and frost-shattered rock debris is of widespread occurrence, suggesting that this higher ground was last ice-covered at a much earlier time than the surrounding lower ground (Fig. 59).

In the Midlothian basin a movement of ice from west to east is demonstrated by the orientation of stones in the basal till and shows that an early ice flow was not significantly affected by the considerable obstacle of the Pentland Hills (Kirby 1966). An intermediate till shows that at a later time Southern Upland ice moved northeastwards into the Midlothian basin and fused with Highland ice in the northern part of the basin. Subsequently the ice-masses withdrew slightly and then advanced again, thick deposits of sand being laid down between the southern fringes of Edinburgh and Penicuik by meltwaters that ultimately escaped into East Lothian through the large meltwater channel near Gorebridge (p. 123). With continued advance of the ice this channel was occupied by the ice and a layer of till a few feet thick was laid down on top of the fluvioglacial sands south of Edinburgh. At this time the Pentland Hills strongly influenced the ice flow, for a stream of Highland ice curved round their northern end and extended southwards to the vicinity of Penicuik. Here it was confluent with the Southern Upland ice whose general northeastward movement is recorded by the distribution of erratics of Tinto felsite (McCall and Goodlet 1952), ice-moulded forms and numerous fluvioglacial features. The zone of junction between the two ice-streams continued eastwards to intersect the Southern Uplands near Lammer Law. Southwestwards from here no meltwater channels run along the scarp of the hills, implying that the Southern Upland ice-sheet had a component of movement away from the hills. On the other hand, northeastwards from the vicinity of Lammer Law meltwater channels abound along the northern face of the Lammermuirs, implying that here the great stream of Highland ice that had moved down the Forth valley pressed against the hills. The limit of this ice, to the extent that it is represented by the highest well-defined meltwater channels, declines eastwards at about 15 feet a mile and passes out to sea at St Abb's Head (Sissons 1961c).

On the other side of the Central Lowlands along the Highland border of Strathmore a similar ice-limit cannot be identified, for the high ground of the Southeast Grampians nourished its own mass of ice that merged with the great ice-stream that flowed through the Central Lowlands from more westerly sources in the Grampians. The part of this latter ice-stream that traversed Strathmore had previously crossed the high ground between the sites of Pitlochry, Dunkeld and Kirriemuir on a gently-curving eastward course and carried erratics of Ben Vuroch granite to Kirriemuir (Barrow et al. 1905). Northeastwards from this vicinity this ice-stream was sufficiently powerful to extend over the Highland edge for a short distance despite the pressure of local ice. Thus Old Red Sandstone erratics have been found 2 miles north of the Highland fault in Glen Prosen, 4 miles north of it in Glen Clova, and $1\frac{1}{2}$ to 2 miles beyond the fault in the valleys of the West Water, North Esk and Bervie Water (Bremner 1934b). Meltwater channels trending parallel with the coast along with Old Red Sandstone erratics occur in a narrow coastal strip between Stonehaven and Muchalls, and again between Findon and Aberdeen, and mark the further course of this ice-stream, which here flowed in a north-northeastward direction towards the site of Aberdeen (Synge 1956). Between Muchalls and Findon grey

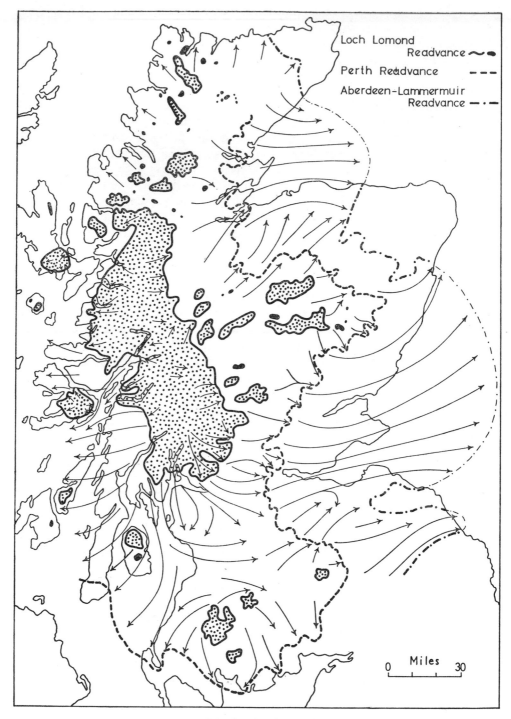

Loch Lomond
Readvance ～●

Perth Readvance ------

Aberdeen-Lammermuir
Readvance —·—

Miles
0 ├────┤ 30

FIG. 59. Successive limits of the last ice-sheet and associated directions of ice
movement.

drift from the west extends down to the coast, implying that ice nourished on the South-east Grampians was locally able to exclude the Strathmore ice-stream. Such exclusion is more effectively demonstrated around Aberdeen, where grey till with granite erratics deposited by the large glacier that flowed down the Dee valley is widely distributed. Close to the city a much-discussed cliff section at the Bay of Nigg shows some 50 feet of till: the lower part, which is grey in colour, contains abundant granite and gneiss erratics and merges upwards into a red till containing Old Red Sandstone erratics (Synge 1963). This section indicates that the Dee glacier at one time crossed the coastline here but that it was subsequently pushed aside by the Strathmore ice-stream. The pressure of the Strathmore ice caused the Dee glacier to flow northwards and northeastwards across the lower part of the Don valley, the striae, meltwater features and till demonstrating this advance extending as far north as Belhelvie.

These ice movements in coastal Aberdeenshire and Kincardineshire are clearly quite different from the southward movement in this area described on p. 130. Proof that this southward flow was the earlier is provided by the Bay of Nigg section where, between the tills referred to above and the solid rock, is a bed of sand and gravel containing Scandi-navian erratics and stones from the Belhelvie igneous complex. Similarly, around Inver-bervie and Benholm a grey-black till with marine shells, Mesozoic erratics and Aberdeen-shire igneous rocks is overlain by the red till of the Strathmore ice-stream.

At the time of the Aberdeen–Lammermuir Readvance the ice-stream from the Great Glen and the mountains of Northwest Scotland formed a great lobe in the Moray Firth area. Its southern limit is marked by the limit of Old Red Sandstone erratics that follows the high ground from Tomatin in the Findhorn valley past the northern end of Lochin-dorb to cross the Spey valley a short distance south of Rothes (Fig. 31). Its limit on the coast may be in the vicinity of Cullen, for T. F. Jamieson (1906) stated that west of this village the shelly Jurassic drift is replaced or covered by a lighter, more varied drift lacking shells.* The Moray Firth ice was confluent on its southern side with the ice-mass that flowed northeastwards from the Monadhliath Mountains as well as down the Spey valley. A 200-foot high section of drift in the Spey valley at Rothes reflects the varying pressures of the two ice-streams in their zone of contact. At the base of the section red till brought by ice from the northwest is overlain by grey till deposited by the Spey ice. Temporary withdrawal of the ice is indicated by the succeeding 40 feet of sands, silts and clays laid down in the ice-dammed lake that was at this time held up in this part of the Spey valley by the Moray Firth ice (p. 123). A slight readvance of the Moray Firth ice into the lake is demonstrated by the overlying 20 feet of red till and this in turn is followed by a further 50 to 75 feet of lake deposits capped by sands and gravels.

On the opposite side of the Moray Firth in Sutherland the ice moved in a general southeastward direction parallel with the principal valleys, such as those of the Fleet, Brora and Helmsdale rivers. This movement is very different in direction from that of the earlier more extensive ice-cover recorded by the shelly drift and related evidence in Caithness (Fig. 39). The line of junction (at the surface) between the two sets of pheno-mena, marking the limit of the Aberdeen–Lammermuir Readvance, appears to cross the coast in the vicinity of Berriedale. In the interior of Caithness upstream from Dirlot on the Thurso Water this readvance is apparently represented by till, morainic mounds and

---

* At an earlier time, according to J. K. Charlesworth (1955) and F. M. Synge (1956), the Moray Firth ice-stream extended to the vicinity of Peterhead where it met the Strathmore ice. As a result some 800 square miles of Northeast Scotland remained ice-free although completely surrounded by ice.

kames of local rock, which rest on the shelly till, and by striae pointing northeast and north that cross the earlier ones pointing northwest (Peach and Horne 1881).

Very few organic remains have been found in association with the deposits of the Aberdeen–Lammermuir Readvance. They comprise a buried soil horizon recently discovered near the lower Spey (p. 145), a mammoth tooth obtained near Ayton in Berwickshire (Ritchie 1928), a mammoth tusk found in till in the valley of the River Almond west of Edinburgh, and a bed of peaty material beneath 30 to 40 feet of till in the valley of the Slitrig Water near Hawick (A. Geikie 1863). Apart from the soil horizon none of these discoveries has been investigated in any detail.

The Perth Readvance

Following the culmination of the Aberdeen–Lammermuir Readvance there was widespread deglaciation accompanied by the formation of some of the large sequences of fluvioglacial features mentioned in Chapter 6, such as those of Nairnshire, Morayshire and the Lothians. This was followed by a major readvance of the ice that was first identified near Perth by J. B. Simpson (1933) and hence may be called the Perth Readvance (Fig. 59). Evidence of a renewed forward movement of the ice is provided by a section by the River Almond about two miles northwest of Perth. This shows a layer of till, covered by 40 feet of fine laminated sediments followed by 15 feet of sand and gravel. The fine sediments suggest that, after the Aberdeen–Lammermuir stage (represented by the layer of till) the ice withdrew a considerable distance and allowed them to accumulate. The later proximity of the ice is recorded by the sands and gravels, which form part of an extensive sheet of outwash leading down-valley towards Perth, and by kettle holes that occur in this outwash near Almondbank. The laminated sediments are composed of alternating fine and slightly coarser layers, each pair of which probably represents an annual increment. Simpson found the average thickness of these varves in the accessible lower part of the section to be three-quarters of an inch, and from this estimated that the whole 40 feet took 640 years to accumulate, thus implying that at least this amount of time intervened between the deglaciation of this locality following the Aberdeen–Lammermuir stage and the culmination of the Perth Readvance.

In the adjacent Earn valley the outwash deposits, formed when the ice of the Perth Readvance was at about its maximal extent and during its subsequent decay, are very extensive and again sometimes rest on varved sediments. Adjacent Strath Allan was occupied by ice from the west that had passed over the Callander area. The limit of this ice-stream on the slopes bordering the strath is approximately defined by the upper limit of complex meltwater channel systems. It attains about 900 feet on the flanks of the Ochils south of Braco and about 950 feet on the hill slopes north of this village, rising westwards to over 1100 feet on the hill slopes north of Doune. A branch of this ice-stream pushed through the Stirling gap and spread out over the low ground of the Forth valley beyond. From Stirling past Bannockburn the course of the ice is recorded by southeastward-pointing drumlins, and near Kincardine and Plean coarse outwash deposits formed at or close to the limit of the readvance rest on fine laminated marine sediments.

The movement of an ice-stream up the Clyde valley over the site of Glasgow to spread out over the Clyde coalfield basin is clearly demonstrated by the way in which the drumlins splay out towards directions between east-northeast and southeast (Fig. 38). This ice-stream blocked the Clyde valley to produce the lake referred to on p. 123, the sands, silts and clays that accumulated in the lake being covered by a sheet of till as the ice moved forward ultimately to extinguish it. In the steep-sided buried river valleys of the Clyde

PLATE XVII. Connel Bridge at entrance to Loch Etive links outwash plain on left with lava hills on right, behind which are granite mountains culminating in Ben Cruachan. Elevated marine platforms and smooth raised beaches in foreground. *Photograph by Aerofilms.*

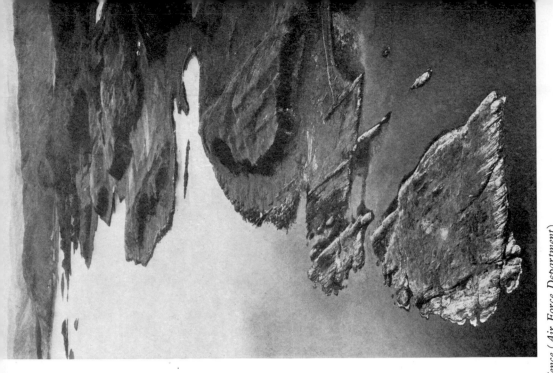

PLATE XVIII. A. Flood-plain at the mouth of the Spey. *Ministry of Defence (Air Force Department) photograph. Crown Copyright reserved.* B. Elevated marine platform and cliff, Craignish, Argyllshire. *Photograph by Aerofilms.*

coalfield basin no till intervenes between the lake deposits and the solid rock, indicating that the valleys were excavated (or, at least, cleaned out) in the interval between the decay of the ice of the Aberdeen–Lammermuir stage and the time of the Perth Readvance. This in turn suggests that in this interval drainage down the Clyde was established, thus implying that the Clyde area became ice-free. The presence of marine organisms in the till of the Perth Readvance in the Glasgow area and near Airdrie (Fig. 33) carries the same implication, for it means that the sea gained entry to the Clyde estuary before the readvance took place. A forward movement of the ice of at least 50 miles at this time in the Clyde area is thus indicated (Sissons 1963a, 1964).

In addition to the marine organisms the deposits associated with the Perth Readvance have yielded other organic remains at various places. Beneath a drumlin composed of till at least 50 feet thick at Queen's Park on the southern side of Glasgow, sewer excavations revealed a continuous bed of gravel that yielded remains of reindeer (Macgregor and Ritchie 1940). A reindeer antler with well-marked glacial striae has been obtained from till near Carluke, while at Baillieston on the eastern side of Glasgow remains of mammoth have been found (Gregory and Currie 1928). Single bones and a tooth of woolly rhinoceros have been found at four points in the Bishopbriggs area on the northern side of the city. One of these discoveries was made in 1964 (the only such find in Scotland in the last quarter century) and came from fluvioglacial sands and gravels that had been severely contorted by the over-riding ice and were in part overlain by a sheet of till (Rolfe 1966). A mammoth tooth has been discovered in similar deposits near Larbert (Absalom and Henderson 1947) and remains of mammoth have also been obtained from bedded sands covered by till at Chapelhall near Airdrie. Also in the Airdrie area wisps of peat in till contained *Salix herbacea*, which is now resitrcted to high mountains in Britain (Bennie 1896a). A sample of this peat yielded five species of beetle, all of which have a pronounced northern distribution today and two of which no longer live in Britain (Coope 1962). In the same area bedded sands and laminated clays containing layers of peat, twigs and branches were observed in underground workings beneath more than a hundred feet of till (A. Geikie 1863). There is also a record from Carluke of 4 feet of peat covered by 48 feet of 'surface clay'. Taken together these various discoveries demonstrate a readvance of ice over an area it had previously vacated and show that the climate was considerably colder than at present during the interstadial that preceded this readvance.

The limit of the Perth Readvance can be followed along the slopes of the rising ground east of Airdrie and Carluke. Below this limit, which declines northwards from an altitude of about 800 feet near Airdrie to near sea-level at Larbert, fluvioglacial features are often abundant whereas above it they are scarce or absent. A section at Larbert shows till of the Aberdeen–Lammermuir stage covered successively by laminated clays, sandy clays, sands and outwash gravels. The upward increase in coarseness of these stratified sediments suggests the approach of the ice at the time of the Perth Readvance, the close proximity of this ice to this locality at its maximal extent being demonstrated by the outwash gravels and by nearby kames and kettles. The ice approached Larbert from the west-southwest, bringing with it erratics from Lennoxtown, and together with ice from the west and northwest enveloped the Kilsyth, Fintry and Gargunnock Hills. Probably only the highest parts of these hills stood above the surface of the ice, for the numerous meltwater channels show that the ice reached about 1000 feet above sea-level on the slopes of the Kilsyth Hills within seven miles of its limit at Larbert.

The movement of a great ice-stream up the Clyde valley over the site of Glasgow implies that an even greater mass of ice occupied the Firth of Clyde and adjacent territory at this time. The flow of this ice into central Ayrshire is recorded by drumlins pointing to directions between east-southeast and east around Kilmaurs and by the distribution of shelly drift. Beneath the till of this readvance in the Kilmaurs area (near Kilmarnock) stratified deposits have been found at various places. The fossils obtained from them at various times since about the year 1816 include 9 or 10 mammoth tusks, a mammoth tooth, reindeer antlers, beetles, marine organisms (shells, foraminifers and ostracods) and plant remains (Richey *et al.* 1930). The plant remains include seeds of *Hippuris*, which is common in British lateglacial deposits. Among the shells at least three species – *Pecten islandicus*, *Tellina calcarea* and *Leda oblonga* – are now extinct from British seas but exist in more northern waters, while the foraminifers and ostracods also indicate arctic or sub-arctic conditions. Thus, like the organic remains in the basin of the River Clyde, the Kilmaurs evidence demonstrates a readvance of the ice following an interstadial during which the climate was considerably colder than at present.

The distribution of shelly drift in Ayrshire (Fig. 33) shows that the ice from the Firth of Clyde pushed farthest inland along the Ayr valley over the site of Muirkirk, to attain an altitude in excess of 1000 feet. Along part of its northern flank this mass was confluent with ice that had moved up the Clyde estuary towards the site of Glasgow and then curved round from the main stream to flow southwestwards across the watershed into Ayrshire (Fig. 59). This southwestward flow is demonstrated by striae and crag-and-tail features in the hilly country between Eaglesham, Stewarton, Beith and Neilston (Richey *et al.* 1930). It is also marked by the carry of local erratics as well as by the transport of Glen Fyne granite (Fig. 30). At the same time the high ground of northernmost Ayrshire and the adjacent part of Renfrewshire was over-run by Highland ice moving towards the south and southeast. In the country between Beith, Dalry and Stewarton the varying pressures of the different ice-streams in their zone of contact are recorded by striae in different directions, including crossing striae, and by variations in the direction of transport of erratics (for example, near Beith a southwestward flow was succeeded by a south-eastward one).

South and southeast of a line passing close to Cumnock and Maybole the shelly drift and Highland erratics are absent, even in ground no more than a few hundred feet above sea-level. This is of considerable significance for it implies that, at the time the Highland ice pushed into Ayrshire from the Firth of Clyde to deposit the shelly drift, a considerable mass of ice existed in the Southern Uplands. The main centre of this ice-mass was the Loch Doon area and the granite erratics from here are abundantly distributed as far as the shelly drift limit (Figs 29 and 33). The limit of the Southern Upland ice in the Solway area as shown in Fig. 59 is based on the mapping of J. K. Charlesworth (1926a, 1926b). In the vicinity of Newton Stewart and Wigtown the limit corresponds with the line (passing through Kirkcowan) that separates an earlier set of drumlins pointing southwest from a later set pointing south-southeast, while around Dumfries it accords with the margin of the great mass of fluvioglacial deposits that occupies this part of the Nith valley. The ice nourished in the central Southern Uplands at this time appears not to have extended very far to the east and in the Yarrow valley its limit may perhaps correspond with the moraines that occupy the valley floor immediately west of the Gordon Arms Hotel.

If we return to the Perth area, outwash terraces can be followed up the Tay valley from Perth, but towards Bankfoot they become increasingly fragmentary to die away in an area of kames and dead-ice hollows that mark the marginal zone of the ice at the culmination of the Perth Readvance. The ice limit crosses the Tay south of Bridge of Isla and marks the southern margin of the glaciers that, emerging from the Bran, Tay and Ericht valleys, combined to form a piedmont lobe in western Strathmore. Farther along the Highland edge none of the valley glaciers extended into Strathmore at the time of the Perth Readvance. This is shown by the fact that the southwest to northeast meltwater channels and kames of the Aberdeen–Lammermuir stage have not been modified or destroyed by glaciers emanating from the Highland valleys, while the red Strathmore till is not overlain by Highland till. The readvance in Glen Clova is demonstrated by outwash terraces that occupy the valley of the South Esk in its course across Strathmore, for the sands and gravels of which these are composed are derived mainly from Highland rocks and as far as seven miles inland from Montrose they rest on marine clays (Howden 1870). The extensive terraced outwash plains around Edzell are also composed essentially of Highland rocks that increase in coarseness towards the Highland edge, where the terraces end amidst the kames and moraines that largely block the exits from the Highlands of the West Water and North Esk and mark the local limit of the Perth Readvance.

Farther north the limit of the Perth Readvance as depicted in Fig. 59 must be regarded as very tentative. In the Dee valley it is placed near Dinnet at the head of the massive outwash deposits that here slope down the valley. Large fluvioglacial accumulations also border the firths of Inverness, Cromarty and Dornoch and their relations to raised beaches (p. 200) suggest the limit shown in Fig. 59.

On the western side of the country striae and ice-moulding show that the Highland ice moved southwestwards over Kintyre at the time of the Perth Readvance, although the Mull appears to have remained ice-free, for here the striae point westwards and the slopes are smoothed by solifluction (Synge and Stephens 1966). On the west coast of the peninsula north of Kilchenzie fossiliferous marine deposits are buried beneath till in several glens (p. 196). Striae show that the Highland ice-stream split to go round the mountains of northern Arran and deflected the local ice nourished on these mountains. As in Arran, a simple radial flow of glaciers from the mountains of Mull, Rhum and Skye appears to have been possible only at the time of the Loch Lomond Readvance, and the limit of this readvance as shown in Fig. 59 represents the maximal independent extent of the local glaciers in these islands. One may therefore infer that at the time of the Perth Readvance the Highland ice largely covered each of these islands and deflected the local glaciers. The interaction between local and mainland ice has been demonstrated very clearly in Mull, where erratics and striae show that the mountains bordering the Sound of Mull and the Firth of Lorne were overwhelmed by the mainland ice, whereas the more protected part of the mountain mass towards the southwest was able to maintain its own ice-cover which, however, was deflected by the enveloping Highland ice (Bailey et al. 1924). The implication of such evidence is that along most of the west side of Scotland the ice terminated in the sea at the maximum of the Perth Readvance.

The Loch Lomond Readvance

The widespread deglaciation that followed the Perth Readvance may well have resulted in glaciers disappearing completely from Scotland. Following this milder phase glaciers once again built up. This readvance – the Loch Lomond Readvance – differed from the earlier ones in that the ice rarely extended beyond the upland margins and no large ice-cap or ice-sheet developed. Instead hundreds of valley and corrie glaciers existed, many of the former joining together to produce large valley glaciers, especially in the western Highlands. It must be emphasised that the limits of the Loch Lomond Readvance as shown in Fig. 59 are very generalised, for the small scale does not permit the intricate edge of the ice to be accurately represented even where it is known. Within the area

FIG. 60. Limit of the Loch
Lomond Readvance in the
ground between Loch
Carron and Loch Torridon.
Arrows represent directions
of ice movement as recorded
by fluted moraines.

shown as ice-covered there were considerable areas of ice-free ground, for much of the higher land stood above the glacier surfaces, as can be seen in Figs 41, 42, 44, 55, 60, 61 and 62 which show the limit of the Loch Lomond Readvance in several areas in more detail than does Fig. 59.

On many valley floors in the Highlands, islands and Southern Uplands this limit is very well defined by the sharp down-valley limit of the fresh hummocky morainic topography described in Chapter 5 and illustrated in Plates XB and XIB or by the limit of equally-fresh fluvioglacial features. It was the clear moraines of this stage that were cited as proof of the former existence of glaciers in Scotland by the early exponents of the glacial theory in the 1840s, and during the subsequent years of last century it came to be accepted by all Scottish workers that a stage of valley glaciation succeeded the great *mer de glace*. The sudden down-valley termination of the hummocky moraines in numerous valleys suggests that they were formed as a result of a readvance of ice, a suggestion that is greatly strengthened when, as sometimes happens, the last feature is a large arcuate end-moraine. Proof of a readvance is provided by the shells in the moraines by Lake of Menteith and by lochs Lomond, Creran, Spelve and Uisg (p. 79).

The directions of ice movement at the Loch Lomond stage were sometimes very different from those of earlier stages. Thus, whereas the Rannoch Moor basin in the Southwest Grampians and the Loch Doon basin in the western Southern Uplands were for long periods major centres from which ice flowed outwards, glaciers flowed into them during the Loch Lomond stage and distributed moraines over the basin floors. In the western part of Rannoch Moor this inward flow is also demonstrated by the eastward transport of volcanic rocks from Glen Coe and down the valley of the River Ba (Hinxman *et al.* 1923). The difference arose because the Loch Lomond stage was relatively short-lived: had it lasted considerably longer ice would doubtless have continued to pour into the Rannoch and Loch Doon basins from the surrounding mountains until the basins were filled to overflowing and an outward movement established as during earlier times. In islands such as Arran, Mull and Skye the simple radial movement from the highest ground caused some valley glaciers to be flowing in the opposite direction to the ice-flow at the Perth stage. Similar reversals of movement are evident in many mainland localities. For example, in the area shown in Figs 60 and 61 the radial flow from the main mountain groups was in some valleys directly opposed to that of the ice-mass of earlier stages, striae and erratics demonstrating the earlier flow being found especially on the ridges and summits.

The glaciers of the Loch Lomond stage varied considerably in size and character. Some were very small and barely extended beyond the corries in which they were nurtured. Many in the Northern Highlands, central and eastern Grampians, Southern Uplands and the islands were a few miles long and flowed out radially from the higher mountains. Some of these glaciers, especially in the isolated mountains and mountain groups of Northwest Scotland, must have flowed very rapidly down the steep slopes towards the adjacent low ground. In the western mountains from southern Ross-shire to Loch Lomond the altitude coupled with the heavy precipitation produced a greater accumulation of ice than elsewhere and the main valleys were occupied by large glaciers fed by many tributary glaciers. At the western ends of lochs Morar, Shiel, Creran and Etive, at Corran on Loch Linnhe, and at Ballachulish on Loch Leven large outwash plains built into the sea were probably formed at or close to the limit of the Loch Lomond Readvance (McCann 1966a). Outwash was also poured into the sea near the head of the Forth lowlands (for the sea then extended much farther inland than now), down the Leven valley leading southwards from Loch

Lomond, and at the head of Loch Carron in Wester Ross. In each of the last three localities conspicuous moraines mark the limit of the readvance. Ice from the western mountains occupied the southern part of the Great Glen and, along with ice from Ben Nevis and adjacent mountains, formed the barrier that held up the lakes of the Glen Roy area (p. 119). The ice-dammed lakes of Rannoch Moor (p. 122) also existed at this time and there

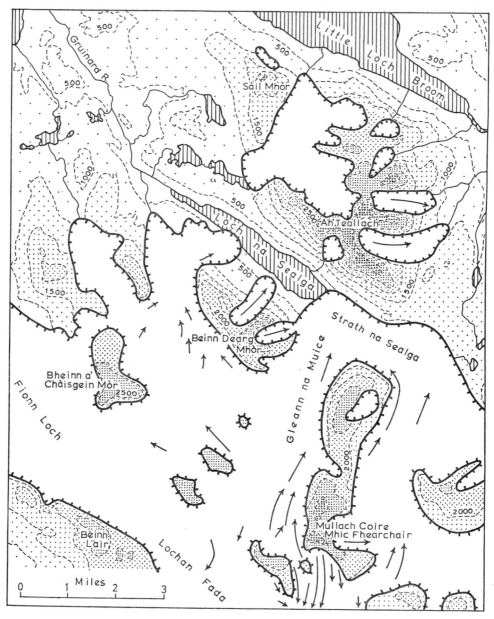

Fig. 61. Limit of the Loch Lomond Readvance in the ground south of Little
Loch Broom. Arrows represent directions of ice movement as recorded by
fluted moraines.

were doubtless other small ones of which little is known as yet (for example, in valleys between Loch Hourn and Loch Duich).

In only a few places did the ice spread out beyond the mountains to form piedmont glaciers on adjacent lowlands. One such glacier in eastern Mull extended into lochs Don and Spelve, while other piedmont tongues produced the Loch Lomond and Menteith moraine complexes. The rapid increase in thickness of these ice tongues back from the margin, represented by contours in Fig. 44, was a feature of many other glaciers. On the hill slopes bordering the Gare Loch an end-moraine rises northwards to reach 650 feet above sea-level 3½ miles back from the glacier limit now probably represented by the basal deposits of Row Point (Anderson 1949). In Glen Dochart the ice reached the head of Loch Tay, upstream from which the limit of the abundant fluvioglacial deposits and moraines rises quickly up the valley sides to indicate a former glacier at least 600 feet thick 3 miles from its terminus. A similar distance back from the end-moraine near the head of Loch Carron moraines demonstrates that the ice had a thickness of about 900 feet (Peach *et al.* 1913a).

While many of the glaciers of the Loch Lomond stage commenced in corries – in fact it seems likely that every well-developed corrie possessed a glacier at this time – some glaciers were nourished in other situations. For example, fresh moraines show that a tiny glacier was able to form at the base of the steep northern face of Sàil Mhòr by Little Loch Broom (Fig. 61). Abundant morainic mounds record the presence of glaciers in the valleys of the north-bank tributaries of the Meggett Water in the Tweedsmuir Hills (Fig. 62), but there are no corries at the heads of these valleys and it appears that the snows accumulated in the valley heads and perhaps on the plateau above. In the same area the moraine-littered floor of the Talla valley forms an open route that leads up to the plateau behind

Loch Skene, and it seems that some of the snow that nourished the Talla glacier accumulated on the plateau. In this context it is worth noting that under present conditions the largest snow patches in spring are to be seen, not in the Loch Skene corrie, but on a broad step in the plateau above the corrie. In the high ground north of Loch Kishorn in Wester Ross the contrast between fresh ice-swept bare rock and intensely - frost - shattered summits (p. 224) suggests that the plateau traversed by the Applecross road nourished a small ice-cap that augmented some of the adjacent valley glaciers (Fig.

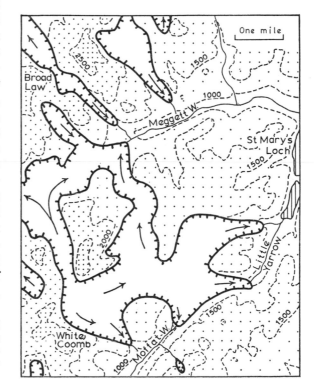

FIG. 62. Limit of the Loch Lomond Readvance in part of the Tweedsmuir Hills. Arrows indicate directions of ice movement.

60). The presence of plateau ice at this late stage of the Scottish glacial story leads one to suspect that at earlier times, when climatic conditions were more severe, plateau ice-caps of considerable dimensions may have developed.

We have so far made little reference to local glaciation in the outer islands since the relation of the ice limits in these islands to those on the mainland is not known. Following the waning of the last ice-sheet to cover the Outer Hebrides local glaciers existed on a considerable scale in the mountain area of Harris and southern Lewis and, apparently, on a very limited scale in the highest ground of South Uist. The presence of these local glaciers in Harris and Lewis is amply demonstrated by moraines and striae (Charlesworth 1955). That their farthest limit was achieved after the disappearance from the area of the mainland ice-sheet is shown by their unhampered radial flow and by evidence such as crossing striae. For example, where glens such as Meavaig and Eavat that lead south from the central axis of Harris approach the coast, ice-sheet striae pointing northwest are crossed by fresher ones pointing south or southwest (Jehu and Craig 1934). Since the early work of Peach and Horne (1879) the glaciation of the Shetland Islands has received little attention until very recently. Work now in progress, of which only a brief provisional account is so far available (Hoppe *et al.* 1965), shows that, following the disappearance of the Scandinavian ice-sheet from the islands, they were covered by local ice that streamed out from the central parts in all directions towards the sea. The ice was attacked by the sea and, during deglaciation, recession of the ice-front was faster where the sea was deep, causing the ice movements to change as they adjusted to the new ice-margins. A peat bed has been recently discovered beneath more than 20 feet of till at Fugla Ness, North Roe. At one point it has been found to be nearly 5 feet thick and provisional results of pollen analysis suggest it was formed during an interstadial (Chapelhow 1965).

Some climatic considerations

In discussing climate in relation to the landforms produced by glacial erosion the importance of the western centres of high precipitation has been emphasised (p. 61). Their importance is again evident from the limits of the readvances shown in Fig. 59. It is generally believed that at times of extensive ice-cover a cold but open ocean lay to the west of the Outer Hebrides and sea surface temperatures of 0° C. for January–February and 6° C. for July–August have been estimated. The associated climate must have been raw, cold, cloudy and stormy and thus extremely unpleasant (Manley 1964). On the other hand, the eastern side of the country, sheltered by the western mountains and the bulk of the ice-sheet, was sunnier and much drier, but in winter temperatures were far lower than in the west, for the North Sea (frozen over, occupied partly by glacier ice, or with its bed partly exposed owing to world lowering of sea-level) was unable to exert an ameliorating influence. The last episode of such severe conditions appears to have been associated with the Perth Readvance and to have terminated as the ice subsequently began to decay. Thus there is no evidence of the presence in Scotland of mammoth after the Perth Readvance, although (as the Kilmaurs finds show) it existed at the time the ice moved forward. The organic remains in the marine deposits preceding and associated with the Perth Readvance also indicate a severe climate in the east of Scotland, whereas those associated with the Loch Lomond Readvance indicate much less harsh conditions (Chapter 8). The great majority of the fossil frost wedges so far found in Scotland are outside the limit of the Perth Readvance or are in deposits associated with it (p. 221).

G. Manley (1964) has estimated that at the time of the Loch Lomond Readvance mean summer temperatures in northwestern Britain were lowered by about 4 to 5 degrees Centigrade and that in the wettest areas the associated lowering of the snowline was about 2000 feet. That the snowline sloped up towards the east is indicated by the altitudes to which glaciers descended in various parts of the country. At many places on the west coast of the Highlands and in the islands glaciers descended to sea-level or to within one or two hundred feet of it. On the other hand, in the Ben Armine range in central Sutherland glaciers terminated at about 1000 feet above sea-level and in Glen Dee, Glen Lui and the valley of the River Gairn in the Cairngorms they descended to between 1400 and 1600 feet. The differences are especially clear if one compares conditions in Arran, the western and central Southern Uplands and The Cheviot, bearing in mind that the highest point in each of these areas lies between 2670 and 2970 feet. Thus in Arran the glaciers descended to sea-level, in the Merrick area to 500 feet and in the Tweedsmuir Hills to 1000 feet, while on The Cheviot glaciers appear not to have existed at this time (although there are masses of frost-shattered rock debris in the highest valley heads). The equivalent readvance in the Lake District was associated with glacier limits as low as 500 feet whereas in the northern Pennines the glaciers failed to extend below 1250 feet. Although in part the altitudinal limits of these various glaciers were influenced by the altitudes of the valley floors down which they flowed, the strong eastward rise of the snowline is nevertheless apparent. This evidence thus agrees with that revealed by the altitudes of corrie floors (Fig. 23), but it does not mean that the corries were fashioned at this time. One strongly gains the impression that in many corries the glaciers that formed at the time of the Loch Lomond Readvance did little more than sweep out the frost-shattered rock debris that had accumulated in the preceding milder phase, subsequently depositing it, along with debris from the valley slopes, as the innumerable mounds that characterise this stage. The corries are far older than this stage and their altitudes imply that an eastward-rising snow-line was an essential feature of glacial conditions in Scotland for long periods.

The periods of cold climate were interrupted by times when climate greatly ameliorated. In the time covered by the three readvances whose limits are shown in Fig. 59 a marked amelioration of climate following each readvance is implied by the extensive evidence of glacier downwasting and of powerful meltwater activity. The existence of such evidence to high levels on the mountains appears to imply that the snowline rose above many or all of the mountain summits, thus presenting a marked contrast with conditions during times of glacier advance or readvance. Since the theoretical snowline today passes less than a thousand feet above the summit of Ben Nevis, it would seem that summer conditions at least might not have been very different from those of today had it not been for the presence of the glaciers themselves. Certainly the glaciers became out of harmony with the climate and rapid decay ensued. The change from actively-advancing ice to ice decay appears to have taken place rapidly. Thus end-moraines, implying a balance between accumulation and ablation, rarely mark the limits of the Aberdeen–Lammermuir or Perth readvances, but dead-ice features often abound immediately within these limits. A similar abundance of dead-ice forms is often found up to the limit of the Loch Lomond Re-advance, although in some places a period of balance is indicated by the large moraines that mark the limit. Yet even here a marked change in climate is indicated, for the evidence of rapid increase in ice thickness back from the ice limits strongly suggests that powerful glaciers were suddenly checked, their subsequent decay being recorded by kames, kettles and related features that occur immediately within the moraines and are sometimes intimately mixed with them.

Absolute dating of glacial events

Having considered the sequence of glacial events, we now turn to the question of when these events took place. No evidence is available on the dates of the earlier glacial events and we can only infer by analogy with other parts of the world that glaciers have existed intermittently in Scotland for hundreds of thousands of years at least. A beginning has been made, however, towards establishing the times of certain events in the final part of the glacial story. The principal technique available for this purpose is radiocarbon dating. By this technique the age of organic materials less than about 70 000 years old can be determined in specially-equipped laboratories. Although the dates obtained are subject to various errors (and the original published dates as quoted below and elsewhere in this book are therefore rounded off) the technique can provide the basic information for establishing a time-scale.

Unfortunately only a few radiocarbon dates directly related to glacial events in Scotland are available at present, so that as yet only a provisional time-scale can be suggested. In making these suggestions analogy with events in continental Europe and in North America is helpful. In these areas it appears that the last interglacial came to an end about 70 000 years ago when large ice-sheets began to build up. These ice-sheets persisted, with various oscillations of the margins, for a considerable time, but eventually widespread decay prevailed. There followed an interstadial that appears to have lasted for perhaps

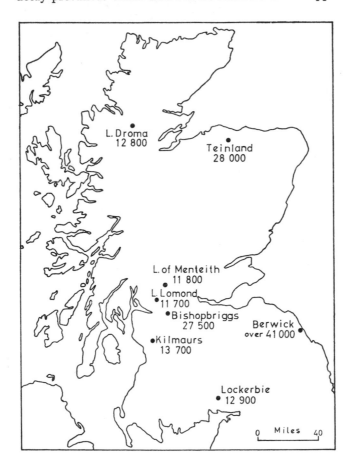

15 000 to 20 000 years and this in turn was succeeded by the last great build-up of the Scandinavian and North American ice-sheets commencing about 25 000 years ago. These ice-sheets attained their maximal extent between 20 000 and 17 000 years ago, following which there were periods of decay and re-advance until the main ice-masses finally disappeared less than 8000 years ago.

The oldest radiocarbon date so far obtained that is directly related to glacial events in Scotland is for marine shells from sands and gravels and overlying till near Berwick. These gave an age of more than 41 000 years, their full age being unknown since it lay

FIG. 63. Radiocarbon sites that are closely related to former glacial limits.

beyond the range of dating of the particular equipment used. This date suggests that the southward and southeastward movement of ice along the east coast of Scotland referred to on p. 130 predates the long interstadial mentioned in the last paragraph (Sissons 1967).

Two dates in Scotland can be assigned to this long interstadial. One of these is a date of 28 000 years for a buried soil horizon at Teindland in Morayshire (Fig. 63). The other is a date of 27 500 years for a water-worn woolly rhinoceros bone obtained from fluvioglacial sands and gravels at Bishopbriggs near Glasgow (Rolfe 1966). The latter is important because it implies that the Glasgow area, not far distant from the central part of the Scottish ice-sheet, became ice-free during the long interstadial, and it may well be that the whole country was ice-free at this time. E. A. Fitzpatrick (1965) states that the dated soil in Morayshire is covered by till and outwash gravel, thus implying that after the long interstadial the ice-sheet built up sufficiently to cover this area. A great movement of Scottish ice southwards at this time is indicated by the occurrence in Cheshire of glacier-transported marine shells dated at 28 000 years old (Boulton and Worsley 1965). By analogy with continental Europe and North America we may assume that this ice-sheet reached its maximal extent between 17 000 and 20 000 years ago, having advanced at least 200 miles in a southward direction. It is possible that the maximal extent of this ice-sheet is represented in Scotland by the limit of the Aberdeen–Lammermuir Readvance, but it is also possible that this readvance is of rather later date.

One of the mammoth tusks from the stratified deposits that underlie till laid down at the time of the Perth Readvance in the Kilmaurs area of lowland Ayrshire (p. 136) has yielded an age of $13\,700^{+1300}_{-1700}$ years. This implies that mammoth were living in Ayrshire around 14 000 years ago and that the remains of some of them were interred as the ice spread over the area during the Perth Readvance. On the other hand, peat interbedded with silts, clays and sands in the banks of the River Annan near Lockerbie has given a radiocarbon date of 12 900 years (Bishop 1963). These sediments, including the peat, are gently warped, suggesting that they accumulated on top of decaying ice and that 12 900 years ago deglaciation was in progress. An age of 12 800 years has been obtained for plant remains in varved silts at Loch Droma, which is situated by the main road to Ullapool on the watershed between Atlantic and North Sea drainage (Kirk and Godwin 1963). Loch Droma lies in the heart of the area that was ice-covered at the time of the Perth Readvance and is only a few miles from large corries in the mountain backbone of Northwest Scotland. Yet the sediments containing and overlying the dated plant remains show no sign of having been over-ridden by glacier ice, implying, if the radiocarbon date is valid, that Loch Droma has been ice-free for the last 12 800 years at least. Taking the dates from Kilmaurs, Lockerbie and Loch Droma together it thus seems that the Perth Readvance probably culminated between about 13 500 and 13 000 years ago.

In this context it is interesting to recall a 'teleconnection' made by G. de Geer more than thirty years ago (de Geer 1935). He compared the relative thickness of a succession of 59 varves in a section near Dunning in the lower Earn valley with the results of the very detailed varve measurements in Sweden that had enabled him to establish a time-scale for that country. From this comparison de Geer concluded that the Dunning varves accumulated about 13 100 years ago. Since these varves are part of the series in the lower Tay, Almond and Earn valleys that underlies outwash laid down when the ice of the Perth Readvance was at or close to its maximal extent (p. 134), the date given by de Geer seems to suggest that the Perth Readvance culminated about or shortly after 13 100 years ago. While this is in broad agreement with the limited evidence from radiocarbon dating, the tenuous nature of the varve correlation and subsequent revision of the Swedish varve chronology do not allow us to attach much significance to this date. Rather must we regard it as intriguing and hope that further radiocarbon dates will test its validity.

The date of the Loch Lomond Readvance was first established by J. J. Donner (1957) through pollen studies. Such studies, based on the identification of the pollen grains trapped especially in accumulating lake sediments and peat bogs, have revealed the successive changes in vegetation (and, hence, of climate) that have taken place in the British Isles during the final stages of glaciation and through postglacial times. The succession is divided into eight main zones, of which the first three are grouped together as lateglacial and the last five as postglacial, and the ages of the zonal boundaries have been approximately determined by radiocarbon dating (Godwin 1961). Following the variable but mainly cold conditions of Zone I, Zone II apparently began about 12 000 years ago and represents a period of milder climate. This was in turn followed by a renewal of cold conditions during Zone III, which lasted from about 10 800 to 10 300 years ago. Donner found that all three lateglacial zones were represented in Loch Mahaick, which lies a few miles east of Callander outside the limit of the Loch Lomond Readvance. He also found all three zones in a lake situated north of Drymen on the high ground that separated the Menteith glacier from the Loch Lomond glacier. Earlier G. F. Mitchell (1952) had recorded the lateglacial zones at Garscadden near Glasgow. On the other hand, in the deposits of a lake near Gartmore, within the area covered by the Menteith glacier, the lowest zone present was Zone IV. Donner therefore concluded that the readvance of glaciers to the limits represented by the Loch Lomond and Menteith moraines took place during Zone III, implying that the moraines were formed around 10 300 years ago. This interpretation is now confirmed by radiocarbon dating of shells from the two areas. Shells from the Menteith moraine gave a date of 11 800 years, while those from the Loch Lomond area yielded an age of 11 700 years, thus implying that the sea extended to the head of the Forth lowlands and into the ground now occupied by Loch Lomond during Zone II, its deposits subsequently being redistributed by the glaciers that advanced into these two areas during the Zone III cold phase (Sissons 1967).

In concluding this chapter we must emphasise that the pattern of glacial events we have described can be regarded only as a provisional one for much has yet to be learned about the glaciation of Scotland. For many parts of the country very little information is available and in very few areas have detailed studies been carried out. We must hope that when many such studies have been made and many more radiocarbon dates have been obtained, it will be possible to present a much more detailed and accurate picture of the glacial story than current evidence permits.

8

Changing sea-levels and changing climates

THE nearness of the sea has long encouraged speculation concerning its former extent in Scotland and, as we have seen, widespread submergence of the country was early favoured to explain the abundant drift deposits. The most important factor influencing the adherents to the submergence idea was the frequent discovery of marine shells, some of them in perfect condition, in the glacial tills. Thus John Smith found shells in till at so many places in Ayrshire that he felt forced to conclude in 1898 that submergence to over a thousand feet above present sea-level had taken place, a notion that was maintained as late as 1926 by J. W. Gregory. Meanwhile, others preferred a more modest submergence, and in the final years of last century a limit of 500 feet or so was often mentioned. This figure was based particularly on the discovery of a puzzling deposit of marine clay at this altitude at Clava, near Inverness, and on the finding of shells in till at about the same altitude in Lanarkshire near Airdrie. Yet others preferred a submergence of only 100 feet or so. This figure emerged particularly as a result of the work of the Geological Survey, the officers of which found evidence of sea-levels up to about this altitude in various parts of Scotland. Unfortunately this figure of 100 feet has attained undue prominence in the story of Scottish sea-level changes, and the concept of a sea-level at about this altitude has long been regarded as an established fact. We shall show later that this 100-foot sea is as much a myth as the Great Submergence that was so popular in the first part of last century.

Most of the available evidence relating to sea-level changes in Scotland demonstrates that the sea has in the past been higher in relation to the land than it is at present. The evidence relating to times when sea-level was lower than now is rather sparse (except in the peripheral parts of the country), largely because such evidence has been buried beneath later deposits or has been subsequently submerged or destroyed by the sea. Fringing the coast of many parts of the Scottish mainland and of some of the islands is a strip of marine deposits in part representing beaches now elevated above sea-level. This belt with raised beaches is often no more than a few hundred yards broad, but in some areas, such as the Moray coastlands, the shores of the three firths of central Scotland and central Ayrshire, it is much broader, attaining a width of a mile or even several miles. Sea-levels higher than the present are also demonstrated by elevated cliffs and wave-cut rock platforms, such features being most remarkably developed in some of the western islands, including Islay, Jura and Mull, where rock platforms reach over 100 feet above sea-level. At lower levels there is much more widespread evidence of marine erosion, and cliffs,

147

caves, wave-cut notches, stacks and rock platforms occur on many stretches of coastline above the level at which waves operate today (Plate XVII). Sometimes these features are not associated with deposits apart from a few worn boulders. More often, however, the rock platform is itself covered with raised beach sand and shingle, the whole being backed by an abandoned cliff-line. That rock platform, cliff and raised beach deposits were all formed at about the same time seems the obvious interpretation of such assemblages of features, yet there are often good reasons, as we shall see, for doubting this simple explanation.

Most of the evidence associated with sea-level changes in Scotland can be grouped into four main categories: (*i*) the arctic phenomena formed while glacier ice still covered a large area of Scotland; (*ii*) the subarctic, formed when the ice cover was much less extensive; (*iii*) the postglacial, formed after the glaciers had decayed; (*iv*) the buried and submerged peat deposits. Groups (*i*) and (*ii*) may be together referred to as the lateglacial phenomena.

Arctic seas

The arctic deposits are far thicker and more widespread in the east of Scotland than in the west. They are particularly abundant in the Forth valley between Stirling and Falkirk, in East Lothian between Aberlady and Dunbar, around St Andrews and Leuchars, and around the Tay–Earn confluence. Farther north they are well developed in the valley of the South Esk near Montrose, around the mouth of the Ythan north of Aberdeen, and on the coasts of the Moray Firth. These deposits have naturally been most frequently described where they occur above sea-level as raised beaches, but they also occur widely beneath later deposits as well as beneath the surrounding seas. On the west coast of the Scottish mainland in the Clyde area the arctic deposits are typically only a few feet thick. In both east and west Scotland the arctic deposits are, where present, the lowest members of the marine sequence, and usually rest on till or fluvioglacial sand and gravel.

Quite often the arctic deposits contain very few shells, although a few sites have provided a considerable number. Some of the species found inhabit the Scottish seas at the present time but others, some of them abundantly represented, are to be found only in sea areas well to the north of Scotland, and it appears that we must envisage sea temperatures comparable with those off west Greenland today (Davidson 1932). Among the most common of the arctic shells of the east of Scotland are *Leda arctica*, *Pecten groenlandicus*, *Cardium groenlandicum* and *Thracia myopsis*. These, and some other arctic species, have been found only rarely or not at all in the west. Other evidence of the very cold conditions associated with the eastern clays includes the discovery in them of the remains of the small arctic seal, *Pagomys foetidus*, at Grangemouth and Portobello, and near St Andrews and Montrose. Other seals found in these deposits near St Andrews, and also at Camelon near Falkirk, Tyrie near Kirkcaldy, Dunbar, Errol, and Invernetty in Aberdeenshire also probably belong to this species (Turner 1872).

There is only limited evidence of erosion by the arctic seas. Although the raised beaches are often backed by sharply-rising ground, this almost always represents a pre-existing slope, such as the side of a glacial trough or the flank of a drumlin, against which the deposits accumulated. Along much of the coastline the most the arctic seas have done in the way of erosion is to remove a cover of drift from the solid rocks. The well-known elevated cliffs at Kincraig Point in Fife, which are so conspicuous when viewed from the west, are the exception rather than the rule and are developed in easily-eroded volcanic tuffs. The general lack of significant erosion is probably partly a result of the rapid changes in relative levels of land and sea and partly a result of the sea being frozen in winter.

For the most part the arctic sediments comprise finely-laminated deposits of clay, silt and fine sand. When freshly exposed the lamination is not always obvious, but if a sample of the material is taken from an exposed face it will be found possible to peal off numerous thin layers. Each layer consists of a mixture of silt and clay and has the consistency of fresh cheese. Between the clay-silt layers, and enabling them to be separated, thin layers of fine sand may be observed, sometimes so delicate that they appear no more than a grain or two thick. When the deposits dry and harden the lamination becomes very apparent for, where free to do so, the individual clay-silt layers curl up and separate along the sand partings. The pairs of layers are very probably varves and reflect the annual cycle of sedimentation under glacial conditions.

Within the fine arctic sediments, and greatly contrasting with them, stones and boulders are usually found. Sometimes these are very numerous, as is well displayed at the present time in a clay pit about three miles southwest of Errol, between Perth and Dundee. Here laminated clays and silts are being excavated to form a pit about 15 feet deep. As the clay is removed the included stones, some of which are three feet long, are left on the flat floor of the pit where they are so abundant that one can traverse the floor only by stepping from stone to stone. Such stones amidst fine sediments must have been deposited through the agency of small ice-bergs or ice-floes, which released their contained debris as they melted. Some of them are striated, a feature that has been noted on stones in other arctic clay pits.

Most of the stones in the arctic marine deposits appear to have been derived, as one would expect, from the rocks or glacial drift in the vicinity of where they have been found. An exception, however, is provided by some of the chalk flints and pieces of chalk that have been discovered. Several dozen flints, some encrusted with chalk, were obtained last century from a pit in Edinburgh. Chalk or chalk flints have also been found in the arctic clay at or near Tyrie, Elie, St Andrews, Errol and Montrose. J. C. Howden (1870) said that the pieces of chalk near Montrose, although seldom more than four or five pounds in weight, were of very frequent occurrence and observed that they were generally rubbed or scratched on at least one side. That the stones were transported by floating ice cannot be doubted. It is equally clear, however, that they were not picked up by sea ice from an adjacent shore since, except for one small area, chalk and flints have not been reported as occurring in the glacial deposits of east-central Scotland. They may well have been brought by floating ice from the Moray Firth area.

The presence of floating ice in the sea is indicated in another way. In some sections in the arctic deposits, as at Portobello and Camelon, the beds may be seen to be greatly contorted in places. Such contortions may be produced in various ways: for example, by the melting out of buried masses of glacier ice, or by freezing and thawing of the surface layers. In the instances cited, however, such agencies seem to be excluded since the greatly-disturbed beds are underlain and overlain by similar deposits in which the normal horizontal bedding is undisturbed. The explanation appears to be that, while the sediments were accumulating, ice-floes or small ice-bergs grounded in them and thus produced the contortions.

Although the arctic deposits for the most part comprise layers of clay, silt and fine sand with scattered stones they often become rather coarser in their upper parts. The surfaces of the raised beaches formed of these deposits are often composed mainly of sand, sometimes with a little gravel. The sand is usually most abundant and the raised beaches most clearly developed in the vicinity of former glacier margins, implying that much of the material that constitutes the beaches was provided by rivers pouring out of the glaciers. That the beaches were formed while glacier ice existed in their immediate vicinity can be demonstrated quite conclusively at many places. Thus, in the Forth valley southeast of Stirling, the arctic raised beaches form conspicuous terraces up to an altitude of almost 125 feet above sea-level. To the west of Stirling, however, these high beaches are quite

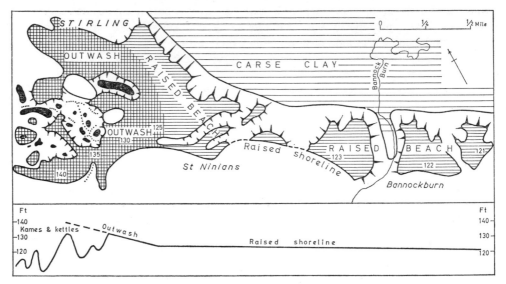

FIG. 64. Raised beach and related fluvioglacial deposits near Stirling. Kettles shown in solid black and kames by lines of dots.

absent, no raised beach in fact exceeding 76 feet in altitude. This absence of the high beaches can hardly be due to later marine erosion in this very sheltered locality, so that we must conclude that, at the time these beaches were formed, glacier ice occupied the ground west of Stirling. The approximate position of the margin of this ice-mass is indicated by other evidence. Around Bannockburn a raised beach forms a flat up to a quarter of a mile broad (Fig. 64). This beach, partly destroyed by gullies, can be followed as far as St Ninians on the southern outskirts of Stirling, where its sandy deposits merge into an outwash plain composed mainly of coarse gravel. The outwash plain rises gently towards the west, but after a few hundred yards it gives way to a kame and kettle landscape. We can therefore visualise an ice-mass occupying the low ground west of Stirling with its margin situated in the Stirling gap. Streams deposited large quantities of debris amidst the ice and in addition spread out in front of the ice a large fan, which was built out into the sea.

The situation at Stirling is repeated many times along the east coast of Scotland. This is possible because the arctic deposits form many distinct raised beaches. It is often found that the highest raised beach in a given locality, after having been traced for a certain distance – sometimes for less than a mile, sometimes for many miles – merges into outwash, and that thereafter the highest beach is a different feature, which itself in turn later displays the same relationship to outwash.

The arctic deposits of the coastlands of Scotland began to be laid down when the present

PLATE XIX. A. Smoo Cave, near Durness. Limestone cave at sea-level. *Photograph by W. A. Sharp.* B. Wife Goe, Caithness. *Geological Survey photograph. Crown Copyright reserved.*

PLATE XX. A. Low plateau of Caithness ending in cliffs and stacks of Duncansby. *Photograph by Aerofilms.* B. Elevated marine platform and cliff, Islay. *Geological Survey photograph. Crown Copyright reserved.*

land areas first began to be vacated by the decaying ice-sheet, much of Scotland then being lower in relation to the sea than it is at present, so that as the ice withdrew the sea replaced it in coastal areas. They ceased to accumulate as the ice decayed following the Perth Readvance. At this time the harsh arctic climate was replaced by less severe conditions, which we will refer to as subarctic.

Subarctic seas

The deposits of the subarctic seas are especially typical of the west coastlands of Scotland southwards from Loch Linnhe. The comparison of the shells in them with those of the present sea enabled James Smith to prove in 1838 that the sea had been much colder in the past than it is now. The subarctic deposits are well developed along the Clyde valley downstream of Glasgow and the fossils are much more abundant than those of the arctic beds of the east of Scotland. The contrast may not be quite as great as the considerable literature on the Clyde deposits suggests, however, for the abundance of artificial excavations and the eager researches of a host of geologists last century, most notably of D. Robertson and H. W. Crosskey during its later years, have resulted in far more information being available on the fauna of the Clyde marine deposits than is available for any other part of Scotland. There is, however, no doubt that the difference between the two sides of the country is great, as witness the words of T. F. Jamieson (1865): 'In 1860 I examined several of these clays of the west coast; they occur in a great number of places along the shores of Argyleshire, and, coming from the comparatively barren district of the east coast, I was delighted with the abundance and fine preservation of the fossils'.

The fossils in the western deposits also reveal a much less severe climate than those in the eastern ones, a point emphasised by F. W. Anderson (1947), who studied particularly the clays around Paisley. Among the ostracods he identified in this area Anderson found that, of those that now have a limited geographical range, 30 per cent were southern species (England to the Bay of Biscay) and 70 per cent were subarctic species (Scotland to the Arctic Circle), true arctic species being absent. He also examined the ostracod identifications of earlier workers and found that at 23 sites studied in the west of Scotland the percentage of arctic species was only 2·65. In contrast, at five localities in the east of Scotland 20·6 per cent of all the species present were arctic.

The molluscan fauna in the Paisley area was also studied by Anderson. He found that 7 of the species, comprising 37 per cent of the individuals, are now restricted to arctic regions and 14 species, comprising the remaining 63 per cent of the individuals, were of the subarctic type. The molluscan fauna thus suggests much colder conditions than the ostracod fauna. Even so, certain arctic species that are quite common in the east of Scotland (e.g. the four mentioned on p. 148) were not found by Anderson. Since the ostracods are free-swimming they are much more sensitive to changes in sea temperature than the molluscs. Anderson therefore concluded that, at the time the Paisley clays were being deposited, the climate was ameliorating and the Scottish glaciers were in their final stages of decay. A fairly similar fauna to that found by Anderson around Paisley has been obtained at other points near the Clyde estuary as well as around the coasts of Ayrshire, Bute and Argyll. Among the most common shells are *Tellina calcarea*, *Astarte borealis*, *Pecten islandicus*, *Cyprina islandica* and *Littorina littorea*.

The subarctic deposits are represented by accumulations of laminated clay and silt along the Clyde valley westwards from Glasgow. Here they extend up to 70-80 feet above sea-level but are most fossiliferous below about 30 feet. Within the city the number of marine organisms diminishes as the deposits are traced eastwards and it appears that the clays east of the city are estuarine. There is a similar change in the number of stones in the deposits, for these are few in number in the clays east of the city but often abundant in those to the west.

The most interesting account of boulders in the clays was provided by T. F. Jamieson (1865), who was able to show that some of them, at least, were transported by ice-floes rather than by ice-bergs. In clay pits at Paisley he observed a number of boulders up to three feet in length and one block six feet long. Quite often the boulders were encrusted with barnacles. Where these occurred on the upper surface and sides of a stone they could have grown after the stone was deposited in the clay. However, in some instances he saw a thick crust of barnacles on the underside of a stone, with the points sticking downwards into the clay beneath. He therefore concluded that the barnacles on such stones grew when the stones lay on some shore; that, subsequently, the stones were encased with sea ice; and that, later, when the ice broke up, it and the included stones floated from the shore, the stones being dropped on to the sea floor as the ice-floes melted. As further proof Jamieson mentioned that sometimes on heaving up a boulder he found a number of crushed mussel shells beneath, as if they had been squashed by the fall of the boulder. Furthermore, he occasionally noted that the surrounding clay showed black stains, as if from the decay of seaweed that had been attached to a stone. Barnacles on the undersides of stones have also been observed in excavations near Kilwinning in Ayrshire and here, in some instances, barnacles girdled the stones obliquely, again implying that the stones with their attached shells have been transported from some previous resting place.

Away from the vicinity of the Clyde estuary shells have rarely been found in the more elevated subarctic deposits. In brick-clay near Kilmarnock at about 70 feet above sea-level they are said to be present but very scarce, and they have also been mentioned as occurring in a clay at a similar altitude near Loch Craignish. Marine deposits with abundant shells are restricted to locations quite close to present sea-level. Such deposits have been described from Ayrshire, Kilchattan in Bute, the shores of the Kyles of Bute, the coasts of lochs Fyne, Sween, Caolisport, Gilp, Crinan and Craignish in Argyll, as well as from the northern end of Loch Linnhe close to Fort William. At all these localities the clays are no more than 30 feet above present sea-level and at most of them they extend down to or below sea-level. Despite this it has often been suggested that these clays relate to a shoreline at about 100 feet above present sea-level. While this is by no means impossible, for clays may be deposited far below sea-level, their rather persistent occurrence some 70 to 100 feet or more below the shoreline with which they are supposed to be associated is a little disconcerting. One is even more surprised at this correlation when one finds that some of the original accounts themselves contain evidence that is not fully consistent with this interpretation. Thus the expert who examined the shells from Loch Gilp said they may have been living in comparatively shallow water (Peach *et al.* 1911). H. W. Crosskey (1886), in his discussion of the Loch Sween clays, emphasised that the water became gradually shallower as they accumulated: he pointed out that *Littorina littorea* is very abundant in the upper layers of the clay, giving this part of the deposit a distinctly littoral facies. Near Fort William, not far from the site where subarctic clay was found, is a considerable area of low ground littered with mounds of loose morainic drift that bears no signs of having been reworked by the sea at altitudes of a hundred or even fifty feet. One must therefore conclude that some, at least, of the highly-fossiliferous subarctic clays accumulated when the sea was well below a hundred feet and probably close to its present level.

A further significant aspect of the clays is their lack of gradation into overlying deposits accumulated in postglacial times. Although at most of the localities where fossiliferous subarctic clays have been studied these clays lie partly or wholly beneath postglacial marine sediments, in no instance has a gradation from the one to the other been observed. On the more exposed coasts this might be a result of marine erosion, but it seems unlikely that this explanation applies in the very sheltered bays and inlets in which some of the subarctic deposits have been located. The inference to be drawn from this evidence is that, by the time the subarctic deposits had ceased to accumulate, the sea had fallen to about its present level and may well have been below this level.

The subarctic deposits of the west of Scotland are not restricted to the fossiliferous clays so far considered. There are in addition extensive deposits of clay, silt, sand and gravel along many parts of the coastline of the mainland and adjacent islands. From Ayrshire to southeastern Skye these deposits in many places extend up to a maximum altitude of very roughly 100 feet above sea-level. They often form distinct raised beaches, several steps sometimes occurring one above the other. In some places, however, the material forms a sloping bank against the ground behind and it is not possible to identify different beach levels. Gravel appears to be more common among the western deposits than in the arctic ones of the east and on exposed coasts may form ridges cast up by waves during storms. This difference may be simply a result of exposure of the west coast to prevailing winds, but is probably also a result of higher sea temperatures and consequent longer period free of sea-ice as compared with the east. Despite this evidence of wave action, however, there is little indication of erosion of solid rock by the subarctic seas, and

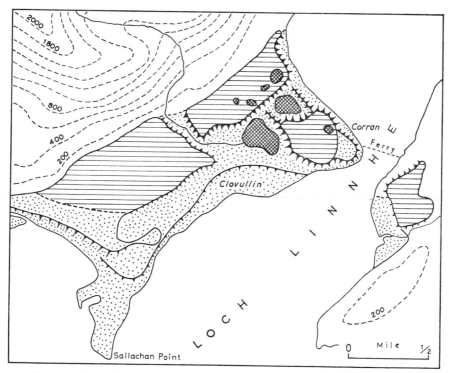

FIG. 65. Outwash deposits at Corran Ferry, Loch Linnhe. Main outwash plain represented by horizontal shading, lower outwash deposits and raised beaches by dots, and kettles by close shading.

their erosional activity, as with the arctic seas of the east, appears to have been restricted essentially to the removal and modification of drift deposits.

The higher subarctic raised beaches along much of the west coast were probably formed during the decay of the ice-mass that had accumulated during the Perth Readvance. At the time the Loch Lomond Readvance reached its maximal extent sea-level was much lower. In a number of the western sea lochs outwash plains occur at or near the limit of this readvance and descend to altitudes well below those of the highest raised beaches. Thus Loch Linnhe is narrowed by a broad headland on its western side to a passage only a few hundred yards wide, a feature that is taken advantage of by Corran ferry (Fig. 65). The headland consists mainly of a mass of outwash gravels pitted by several kettle holes containing lochans, one of which is 74 feet deep. The gravels are highest (about 85 feet above sea-level) at their northeastern margin and from here slope gently outwards down the loch to an altitude of about 40 feet (below which altitude they have been modified by the sea). This implies that at the time the outwash plain was formed sea-level was no higher than 40 feet and may, of course, have been considerably lower (McCann 1961a, 1966a).

Other outwash plains were formed by streams pouring out of the valley glaciers of Mull, and were described in detail by W. B. Wright (in Bailey *et al.* 1924). One of these plains, situated at the end of a steep-sided glacial trough, encloses the western end of Loch Ba. It forms a coarse gravel spread that begins some 30 feet above the level of the loch and slopes down regularly westwards, falling from 75 feet above sea-level to 35 feet, at which latter altitude it becomes obscured owing to the action of postglacial seas. A moraine partly surrounds the outwash, showing that the outwash spread was formed slightly within the maximal limit of the local valley glacier. Some three miles away a similar gravel fan occurs at the northern end of Glen Forsa by the shores of the Sound of Mull. Here the floor of the valley is occupied by peat and alluvium instead of a lake and the steep valley sides are littered with hummocky moraines. From the valley floor rise several small eskers, one of which can be traced into the fan, which has a steep ice-contact slope facing up Glen Forsa. The fan descends regularly outwards to about 35 feet above sea-level, where it passes beneath deposits of a postglacial sea. As at Loch Ba, one thus has a clear picture of a valley glacier with streams discharging from its snout and building up a fan of gravel. From this evidence Wright concluded that in neither case could the sea have been more than 35 feet above its present level, and in neither case has it been above this altitude since, for the deposits above this altitude are unaffected by marine action.

The subarctic marine deposits of the eastern side of Scotland have received but scant attention. This is partly because they are restricted to low altitudes and are consequently often buried beneath postglacial deposits. This happens, for example, in the Forth valley, the deposits here being almost entirely concealed except in the Menteith moraine, where they have been thrust up into ridges by glacier ice.

Postglacial seas

Around the coasts of most of the mainland and adjacent islands there exists a zone of uplifted marine features of much greater clarity than most of those already described. Indeed, the features are in many areas much more marked than those of the present shore.

Elevated cliffs and rock platforms are particularly conspicuous along the west coast and island coasts of Argyllshire. The inner edge of the platform is usually at about 25 to 35 feet above sea-level, although it reaches about 40 feet on parts of the shore of Loch

Linnhe. Very small islands may be completely truncated or may have a small unconsumed rock knob rising in their centre. Islands of the latter type can be seen from the coast road a few miles north of Oban and in profile resemble submarines. The older part of Oban itself is built on an old rock platform with an irregular cover of shingle, while immediately north of the town a prominent isolated stack stands in front of the old cliff. The abandoned cliffs and wave-cut platforms often appear remarkably fresh and there is no difficulty in visualising the waves breaking against the former shore (Plate XVIIIB). The old abrasion platform is sometimes as much as a hundred yards broad and, where the rocks are favourable, the abandoned cliffs still remain vertical. Wave-cut notches, caves and stacks may be seen at many points: they are particularly clear, for example, around parts of Kintyre and Arran. This conspicuous rock erosion does not typify the whole west coast of the Highlands, however. Along many parts of the northwest coast ice-smoothed rocks, sometimes with glacial striae inscribed in them, may be seen to pass down beneath the sea, and show little evidence of having been eroded by the sea either at its present level or at higher levels.

Raised features of marine erosion are found intermittently on many parts of the east coast. For example, in Caithness a narrow bench a few feet above high-water mark is sometimes present, while a broader rock platform with a veneer of sand and gravel occurs on parts of the East Lothian coast for several miles south of Dunbar. Old cliffs, sometimes with caves at their foot, may be seen on many parts of the Fife coast or again on the coast of Banff. It must be emphasised, however, that despite the apparent relation on both east and west coasts between many of these erosional forms on the one hand and the deposits of the postglacial seas on the other, there are good reasons for believing that the former are often basically of much older origin and have merely been sharpened by the postglacial seas (p. 193).

Very often the old cliff-line is separated from the sea by a belt of raised beach sands and gravels which may be continuous for many miles along the coast. These deposits have provided the sites of innumerable coastal settlements, whether it be crofting hamlets, fishing villages or towns. Along with the wind-blown sands that partly cover them, they have also been utilised for numerous golf courses, including famous ones such as those at St Andrews, Carnoustie and Turnberry. The sands and gravels usually contain many shells and shell fragments, which are sometimes locally so abundant that the deposits appear to comprise little else. C. Maclaren (1866) described a deposit between Leith and Portobello where a thousand oyster shells could probably be found within a space three to four yards square. Near Renfrew cockles are so numerous as to have given rise to the place-names Cockle Hill and Cockle Farm.

While most of the raised beaches appear at first sight to be gently inclined seawards, closer examination sometimes shows that they comprise numerous low ridges heaped up by waves. In some localities these ridges are well-marked features, as in southwest Jura where S. Ting (1936) at one place found 20 parallel ridges composed of quartzite cobbles, and near the mouth of the River Irvine in Ayrshire where J. Smith (1896) counted 26 ridges varying in height from 2 to 8 feet. In favourable localities such ridges become the dominant feature, rising occasionally to heights of 15 or 20 feet, and were thrown up across many small coastal indentations, sometimes converting their inner parts into lagoons in which fine sediments with abundant plant remains accumulated. Partial blocking of certain important coastal indentations also occurred. For example, part of Montrose is built on a ridge of gravel and boulders through which a passage from the sheltered waters of the Montrose Basin is maintained by the River South Esk. Similarly, a barrier was built by waves most of the way across the mouth of the estuary of the River Fleet, thus producing the present Loch Fleet (Ogilvie 1923). The barrier is composed of a large number of shingle ridges, each about 8 to 10 feet high, which together form a complex recurved spit that was built southwards from Golspie (Fig. 66). The details of most of the ridges, including their recurved ends, are still clearly preserved, but the ridges now stand well clear of the sea, their higher parts reaching 35 feet above sea-level. Not far to the south other complex systems of raised postglacial spits form Cuthill Links, Ferry Point and Ardjachie Point in the Dornoch Firth.

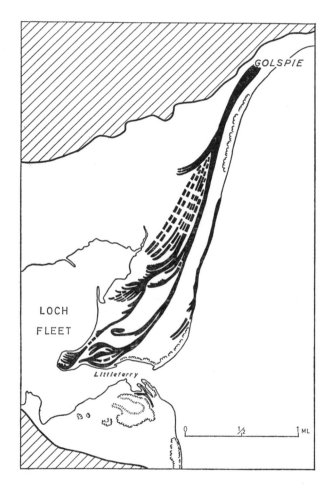

FIG. 66. Raised shingle ridges responsible for the formation of Loch Fleet. The unshaded area is mostly postglacial raised beach deposits, except for a strip along the coast at about present sealevel, with which the separate ridges are associated. The main areas of sand dunes are also shown. After A. G. Ogilvie 1923.

Other elaborate patterns of elevated shingle ridges line the coast of Morayshire, except for the stretch from Burghead past Hopeman to near Lossiemouth where the coast is mostly cliffed. For a time the postglacial seas completely surrounded the rocky hill on which Lossiemouth now stands, and on either side of this island, as it was then, numerous ridges were thrown up by the waves (Fig. 67). South of the shingle ridges a large shallow loch – Loch Spynie – was formed, which was not finally reduced to its present small extent until a canal was constructed to the sea at Lossiemouth. Many of the raised shingle ridges west of Findhorn are partly obscured by the wind-blown sands of Culbin. Ogilvie suggested that these ridges grew in a westward direction and deflected the Findhorn as they did so, the river from time to time breaking through to regain the fairly direct route to the sea it possesses at the present time (*cf.* p. 229).

In marked contrast with the cliffs, platforms and shingle ridges usually found on the more exposed coasts are the flat areas of fine sediment laid down in association with the postglacial seas in many sheltered coastal indentations. Two such areas occur at the head of the Beauly Firth, one extending for several miles around Beauly itself and the other a short distance away south of Kirkhill. A similar strip of flat land follows the lower course of the Ythan in Aberdeenshire and another borders the South Esk inland from Montrose.

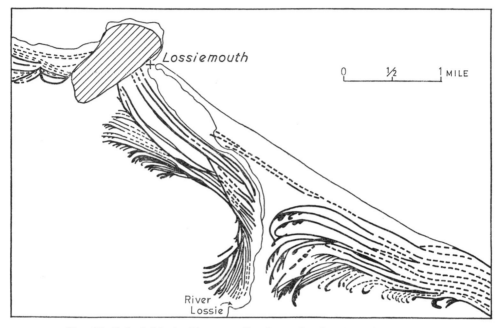

FIG. 67. Raised shingle ridges near Lossiemouth, after A. G. Ogilvie 1923.

In Argyllshire the fine postglacial deposits occupy a considerable part of the low ground between Lochgilphead and Crinan. Near the Solway shores these deposits occur at many localities, as near Gretna, Annan and Kirkbean, along the valley of the Urr southwards from Dalbeattie, and especially on either side of the Cree between Creetown, Newton Stewart and Wigtown. The term 'carse' has often been applied to these flat lands and hence near the Cree one finds such names as Carseminnoch, Carsenestock, Carsewalloch and Carsegown. The most famous carse is that of Gowrie, which extends for a dozen miles southwest from Dundee, with an average width of three miles, and thereafter continues a short way up the Tay valley past Perth and for a considerable distance along the Earn valley past Bridge of Earn. Carselands border the Clyde estuary but have often been much modified by docks and buildings. On the other hand, in the Forth valley they are as yet little disturbed and form the largest area of flat land in Scotland, extending for almost thirty miles, with an average width of three to four miles, from near Grangemouth past Stirling to end not far short of Aberfoyle.

The carselands are elevated mudflats and are identical in origin with the mudflats that are accumulating along parts of the present coastline. Consequently they are usually composed of silt and clay with a very small amount of sand and are almost completely free from stones. The sand tends to become more common towards present or former stream courses, where it may occur as separate beds within the muds. In the upper Solway the present salt marshes are developed on deposits that are rather different in that they are usually composed of over 90 per cent fine sand, and old marshlands now slightly elevated to form raised beaches usually have a similar proportion of fine sand (Marshall 1962).

The top 3 to 5 feet of the carse deposits are often tougher than the part underneath, which comprises very soft mud that normally has a water content of 30 to 60 per cent and is often referred to in older records as 'sleech'. The development of the tougher surface layer, sometimes called the carse crust, has been assisted by artificial drainage by ditches and tile drains: it often thickens towards deep ditches and is absent in badly-drained areas and beneath peat mosses. This crust is very important in building construction, for it carries the lighter structures that have been erected on the carselands such as houses and low factory buildings, care being taken not to pierce the crust when foundations are being constructed. Even so, a loading of 6 to 12 cwt. a square foot is usually the most that this land will safely bear, so that larger structures have to be erected on piles or on other special types of foundation.

The peat mosses that now lie on some of the carselands are the remnants of much larger mosses that existed in times past. They occur, for example, near Wigtown (Moss of Cree), near Linwood in Renfrewshire, and at various places in the Forth valley where the largest, Flanders Moss, occupies several square miles. The mosses are typically between 10 and 20 feet thick and their flattish surfaces are often cut off quite abruptly by steep slopes that lead down to the surrounding carselands. These slopes are artificial and mark the limits of man's clearances. It should not be assumed, however, as is sometimes stated, that all the carselands were once entirely covered with peat: for example, in the Forth valley, where the peat was certainly far more extensive in the past than it is now, there is no evidence that the land around Grangemouth was ever peat-covered. The carselands were, however, generally ill-drained with shallow pools of standing water until transformed as a result of the agricultural improvements of the late eighteenth century. Such conditions are reflected in the occurrence of 'inch' in place-names like Inchyra, Inchcoonen, Inchmichael, Inchmartin and Inchture, which were formerly 'islands' of dry land amidst the badly-drained clay flats of the Carse of Gowrie.

Although the most striking feature of the carselands is their flatness this must not be over-emphasised and an analogy with the English Fenlands or the Somerset Levels is not quite appropriate. Whereas the two latter are more or less at sea-level, large areas of the Scottish flats have been raised distinctly above sea-level, attaining a maximal altitude of almost 50 feet at the western end of the Carse of Stirling. Consequently the larger rivers, such as Earn, Forth, Urr and Cree, normally flow well below the general level of the land, sometimes in steep-banked channels that are rarely over-topped even in times of high flood. It is also apparent that the carselands often comprise, not one flat stretch, but two, three or even more levels, each separated by a slight slope. These various steps, of which the lowest is little above present high-water mark, relate to different levels of the sea in postglacial times. The landward margin of the carse deposits is often sharply defined and sometimes the land rises so abruptly from the carse plain as to suggest a wave-cut cliff. Such steep slopes, however, were formed in earlier times and the carse muds gradually accumulated against them.

The carse deposits often contain abundant organic remains, so much so that the sleech often has a most unpleasant smell caused by decaying matter. Seeds and stems of plants, bits of drifted peat, and branches and trunks of trees have often been observed. Marine shells are scarce in some parts but are very common in others, usually occurring in distinct layers. For example, between Grangemouth and Bo'ness in the Forth valley oyster shells occur at a depth of a few feet in such quantity that in times past they were dug out for use as flux in iron making. D. Milne-Home remarked in 1871: 'Some of these shell-beds are so uniform and regular in position, that I found the labourers who were cutting drains in the fields north of Grangemouth, availing themselves of these beds as a guide for the proper depth of the drains'. Whale skeletons up to 70 feet long have also been found in the Forth valley. Between 15 and 20 have been discovered, some of them many miles to the west of Stirling. Doubtless these creatures were from time to time left stranded on the mudflats as these were bared by the semi-diurnal recession of the tide, an occurrence not unusual in more recent times. (In 1808 a whale 43 feet long was stranded on the banks of the Forth as far upstream as Alloa.) Whale remains have long been known to occur also in the banks of the Irvine near the town of Irvine. They were found here at least as early as 1790 and at one time it was not uncommon to find weavers in the town using whale vertebrae as loom weights.

Almost all the shells found in the postglacial raised beach and estuarine deposits – oysters, mussels, cockles, periwinkles, etc. – are common round our shores at the present time. There are a few exceptions, however, of which *Scrobicularia piperata* is the best known through the elegant account by the elder Hugh Miller (1864) of its occurrence at Portobello. This shell, which favours muddy estuarine locations, is apparently absent from the coastal inlets of eastern Scotland today, but lives in slightly warmer seas. It has been found, however, in the raised estuarine deposits of the Ythan, in former Loch Spynie, and at Aberdeen, and occurs abundantly in the similar deposits near Montrose and Portobello. Oyster shells, often of large size, are also commonly found in the post-glacial raised beaches and have been seen in abundance at points ranging from the Kyle of Tongue to the firths of Forth and Clyde. This contrasts greatly with the situation today, although here man's depradations need to be taken into account. Another shell, *Trochus lineatus*, is common in some of the raised deposits of the Firth of Clyde, but does not exist here today, while *Tapes decussatus*, found in the floor of old Loch Spynie, is now extinct on adjacent coasts. It is thus evident that, at the time these deposits accumulated, the sea – and hence, presumably, the climate – was slightly warmer than it is today, a point appreciated as long ago as 1877 by D. Robertson. This period of milder climate, now often known as the Climatic Optimum, was first clearly demonstrated by R. L. Praeger in Northeast Ireland.

Associated with the postglacial raised beaches there is also abundant evidence of the presence of man. In some instances this evidence demonstrates that man was living in a particular locality at the time the raised beaches accumulated. Such material has given rise to much discussion among archaeologists and we can only mention briefly here the nature of some of the finds. Apparently among the oldest are canoes said to have been found at the base of the carse clays near Perth and Falkirk. Many other canoes have been found in the Clyde area, some of them under the streets of Glasgow itself, the first apparently having been discovered in digging the foundations of St Enoch's Church. Farther down the Clyde the circular wooden structures known as crannogs have caused a good deal of discussion, especially as they are now partly submerged by the waters of the estuary. The elevated caves have also yielded proof of the former presence of man and those at Oban are particularly well known. Flint implements and the sites of ancient burials have been often found in association with the raised beaches, especially in areas where they are partly covered with drifting sand. At the base of the peat that formerly covered large areas of the Forth carselands wooden trackways have been discovered and in the carse clay itself implements have been found close to some of the whale skeletons. Finally we may mention the heaps of discarded shells that occur along some of the ancient shorelines, one of these heaps near Grangemouth having been estimated to have contained some six to seven million oyster shells.

Buried peat

The evidence described so far in this chapter suggests that during lateglacial times sea-level around much of the Scottish coastline was generally falling. As we have seen, along considerable parts of the west coast at least, the sea had fallen to about or below its present level while the subarctic deposits were still accumulating. On the other hand, the post-glacial deposits extend well above the present sea-level, attaining almost 50 feet at the head of the Forth carselands. It thus follows that a major rise of sea-level occurred in postglacial times. This marine transgression was first clearly recognised by G. Buist in 1841, although it was not until 1865 that the broader significance of the evidence of Buist and others was appreciated in T. F. Jamieson's important paper.

Buist observed a bed of peat at many places on both banks of the Firth of Tay and along the lower Earn valley. He described it as containing tree roots, leaves, branches, nuts and fruit. In places it lay below the waters of the firth and was 'a source of great annoyance to salmon-fishers, whose nets it entangles, and is by them often dragged ashore in enormous masses'. Usually, however, it was overlain by 15 to 25 feet of carse deposits containing cockles, mussels and other shells. Buist reasoned that a forest grew 'high and dry above the level of the water of the river' and that later 'some interruption of the drainage . . . or other cause of partial inundation, swamped the forest trees, and converted them into peat'. Subsequently, 'the level of the land rapidly descending', the peat was covered by fluvial, estuarine and marine deposits and, finally, there was a 'general upheaving which brought the present land and water into the relative position they now occupy'.

A layer of peat similar to that described by Buist is very frequently found beneath the carse clay in many parts of Scotland and sometimes occurs also beneath other coastal postglacial deposits. It is particularly well developed in the Forth and Tay valleys and along the indented Solway coast. Other coastal localities at which it has been described range from Ayrshire to Aberdeenshire, the Moray Firth coast and the shores of Loch Linnhe. Normally the peat is only one or two feet thick, although occasionally it is as much as four feet. When covered by a considerable thickness of carse clay it is greatly compressed and the branches of trees have been deformed to an oval cross-section. In some instances numerous stems may be seen to penetrate the deposits beneath, and usually the peat merges gradually into the overlying clay. The peat usually contains evidence of damp conditions such as bright orange bog-beans, the flattened stems of the common reed *Phragmites*, and various species of mosses. It also frequently includes branches of trees and even whole trunks of trees more than a foot in diameter. Sometimes tree stumps are found with the roots penetrating the deposits beneath. Birch, hazel, alder, oak, willow and Scots pine have all been reported as occurring, a variety that leads one to suspect that the peat is not all of the same age, a view supported by other evidence (p. 207). However, that the buried peat and overlying deposits demonstrate a major trangression into most coastal areas and even some low inland areas of Scotland in postglacial times is quite certain.

The pattern we have so far described comprises changes in the relative levels of land and sea as well as those of climate. The period of very cold climate associated with the accumulation in the east of Scotland of the arctic marine deposits, up to altitudes well above that of present sea-level in some places, terminated as the ice decayed following the Perth Readvance. Thereafter subarctic deposits were laid down in relation to a sea that was much nearer its present level or even below it. During the first half of postglacial times climate ameliorated to become slightly warmer than at present. Meanwhile sea-level rose, peat being buried beneath the marine and estuarine deposits in many places. Finally the sea fell gradually to its present level. This pattern of changes, although applicable to much of Scotland, is, in fact, merely an outline of the actual sequence of events which was much more complex and is far from fully established as yet. Furthermore, in some parts of the country, even this broad pattern of changes is not fully applicable. It is to the reasons for these changes that we now turn. In addition we must also direct our attention to the actual altitudes of former sea-levels, a controversial subject that we have avoided so far as was possible in the preceding pages.

9

Causes and measurement
of sea-level changes

IT may not be far from the truth to say that in Scotland every senior schoolboy knows that at one time the sea stood at 100 feet above its present level and the 100-foot raised beach was formed. He may know also that later it stood at 50 feet and the 50-foot beach was formed, while still later the 25-foot beach came into existence. Accounts of these beaches may be found in publications ranging in time from the later years of last century to the present day and in such varied fields as geography, geology, archaeology, botany and engineering. Yet the 100-foot and 50-foot beaches do not exist at all, while the term 25-foot beach has been applied to features that are not all of the same age. In this chapter we shall try to show how the misconceptions have arisen. Before doing so, however, we must consider briefly the reasons for the important changes of sea-level that have occurred in Scotland in the recent geological past.

Causes of sea-level changes

The raised beaches and related features of Scotland are, in general, relatively high in the more central parts of the country and low or absent in the peripheral areas. Thus the postglacial features exceed 35 feet along the shores of lochs Linnhe and Etive, around the northern ramifications of the Firth of Clyde, and in the western part of the Forth valley, all of which lie in or near the Southwest Grampians. Outwards from this area the upper limit of the postglacial marine features falls in altitude in all directions. Postglacial raised beaches have not been found in the Orkneys and Shetlands and they lie only a few feet above high-water mark on parts of the coast of Berwickshire. They appear not to exceed about 25 feet on the Solway coast and have been traced southwards, gently declining in altitude, as far as South Lancashire and North Wales. A similar gentle fall is evident along the east coast of Ireland southwards to Dublin.

The lateglacial raised beaches do not show such a simple pattern but reveal the same general trend. Beaches above about 80 feet occur on various parts of the east coast between the Firth of Forth and Sutherland, although not in Northeast Scotland (Fig. 68). On the opposite side of the country they occur intermittently above this altitude from Loch Torridon to southern Ayrshire. Around the margins of this rather large area the upper limit of lateglacial deposits falls away rapidly in Scotland. The deposits do not occur above present sea-level in the Orkneys and Shetlands and appear to be similarly absent from part of Caithness. On the opposite coast the upper limit falls northwards from Wester Ross through Sutherland and descends westwards towards the Outer Hebrides. This pattern is repeated in the south, where lateglacial deposits are either below sea-level or at a very low altitude in northern Northumberland, and appear to die out on the Cumberland coast.

Two principal conclusions may be drawn from these facts: firstly, that, apart from any change in level of the oceans, the land itself has been uplifted – for otherwise the varying altitudes of the features would not be explained – and, secondly, that this uplift becomes progressively more pronounced towards the Southwest Grampians. The reason for the differential uplift was first suggested by T. F. Jamieson in 1865. He said: 'It is worthy of remark that in Scandinavia and North America, as well as in Scotland, we have evidence of a depression of the land following close upon the presence of the great ice-covering'. He went on: 'It has occurred to me that the enormous weight of ice thrown upon the land may have had something to do with this depression', adding, 'the melting of the ice would account for the rising of the land'. This was the first brief statement of the concept of glacial isostasy. Since the amount of land depression is related to the ice thickness, the Scottish raised beaches increase in altitude towards the Southwest Grampians, which formed the principal centre of the last ice-sheet.

It is generally assumed that isostatic recovery of the land, once initiated by the commencement of ice-sheet decay, is a continuous process. If we accept this premise (but see also p. 186), then we would normally expect any particular raised beach to be less steeply inclined than a raised beach formed at an earlier time. The difference in slope between any two beaches thus represents the amount of differential uplift that occurred in the time between their formation. This is shown diagrammatically in Fig. 69a, which represents ideal raised beach profiles along any straight line terminating in the Southwest Grampians.

This diagram needs to be modified, however, because, as we have seen, ice still covered

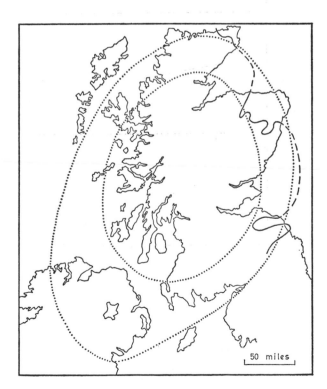

FIG. 68. Approximate limit of area in which lateglacial raised beaches exceeding 80 feet occur (inner dotted line) and approximate line along which outermost lateglacial raised beaches pass below present sea-level. The limit of the Aberdeen–Lammermuir Readvance is also shown.

50 miles

parts of Scotland when the lateglacial beaches were being formed. When the oldest of these beaches was produced most of the country was still beneath an ice-sheet: hence, we can expect to find the oldest and most severely-warped beaches only at a considerable distance from the heart area of the ice-sheet. Ignoring for the moment the complications introduced by glacier readvances, we would expect successively younger lateglacial beaches to terminate nearer and nearer to the central area of the ice-sheet, while the postglacial beaches, of course, would not be excluded by ice at all. This situation is shown in Fig. 69b.

Isostatic movements alone cannot explain the Scottish raised beaches, however. The other major factor that has to be taken into account is the eustatic one, that is, the world-wide changes of ocean level. Such changes may be caused in various ways, but during the period we are concerned with here the main cause was the growth and decay of the world's glaciers. More and more evidence is accumulating to show that the major periods of advance and retreat of glaciers were approximately synchronous in different parts of the world. Therefore, during periods of climatic deterioration and consequent glacier build-

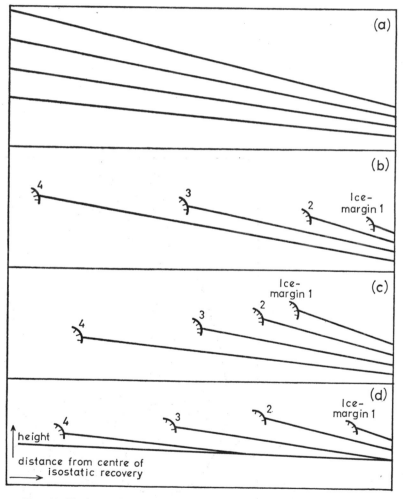

FIG. 69. Various raised shoreline relationships. For explanation see text.

up the level of the oceans dropped. The minimal level achieved when glacier ice was at its maximal extent is believed to have been between 300 and 400 feet below the present level. As the glaciers decayed the water was returned to the oceans. The rise in ocean level following the maximum of the last ice-sheet was not continuous, however, for, from time to time, the general ice decay was interrupted by major readvances. Therefore

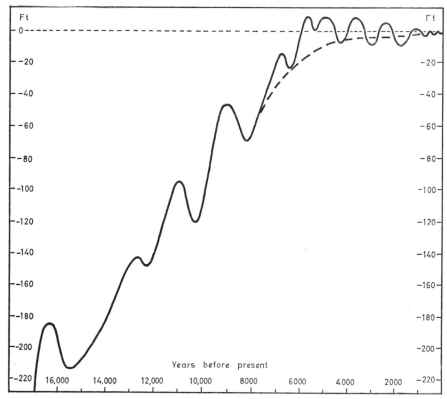

FIG. 70. Eustatic changes of sea-level during the last 17 000 years, based on R. W. Fairbridge 1961. The broken line shows the alternative interpretation of the later part of the curve favoured by a number of other workers.

periods when world sea-level was probably rising rapidly were interrupted by periods when the movement was temporarily reversed. An attempt to plot these variations has been made by R. W. Fairbridge (1961) using evidence from many parts of the world (Fig. 70).

In order to understand the distribution and altitude of the Scottish raised beaches we must combine the effects of isostatic deformation with the eustatic sea-level variations. To do this in any detail is at present impossible because much essential information is lacking. Nevertheless certain relationships may be observed.

For example, when the lateglacial raised beaches were being formed the world sea-level was much lower than it is at present. Therefore for a lateglacial beach to be above sea-level at the present time it must have been isostatically elevated by a greater amount than world sea-level has risen since it was formed. This may be illustrated by considering the raised beach at almost 125 feet near Stirling (Fig. 64) that was produced shortly after the maximum of the Perth Readvance about 13 000 to 13 500 years ago. Since Fairbridge's graph shows that world sea-level was at that time about 150 feet below its present level we can estimate that the beach has been isostatically raised about 275 feet. Had it been raised less than 150 feet it would not now form a raised beach. We would also expect the Stirling beach to slope eastwards down the Forth valley as it gets farther from the centre of isostatic uplift. In fact, the beach should ultimately cross the present sea-level line and continue as a submerged beach until it levels out at a depth of around 150 feet at the limit of the area affected by glacial isostasy. It is very unlikely that it will ever be possible to follow an old beach in this manner. Nevertheless it is interesting to note that at the time the sea was almost 125 feet above its present level near Stirling the southern half of the North Sea and much of the English Channel were land areas.

The existence of lateglacial raised beaches around the coasts of much of the Scottish mainland and of many of the adjacent islands, coupled with the fact that many of these beaches terminate at former ice limits as they are traced inwards towards the centre of isostatic uplift, implies that, owing to the isostatic depression of the land, the sea invaded many of the present coastlands of Scotland as the ice wasted back. Since major periods of glacier decay in Scotland may be presumed to correspond with widespread deglaciation in other parts of the world, the level of the oceans as a whole would be rising at such times. If this rise was sufficiently rapid in relation to the isostatic rise, the upper inward limit of successive lateglacial shorelines increases in altitude towards the centre of isostatic recovery. This is shown diagrammatically in Fig. 69b, while Fig. 69c shows the situation where isostatic recovery outstripped eustatic sea-level rise. Clearly, the third possibility, not illustrated, is a horizontal upper limit for a series of shorelines.

Some of the most distinct raised shorelines mark the upper limit of marine transgressions and, of these, the clearest by far marks the upper limit of the major postglacial transgression. By this time the rate of isostatic recovery in Scotland was much slower than it had been earlier and even the central part of the isostatically-affected area was depressed by only tens of feet compared with the present time. However, world sea-level was rising rapidly, owing especially to the final melting of the European and North American ice-sheets (Fig. 70). Consequently the sea overtook the slowly-rising land and invaded the coastal areas of much of Scotland, extending far inland along the major valleys of the Central Lowlands. Since the amount of isostatic warping of the shoreline that marks the culmination of this transgression is small compared with that suffered by the lateglacial shorelines, this shoreline often intersects the latter at a distinct angle. This is shown diagrammatically in Fig. 69d.

Measurement of the altitudes of Scottish raised shorelines

The pattern of shoreline displacement just outlined is similar to the pattern that has been accepted for half a century as applying in Scandinavia, but differs considerably from the type of interpretation long held in Scotland. The idea of the 100-foot and 50-foot raised beaches appears to have come into existence in 1879 when the Geological Survey memoir on the sheet including Falkirk was published. So far as this particular sheet was concerned the use of the term 100-foot beach was fully justified as a first approximation, for in this area raised beaches at about this altitude are very distinct features. As the geological mapping of Scotland progressed, beaches at roughly 100 feet, as well as around 50 and 25 feet, were found in many localities and again, quite justifiably as first approximations, they were referred to by these heights. Unfortunately, it was not usually

PLATE XXI. Quirang, Skye. Tertiary lava escarpment displaced by land-slipping. *Geological Survey photograph. Crown Copyright reserved.*

PLATE XXII. Culbin sand-hills. *Photograph by W. A. Sharp.*

appreciated that a feature called the 100-foot or 50-foot raised beach in one area was not of the same age as a feature to which the same altitude designation had been applied elsewhere. Consequently, in due course, it came to be widely accepted that there are three principal raised beaches in Scotland, although occasionally additional ones such as 125-foot, 75-foot and 15-foot were described. This simple pattern of raised beaches still has many adherents. For example, J. J. Donner (1959, 1963) claims to have identified the 100-, 50- and 25-foot raised beaches, as well as a 15-foot beach, at various points in the coastal areas of most of the Scottish mainland. In another quite recent contribution C. A. M. King and P. T. Wheeler (1963) identify the same four features in northern Sutherland. The latter, as well as Donner, correlate the beaches with pollen zones, radiocarbon dates and glacier readvances, a good example of pouring new wine into old bottles.

The concept of 100-, 50- and 25-foot beaches has persisted for so long because the need for accurate detailed measurements of the altitudes of raised shorelines has not been appreciated. During the basic mapping of the country carried out by the Geological Survey such detailed work could not be expected, of course, for the prime task was to locate and map the principal raised beaches. Even so, the Geological Survey memoir on Mull published in 1924 contains a considerable body of valuable (although approximate) measurements on raised shorelines, a result of the efforts of W. B. Wright. On the other hand, the considerable amount of very recent research carried out by workers outside the Survey that should have provided a new pattern to replace the simple scheme of sea-level changes developed last century, has failed to provide any convincing alternative. The main reason for this failure is that in most recent studies (as in earlier ones) the measurements of raised shorelines are neither sufficiently accurate nor sufficiently close together.

The total number of published measurements on Scottish raised shorelines (excluding recent measurements by the author and his students) is probably about one thousand. Of these, fewer than two hundred have been made by accurate instrumental levelling tied to Ordnance Survey bench marks. The great majority have been obtained by hand levelling or aneroid barometer using high-water mark or the upper limit of seaweed or barnacles as a datum. Such methods introduce inaccuracies that cannot be tolerated. One result of their use is that raised beaches separated by a small vertical height interval

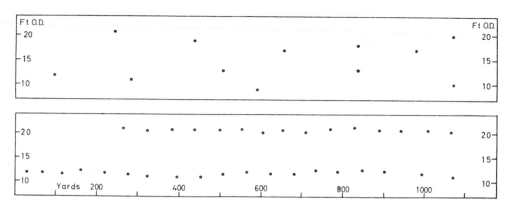

FIG. 71. Measurement of two raised shorelines in East Lothian by aneroid (upper diagram) and accurate levelling (lower diagram).

E.S.S.—M

are unlikely to be differentiated from one another. This is well illustrated by measurements made by the author near the mouth of the River Tyne in East Lothian. In one small area here there are two very distinct raised beach flats, one above the other, separated by a small but steep bluff. As can be seen in Fig. 71, aneroid measurements (made in ideal conditions) completely failed to distinguish these two features but they were clearly separated by accurate levelling. In this example the immediate proximity to each other of the two features shows clearly on the ground that they are quite distinct, but had they been some distance apart, as often happens, the approximate method of measurement would probably have failed to reveal the distinction.

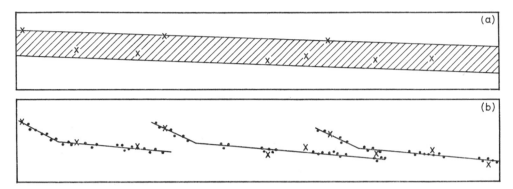

Fig. 72. Resolution of raised beaches and associated outwash deposits by closely-spaced height measurements. For explanation see text.

In most studies of Scottish raised beaches the measurements have been spaced much too far apart, the interval often amounting to several miles (and, occasionally, even tens of miles). One result has been that the surviving remnants of the various raised beaches have been very frequently miscorrelated with each other and the complexity of the story of changing sea-levels has not been revealed. Another common result is that outwash plains have often been mistaken for raised beaches. Closely-spaced accurate height measurements, however, readily enable the gently-inclined raised beaches to be distinguished from the more steeply-sloping outwash plains. Fig. 72 illustrates this point. In the upper diagram (a), crosses represent measurements presumed to have been taken at intervals of several miles on the highest features along a part of the Scottish coast. The heights tend to fall from left to right, suggesting a gently-sloping raised beach, which has therefore been represented by the gently-inclined band of shading. Fig. 72b shows the same coastal stretch following a much more detailed height investigation, the new heights being represented by dots. It will be seen that what was formerly interpreted as one beach has now been resolved into several beaches and associated outwash features. The crosses of the earlier investigation are reproduced in the lower diagram to facilitate comparison. Although Fig. 72 does not relate to a particular area, the type of miscorrelation it represents has been made (and is still being made) in many parts of Scotland.

Quite often the individual beaches of the type shown in Fig. 72b can be traced for only a short distance – sometimes for only a mile or two – and this has caused them to be grouped together in the past as a single feature, referred to as the 100-foot beach in areas where they occur at roughly this altitude. Such a miscorrelation is particularly easy, for each beach is often a very clear feature for a short distance, but then fades away, only to be replaced by another well-developed beach at around the same altitude a mile or a few miles along the coast. This pattern has arisen because, as the glacier ice decayed in coastal areas, rivers often poured large quantities of debris from the ice into the sea, thus building outwash deltas, which merged into beaches that were best developed close to the debris source.

There would be little point in expressing dissatisfaction with the generally-accepted pattern of Scottish raised beaches were it not that a new pattern is available to replace the old. This new interpretation has resulted from investigations in Southeast Scotland during the last few years by D. E. Smith, R. A. Cullingford and the author. The basis of these studies was the entire re-mapping of all identifiable raised beaches and related landforms of the Forth and Tay valleys and the coast of East Fife on a scale of 1 : 10 560. Subsequently the raised shorelines and associated fluvioglacial deposits were accurately levelled wherever practicable at intervals usually of between 60 and 80 yards. This levelling was based on Ordnance Survey bench marks and the altitude of over 10 000 points has been determined. In addition the stratigraphy has been investigated in detail through more than 900 boreholes made by a hand-operated borer to maximal depths of about 30 feet, as well as through a large number of commercial boreholes put down in connection with mining and construction work. This study is still in progress and is expected to continue for a considerable time yet. Inevitably it has produced a number of new problems, some of which are still unsolved. Nevertheless, the main elements of a new story of land and sea-level changes for Southeast Scotland – and, by implication, for much of the rest of Scotland – are now evident, and it is to this sequence of events that we now turn.

10

Changing sea-levels
in Southeast Scotland

AROUND the coasts of the long firths of Forth and Tay and extending inland from them are tens of square miles of elevated marine and estuarine deposits (Fig. 73). Whereas on many exposed coasts such deposits did not accumulate or have been subsequently swept away in part or in whole by the sea, there were long periods of quiet sedimentation in the two firths, resulting in a fascinating sequence of deposits. Even so, the story is not completely one of deposition, for there is also clear evidence of at least one period of significant marine erosion, quite apart from the considerable erosion along parts of the present shore abundantly recorded from historical times.

The oldest lateglacial raised beaches

The oldest raised beaches of Southeast Scotland are to be found in East Lothian and East Fife, for these areas were the first parts to be freed from glacier ice during the period of deglaciation that followed the Aberdeen–Lammermuir Readvance. These beaches are best developed as distinct features in East Fife, where they have been studied by R. A. Cullingford and D. E. Smith (1966). The beaches extend from the vicinity of St Andrews to Fife Ness on the north coast, and from Leven to Fife Ness on the south coast. They are better developed on the north coast owing partly to the very abundant debris supplied by the glacial rivers that utilised the Eden valley west of St Andrews and the Wormit gap northwest of Leuchars. Despite the exposed nature of much of the East Fife coast, there is little evidence of ridges cast up by waves, a fact that may be partly attributable to frozen seas in winter. The various raised beaches are not continuous features, but each occurs at intervals along the coast, the individual remnants varying in length up to a maximum of two miles.

Six separate lateglacial raised beaches have been distinguished in East Fife above an altitude of 48 feet.* Each of these beaches declines in altitude towards Fife Ness. In places they form steps one above the other along parts of the coast and in one locality there is a staircase of five beaches. From the height measurements the best straight line representing each of the shorelines has been calculated. These lines are shown in Fig. 74 along with lines representing the main outwash deposits.

We may infer that the six raised beaches are in descending order of age: otherwise they

---

* All altitudes are related to Ordnance Datum. Where, as in Chapter 11, altitudes related to high-water mark by other writers are used, they have been converted to Ordnance Datum with the aid of Admiralty Tide Tables.

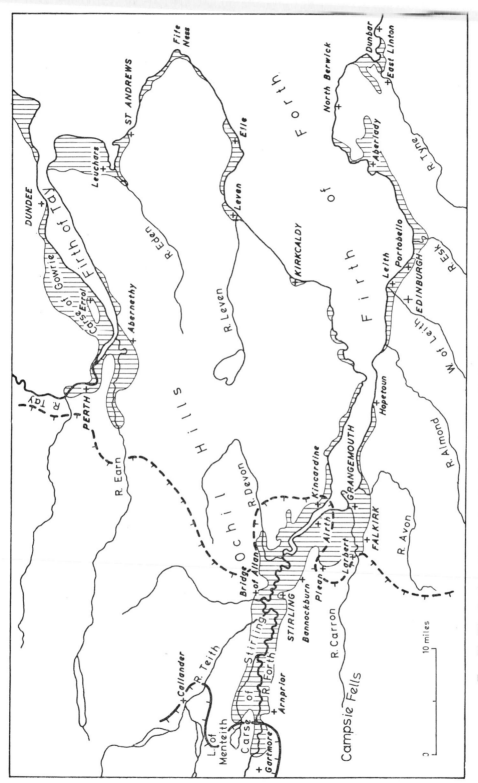

FIG. 73. The Forth and Tay region showing main areas of raised beach deposits and places referred to in the text. The approximate limits of the Perth and Menteith readvances are also shown. After J. B. Sissons *et al.* 1966.

would be unlikely to form such definite features, for the deposits of an earlier, lower beach would have been obscured or modified during the formation of a later, higher one. This also accords with the slopes of the beaches, which become successively less as one descends the series. Thus Fig. 74 gives a picture of the isostatic warping of eastern Fife during and since the time that the beaches were formed. Since the highest beach was

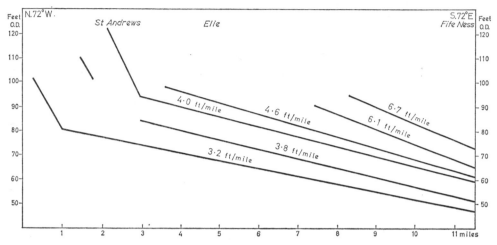

FIG. 74. Lateglacial raised shorelines and some related outwash deposits in East Fife. Based on R. A. Cullingford and D. E. Smith 1966.

produced the total tilting of this area amounts to 6·7 feet a mile, but it is interesting to note that half this tilting had already been completed by the time the lowest of the six beaches had been formed. The beaches accumulated as the ice-sheet wasted away, thus allowing the sea to extend farther and farther westwards along the coasts of East Fife. As can be seen in Fig. 74, the beaches terminate successively farther west at their upper limits. The fourth beach merges imperceptibly near St Andrews into a mass of outwash that was laid down alongside the margin of the ice-sheet, while the lowest beach is similarly related to outwash.

It is not possible, at least as yet, to continue this pattern of shoreline displacement across the Forth into East Lothian, where raised beach deposits of similar age occur. In scattered localities in the low ground of East Lothian are found shorelines likely to correlate with those of East Fife, but few can be traced for any distance. The best example occurs north of the village of East Linton and is almost continuous for about 2½ miles. This shoreline inclines eastwards at slightly over 5 feet a mile.

Following the formation of the series of raised beaches just described, the ice-sheet continued to decay and the sea consequently extended eventually into the Firth of Tay, as well as farther westwards along the Forth valley. This period is in general but poorly represented by raised beaches. Whether this is a function of the relative rates of movement of land and sea, or whether it is a result of the influence exerted by the relief of the coastal zone on glacial rivers, is uncertain. The latter factor appears at least to have been partly responsible, for along the shores of the Firth of Tay and the north side of the Forth where the coastal slopes are steep and large valleys lacking, there are only scattered raised beach fragments related to this retreat phase. On the other hand, on the south side of the

Forth, where the rivers Esk and Almond and the Water of Leith flow into the sea, there are large areas of fluvioglacial and marine deposits. Much of the northern part of Edinburgh is built on these materials, thus obscuring the details of their form. Fortunately, one very clear feature situated within the northwestern part of the city limits has so far escaped the urban spread. The eastern part of this feature is a conspicuous raised beach forming a gently-inclined step up to 400 yards wide that can be followed for over a mile, most of it in Silverknowes Golf Course. In this distance the shoreline rises westwards from 101 feet to 104-105 feet. The gradient of the feature then increases, for it imperceptibly becomes a fluvioglacial terrace, and on being followed for a further three-quarters of a mile attains 124 feet. Another assemblage of similar features occurs on the south side of the Forth a short distance west of the Forth Road Bridge. Here a large outwash plain, fed from the west by a now-streamless meltwater channel, has provided the site for Hopetoun House and its surrounding gardens and walks. Eastwards the outwash can be traced into a narrow raised beach whose shoreline is situated between 110 and 114 feet above sea-level. This shoreline and the one at Silverknowes are shown in Fig. 81.

Farther west on the south side of the Forth valley outwash spreads occur at various places as far as Falkirk, but none appears to be associated with a raised beach. A similar situation appears to prevail on the opposite side of the Forth. This may be the result of a relative rise of sea-level at the time of the Perth Readvance, the raised beach deposits associated with this readvance having buried the beach deposits related to the previous retreat phase.

The Perth Readvance raised beaches

Following the deposition of the raised beaches and fluvioglacial features described above, the ice-sheet continued to waste back up the Forth, Tay and Earn valleys. How far it withdrew and for how long are unknown, but eventually it began to build up and extend down these valleys again as well as up the Clyde valley. When this readvance – the Perth Readvance – culminated about 13 000 to 13 500 years ago the ice limit stood within a few miles of the site of Perth. In the Forth valley ice streamed through the Stirling gap and spread out as a lobe whose farthest limit was in the vicinity of Kincardine. The ice mass that moved up the Clyde valley over the site of Glasgow at this time also had an influence in the Forth area, for at its greatest extent its edge stood within a few hundred yards of where Larbert now stands (Fig. 73).

During the decay of this ice meltwater rivers laid down great quantities of sand and gravel. Some of these deposits now form kame and kettle landscapes or kame terraces while others were laid down as outwash plains composed mainly of coarse gravel. Some of these outwash plains can today be traced into raised beaches, together with which they form continuous features (Fig. 64). One can therefore envisage the outwash plains being built out into the sea, as happens today in Iceland and Alaska, the braided torrents with their constantly-changing courses carrying heavy loads of debris, some of the finer portions of which were transported along the shores of the ancient firths of Forth and Tay to build up broad beaches. These beaches, now raised well above sea-level, are conspicuous features around the western parts of the two firths, where individual remnants often form almost flat terraces 200 yards or more broad and a mile or more long. They reach their greatest development north and west of Falkirk where, before being dissected by the River Carron, there existed a great intertidal delta with an area of about six square miles. A considerable part of this raised delta still remains on the north side of the Carron and includes the flattish sandy ground on which Stenhousemuir stands.

This feature lies close to the limit of the Perth Readvance and owes its dimensions especially to the meltwater rivers from the west that discharged their debris into this area.
The importance of the glacial rivers in providing beach-building debris is also reflected
in the composition of the raised beaches. For example, in and west of Falkirk they are
mainly sand – as witness the various sand pits – but as they are followed eastwards down
the Forth valley they become mainly laminated silts and clays with no more than a
surface layer of sand a few feet thick (Sissons and Smith 1965a).

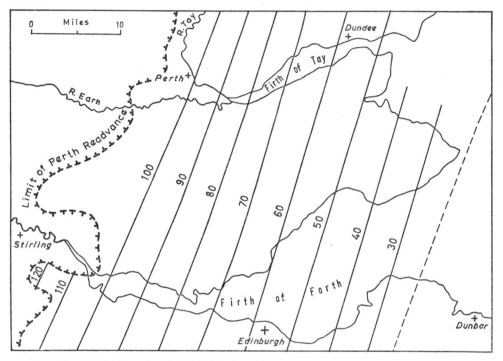

FIG. 75. Isobases for the Main Perth Raised Shoreline. The broken line represents the line along which this shoreline intersects the Main Postglacial
Shoreline.

Several distinct raised beaches are associated with the Perth Readvance and with
the earlier part of the period of glacier decay that followed. The highest of these beaches,
which is usually the best preserved, was formed when the ice was at its maximal extent
or very shortly after the maximum, for it merges into outwash plains at or very close to
the ice limit. This beach, which we may refer to as the Main Perth Raised Beach, is the
clearest of all the lateglacial raised beaches of Southeast Scotland and it has therefore
been possible to trace it widely, while the altitude of its shoreline has been measured at
several hundred points. The results are represented by isobases in Fig. 75, from which it
is apparent that the feature declines in altitude towards a direction slightly south of east
from over 120 feet above present sea-level in the west to below 30 feet in the east, its
average gradient being about $2\frac{1}{4}$ feet a mile. The beach cannot be traced eastwards down
to present sea-level because, at the altitudes one would expect to find it, there exists
instead the Main Postglacial Beach of considerably later age (Fig. 81).
    As the ice decayed following the formation of the Main Perth Beach meltwater rivers

continued to deposit sand and gravel, especially as outwash plains, in both the Forth and Tay areas. At the same time the level of the land in relation to the sea was rising, so that the outwash deposits were fashioned into successively-lower terraces that now flank the course of rivers such as the Earn, Tay and Carron. (In part this terracing was also caused by the retreat of the glacier margins.) Some of the terraces can be traced into raised beaches at lower levels than the Main Perth Beach and these beaches also fall in altitude towards a direction south of east. Such raised beaches are very extensive near Bridge of Earn and thence along the foot of the Ochils towards Newburgh. Cullingford has traced one of the beaches down to the level of the postglacial deposits in the Carse of Gowrie and has found by boring that it continues to decline in altitude eastwards beneath the carse clay. In the Forth area the lower beaches of this period are well developed on the raised delta north of the River Carron, where their shorelines are at 84-88 and 108-109 feet, the Main Perth Shoreline here being at 116-119 feet. The middle member of this trio can be followed past Bannockburn towards Stirling, by which time it has attained almost 125 feet. Here it merges into an outwash plain laid down when the ice margin lay athwart the Stirling gap, as described on p. 150 and illustrated in Fig. 64.

Around the margins of the broad belt of low ground that extends for fifteen miles west of Stirling lateglacial beaches are very poorly developed. A few features occur at about 65 to 70 feet but they are not sufficiently numerous or extensive to permit correlation. One noticeable point about them, however, is that they are definitely absent within the great arcuate loop of the Menteith moraine, so they cannot have been formed after this moraine was built up.

Buried raised beaches

The paucity of lateglacial shorelines in the Carse of Stirling is fortunately more than compensated by the great extent of more recent marine and estuarine deposits. These comprise not only the carse plain with an area of some forty square miles, but also raised beaches buried beneath the carse clay. These buried raised beaches have been investigated by putting numerous boreholes down through the carse clay (Sissons 1966). The boreholes show that, were it possible to view the surface buried beneath the carse clay, the main impression away from the vicinity of the Forth would be of a large, almost flat plain. However, within the buried plain there are small but significant variations: in fact, it comprises three distinct beaches.

As shown in Figs 76 and 77 the beaches form steps one above the other, which we may refer to as the High, Main and Low Buried Beaches. The High Beach occurs only outside the Menteith moraine and its shoreline is at an altitude of about 40 feet. It is mostly composed of pinkish silty sand and is overlain by peat a few inches thick, above which is the carse clay. The Main Buried Beach is a few feet lower and is formed mainly of silty fine sand of light grey colour. It is a very extensive feature with a width of more than a mile in places. The Low Beach is composed of similar deposits except in its upper few feet, which are sticky grey clay. This low feature and the peat that overlies it can be seen at various places in the banks of the Forth when the river level is low. In a belt varying in width between a quarter and three-quarters of a mile and for the most part following the trend of the present meander zone of the Forth, the buried peat is absent and the carse clay alternates with layers of sand and sandy clay in which marine shells occur. It thus appears that this central belt was at one time an estuary in which sandy river deposits mixed with estuarine muds, and it probably looked very much like the Forth does today for a few miles upstream of Kincardine Bridge.

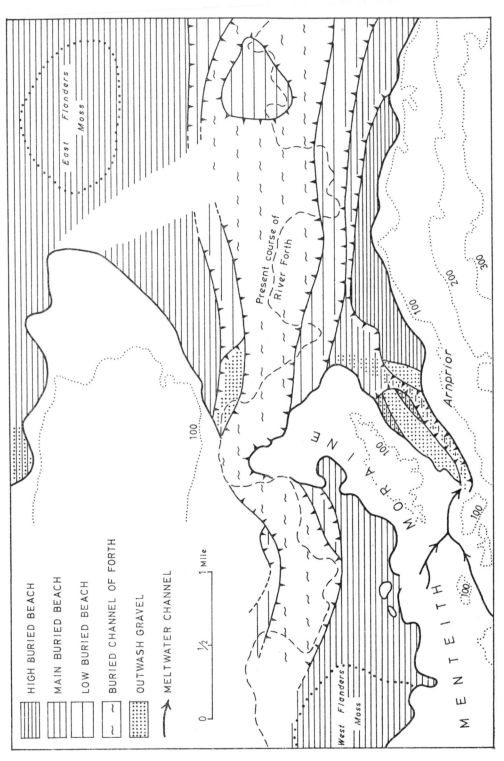

FIG. 76. The buried landforms that would be revealed near the Menteith moraine if the carse clay and peat were to be removed. In addition the two areas where peat bogs grew in a postglacial sea are delimited by dots.

In three areas outwash gravels poured through meltwater breaches in the Menteith moraine occur beneath the carse clay. One of these breaches is now utilised by the Goodie Water, the small stream that drains Lake of Menteith. Near where the Goodie Water leaves the lake is a group of kames and dead-ice hollows, and from these an outwash plain of very coarse gravel passes eastwards through the gap in the moraine. The surface of the

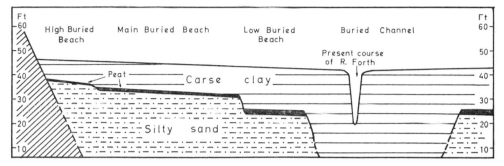

Fig. 77. Diagrammatic section across the buried raised beaches and buried channel of the Forth, showing their relations to the buried peat and carse clay. The section applies to the area immediately east of the Menteith moraine.

outwash falls in altitude eastwards from 77 feet by Lake of Menteith to about 48 feet where it passes beneath the carse clay. Thereafter its continued decline eastwards has been traced down to 33 feet, where it tends to level out (Fig. 78). Clearly this mass of gravel could not have been deposited once the ice in the Lake of Menteith kettle hole had melted. Since the lake lies immediately inside the moraine – its waters in fact lap against it – the gravel must have been laid down very soon indeed after the moraine was formed and while glacier ice still rested against the moraine.

The outwash plain suggests that sea-level was not above 33 feet when it accumulated. It is partly covered by the deposits of the High Buried Beach (Fig. 78), thus implying that sea-level rose to about 40 feet after the outwash was laid down. Since this beach does not exist inside the Menteith moraine, it must have accumulated at the time the ice stood at the moraine. Hence, since the moraine is believed to have been formed about 10 300 years ago (p. 146), we can say that the beach was probably produced about or shortly after this date.

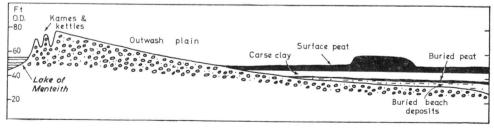

Fig. 78. Section through the outwash plain that slopes down eastwards from Lake of Menteith to pass beneath later deposits. Length of section approximately 1¾ miles.

The Main Buried Beach was clearly formed at a distinctly later time, for it is widespread both within and without the Menteith moraine. Its age can be inferred from pollen analyses of the peat that overlies it (Newey 1966). The base of this peat contains *Chenopod* pollen, which indicates marine influence and implies that the peat began to accumulate on the flat ill-drained surface of the beach as the sea withdrew. This basal peat belongs to the transition from Zone IV to Zone V, which corresponds with an age of about 9500 years. This is therefore approximately the age of the Main Buried Beach.

The top two feet or so of the silty clay that forms the upper part of the Low Buried Beach are usually threaded with innumerable vertical stems of reeds, which merge upwards into the overlying peat, so that one may envisage an estuary with reeds growing on mudflats at its margins, the mud gradually accumulating round the reeds. The base of the peat overlying this material contains *Chenopod* pollen and a sample of this basal peat has given a radiocarbon age of about 8700 years. Since this sample may have been contaminated by the roots of trees that later grew on the peat, the Low Buried Beach is likely to be slightly older than the radiocarbon date. An age of about 8800 years seems probable.

The buried beaches thus indicate a 1500-year period of falling sea-level, probably interrupted by slight transgressions whose limits are recorded by the shorelines of the beaches. After the Low Buried Beach was abandoned the sea once again fell and was restricted to a long relatively-narrow estuary differing in location only slightly from the present meander belt of the Forth. The Main and Low Beaches have a slight but definite slope down the Forth valley that is probably mainly a result of isostatic tilting. Both beaches have been traced past Stirling to Bannockburn, the average gradient of the Main one being about 0·8 feet a mile and of the Low one slightly less (Fig. 81). The High Beach has so far been found only in a very limited area and its representation in Fig. 81 is diagrammatic.

The buried gravel layer

At this point it is necessary to leave for the moment the story of successive sea-level changes and to move back in time in order to look at the sequence of deposits that underlies the broad expanse of nearly flat carseland in the area extending from Grangemouth to Airth. Fortunately these deposits have been penetrated by hundreds of boreholes put down for many firms and organisations, who have kindly allowed access to their records. These boreholes show that, over most of the area, there is a very clear sequence of deposits. This sequence is summarised, along with other evidence, in Fig. 79.

The most significant deposit in the present context is a layer of sand and gravel that forms a distinctive horizon under almost the whole of the Grangemouth–Airth area and is also found under the low ground of Bo'ness. Normally this layer is between two and five feet thick, and it has a remarkably regular slope towards the Forth. Its landward margin often lies within a few feet of present sea-level and it declines to about 20 feet below sea-level near the river. Quite often the stones in the gravel are rounded and some of them are of considerable size, the layer often being referred to as a boulder bed in borehole records. A variety of rock types is represented, ranging from local Carboniferous rocks to pieces of schist from the Highlands. In addition, the stones and sand are often intermixed with marine shells. It is thus apparent that the gravel layer represents an old beach lying at a lower altitude than any of the features we have considered so far.

It is also apparent that this beach is of a very different character from all the other old beaches we have referred to, for the latter are composed mainly of fine sediments.

The gravel layer may partly owe its existence to debris brought down from adjacent higher ground by rivers such as the Avon and Carron. It appears to be essentially a result of marine erosion, however. This erosion is expressed in various ways. In the Forth valley generally the landward margin of the carselands is often backed by a steep slope that is strongly reminiscent of a marine cliff. This appearance is sometimes misleading, as, for

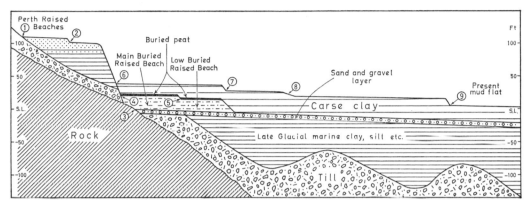

FIG. 79. Diagrammatic section through the superficial deposits of the Grange-mouth-Airth area. Circled numbers relate to shorelines in order of formation, the sequence being slightly generalised (e.g. only 3 of the 4 visible post-glacial shorelines are shown). After J. B. Sissons *et al*. 1966.

example, west of Stirling, where the steep slope is sometimes ice-eroded rock or the ice-moulded flank of a drumlin. Southeast of Stirling, however, including the Grange-mouth–Airth area, this cliff-like slope is often a result of marine erosion. It is noticeable, for example, that the cliffed appearance is present only on the parts of this old coastline that would have been most exposed to former wave attack. It is also evident that the deposits of the Perth Raised Beaches have been considerably eroded, as is shown diagram-matically in Fig. 79. Furthermore, boreholes and sections show that beneath the carse clay along the foot of considerable stretches of this cliff line, the glacial till has been stripped away and the carse clay rests directly on solid rock. Farther out from the old cliff the till is present but its surface has sometimes been planated and on this planated surface rests the buried gravel layer. Still farther out the gravel layer passes on to lami-nated lateglacial silts, clays and fine sands (Fig. 79). There is thus a clear relation between the evidence for marine erosion on the one hand and the depositional evidence of the gravel layer on the other. It appears that erosion of glacial till by the sea was particularly important in providing debris for the beach now represented by the gravel layer, while stones were also derived from the erosion of the lateglacial marine deposits, for these contain much ice-rafted debris. The origin of the gravel layer is thus exactly analogous with that of the deposits of many miles of the present shores of the Firth of Forth, for these shores are often littered with innumerable stones and boulders that represent the coarser constituents of drift deposits eroded by the sea. These shore deposits now extend up the Forth valley to the vicinity of Bo'ness, but when the gravel layer was being formed we may imagine the same type of shore extending much farther up the Forth (the estuary being at that time much wider than it is now).

The age of the gravel layer is suggested by its relation to the buried beach deposits described in the previous section. As shown in Fig. 79, it passes beneath these deposits and hence cannot be less than about 10 300 years old. On the other hand, it was produced later than the deposits of the Perth Raised Beaches (for these were severely eroded during the formation of the gravel layer) and hence cannot be older than about 13 000 to 13 500 years. If, now, we integrate this evidence with that described earlier, we have the following pattern of relative sea-level changes.

(i) A high sea-level around 13 000 to 13 500 years ago as the ice of the Perth Re-advance began to decay.

(ii) A period of rapidly-falling sea-level as this decay continued.

(iii) A period of low sea-level associated with the formation of the buried gravel layer.

(iv) A rise of sea-level, culminating in the formation of the High Buried Beach shortly after the maximum of the Menteith Readvance about 10 300 years ago.

(v) A fall of sea-level, followed by a slight rise ending about 9500 years ago and associated with the deposition of the Main Buried Beach.

(vi) A further fall of sea-level, possibly followed by a slight rise, resulting in the formation of the Low Buried Beach about 8800 years ago.

(vii) A renewed fall of sea-level.

The major postglacial transgression

We have seen that, with the abandonment of the Low Buried Beach, the sea in the vicinity of the Menteith moraine was restricted to a long relatively-narrow estuary (Fig. 76). The peat resting on the Low Buried Beach shows that the sea fell sufficiently for this beach to become forested with trees such as alder and birch, for the middle part of this peat contains numerous branches, trunks and pollen of these trees. The upper part of the peat shows a return to the wet conditions that characterise its basal part and contains abundant flattened stems of reeds. Upwards the peat contains more and more clay, and *Chenopod* pollen and that of *Plantago maritima* become common as the peat gradually merges into the thick deposit of carse clay that overlies it (Newey 1966). An early phase in the rise of sea-level that drowned the ancient forest and resulted in the widespread deposition of carse clay is thus recorded. A radiocarbon date at the very top of the peat layer has given an age of about 8300 years. Comparing this with the date of about 8700 years for the base of the same peat layer, it appears that the time of lowest sea-level immediately preceding the major transgression during which the carse clay began to accumulate was probably very close to 8500 years ago.

At a few places close to the old estuary of the Forth shown in Fig. 76 the buried peat bed contains numerous layers of brownish-yellow sand – in one section thirty were counted – which closely resembles the sand that today veneers the banks of the Forth and is laid down during floods. We may therefore imagine the river, as the sea-level rose, repeatedly overflowing its banks onto the surrounding peat wastes with their dying trees. One flood appears to have been particularly extensive, for one sand layer an inch or two thick has been traced in a series of boreholes for more than a quarter of a mile from the old estuary.

As the sea continued to rise and the estuary to grow wider so the Main Buried Beach with its cover of peat was in turn interred by the muddy carse. In two areas, however, this did not happen. In these areas, each of which is roughly a mile across (Fig. 76), the carse clay is quite absent and thick peat occurs instead. The present land surface around each of these areas is mostly peat and comprises the large bogs known as West and East Flanders Moss, each of which covers several square miles. The present extent of these mosses is artificial, for they represent the remains of much larger peat wastes that have been cleared by man through the centuries revealing the carse clay beneath. In part the present reduced mosses rest on the carse clay, but in the two areas mentioned the peat is much thicker, sometimes exceeding 25 feet, and rests directly on the Main Buried Beach. A typical section through the mosses is shown in Fig. 80, wherein it will be seen that the layer of carse clay gradually tapers out. Towards the point where the clay finally disappears it contains great quantities of reeds, which merge into the peat above and below (Sissons and Smith 1965b).

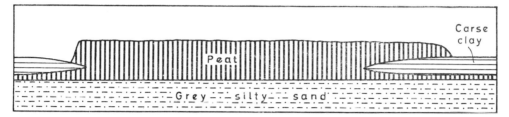

FIG. 80. Typical section through one of the peat bogs that continued to accumulate on the Main Buried Beach as the carse clay was being deposited.

It is clear from Fig. 80 that the peat of the deep parts of the mosses accumulated at the same time as the surrounding carse clay was being laid down. At first the waters of the estuary gradually encroached on the developing peat, their maximal extension being recorded by the apices of the wedges of carse clay. Thereafter the peat gained the upper hand, and the estuarine waters were gradually pushed back as the area of peat growth extended at the expense of the still-accumulating carse clay. We can therefore form a clear picture of the conditions at this time in the Carse of Stirling. At times of highest tides the whole area that is today the carse plain, 15 miles long by 3 to 4 wide, was covered by the sea, shallow for the most part, but deepening somewhat towards the Stirling gap where the rapid ebb and flow of the tide were less favourable for the accumulation of fine sediments. Rising above the waters of the estuary were one or two rock islands near Stirling, the Menteith morainic ridge system along with the tops of a few eskers within it, and the two accumulating mosses. The surfaces of the latter probably stood no more than a foot or two above the surrounding sea and were encircled by a thick belt of reeds. With each semi-diurnal fall of the tide most of the carse plain was exposed as broad mudflats on which, from time to time, whales were left stranded, perhaps to be utilised in some instances by Mesolithic man. The surface of the mudflats was interrupted by channels, particularly that of the Forth, and it is likely that many of the present stream courses, including the peculiar meanders of the Forth itself west of its junction with the Teith, are the direct descendants of these mudflat channels.

It may well be wondered how the two anomalous peat bogs managed to withstand the inundations of the sea when elsewhere (except for a few very small areas at the margins of the carselands) the peat was completely buried beneath the carse clay. It seems likely that a combination of favourable circumstances was responsible. Each of the deep mosses rests on the Main Buried Raised Beach in an area where that feature is particularly flat and extensive. Consequently, peat growth was facilitated, and by the time the carse sea encroached on the area the peat had already accumulated to considerable depth. A second point is that the mudflats would be covered by the sea for only a short time at high spring tides and perhaps not at all during high neap tides. A further consideration is that in the Forth valley it was the western part that underwent most rapid isostatic uplift, and it was therefore in this area that the rising postglacial sea would transgress most slowly onto the buried beaches and their overlying peat.

The culmination of the rise of sea-level associated with the widespread deposition of carse muds is represented in much of the low ground west of Stirling by the surface of the present carse plain. The margin of the western part of this plain where it abuts against the surrounding higher ground, marks the shoreline of this sea and records approximately the highest marine level of postglacial times. In view of this and the widespread nature of the deposits of this phase we may refer to the shoreline as the Main Postglacial Shoreline. At the western end of the Carse of Stirling, near the village of Gartmore, the shoreline reaches its maximal altitude of 49 feet above present sea-level, and from here it slopes gently down the Forth valley with an average gradient of 0·4 feet a mile. By the time Stirling is reached it has declined to 42 feet. Southeastwards from here for most of the way to Falkirk there exists a broad expanse of carseland that lies at about or a little below 40 feet except where shallow depressions caused by mining subsidence have lowered it a few feet. Remnants of formerly-extensive peat bogs overlie the carse clay and disrupt the continuity of the fertile farmlands. The transgressive nature of the sea is recorded by the penetration of the muddy deposits along the floors of many small valleys, which had previously been excavated by rivers in response to the lower sea-level of earlier times. In the sheltered inner recesses of some of these valleys the buried peat managed to keep pace with the accumulating clays in the same manner as in the two Flanders Moss areas. The largest valley up which the transgressive sea penetrated was that of the Carron, where the clay it deposited, owing to subsequent dissection by the river, now forms an almost horizontal terrace, contrasting with the gravel river terraces both above and below it that slope down the Carron valley in the normal manner of river terraces. Farther east, in Leith, as described a century ago by the elder Hugh Miller, the sea laid down its fine deposits to an altitude slightly exceeding 30 feet in the lower reaches of the valley of the Water of Leith. East again, near Aberlady, a former bay contains an almost flat expanse of carse clay that rises at its margins to 25 feet, while in the former estuary of the Tyne the same feature is represented by a distinctive terrace that lies at only 20 feet. On the north side of the Forth the carse clay penetrates several miles up the Devon valley. In the Tay region it extends likewise up the valley of the Earn, the shoreline here attaining 36 feet. At the margin of the extensive flat stretch around Bridge of Earn crossed by the A90 road the limit is 33-34 feet. Almost the whole of the Carse of Gowrie (*sensu stricto*) belongs to the Main Postglacial Beach, the upper margin having declined to 28-29 feet by the time Dundee is reached. Still farther east, carse clay was deposited in a former extension of the sea up the valley of the River Eden, the upper limit here being only 26 feet.

On the less sheltered parts of the coastline deposits of sand and gravel often record the maximal extension of the postglacial sea. Sometimes, as along the southern shores of the Forth from the Road Bridge to near Grangemouth, there is merely a veneer of these deposits resting against a steep slope. In other places a distinct raised beach step of sand and gravel occurs, as on parts of the East Fife coast. Considerable erosion of solid rock, represented by elevated marine platforms and old cliff lines, is also evident along some stretches of the coast, although much of this erosion was not achieved by the postglacial sea (Chapter 11). Ridges of sand and gravel cast up by the waves occur here and there and are particularly prominent on part of the East Lothian coast north of Dunbar.

As the sea-level began to fall following the deposition of the Main Postglacial Beach, peat began to accumulate widely on the ill-drained surface of the carse clay in the western

PLATE XXIII. A. Terraces of frost debris, Fannich Mountains, Ross-shire. *Geological Survey photograph. Crown Copyright reserved.* B. Tors in the Cairngorms. *Photograph by R. B. King.*

PLATE XXIV. A. Gullied slopes by Ben Nevis. B. The Bar, near Nairn.
Ministry of Defence (Air Force Department) photograph. Crown Copyright reserved.

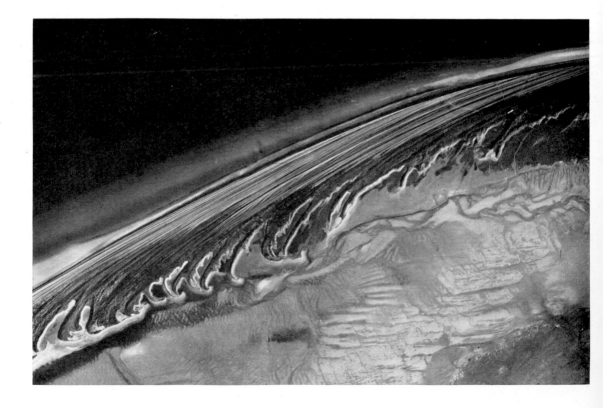

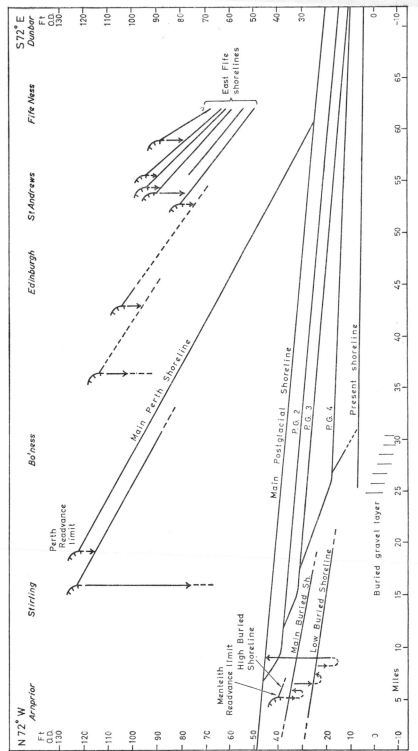

FIG. 81. The shoreline sequence in Southeast Scotland. After J. B. Sissons *et al.* 1966.

part of the Forth valley. A sample from 4 to 5 inches above the base of this peat in East Flanders Moss has given a radiocarbon age of about 5500 years (Godwin and Willis 1962). We can therefore regard the Main Postglacial Beach as around five and a half thousands years old in this area. The beach may well be slightly younger eastwards down the Forth valley, for the western part would have been raised above the reach of the sea earlier owing to more rapid isostatic recovery there. The average thickness of the peat that still remains, as in Flanders, Ochtertyre, Killorn, Dunmore and Letham mosses is usually between 10 and 20 feet, although it is less where artificial drainage has been introduced. Whether or not a layer of peat once covered the postglacial clay of the Carse of Gowrie is uncertain: there appear to be no remains of such a former cover at the present time and the historical evidence seems inconclusive. It is clear, however, that the surface of the carse clay in both the Forth and Tay valleys was, for the most part, badly drained and dotted with shallow pools of water until the agricultural improvements of the late eighteenth century.

As the peat wastes of the Forth valley slowly grew in thickness, so the level of the sea relative to the land gradually moved down towards its present level. This movement was not continuous, however, for below the level of the Main Postglacial Raised Beach occur three other steps indicating halts in the emergence or temporary reversals of the general trend. These lower beaches are best developed in the Forth valley in the carselands between Grangemouth and Stirling and extending thereafter for a few miles west of Stirling. In appearance they are like the Main Postglacial Beach of this area, forming almost flat clay plains. Their differentiation from each other and from the Main Beach is sometimes demonstrated by a small but distinct bluff a few feet high. Often, however, the separation into different levels is not evident until accurate altitude measurements are undertaken.

The altitudes of the four postglacial shorelines are shown in Fig. 81, where it can be seen that below the Main Shoreline are two others with almost the same gradient. The second shoreline is five to six feet below the main one and the third is four to five feet lower still. This third shoreline is probably about 4000 years old, for the base of the peat resting on the faint slope that separates it from the second shoreline has been radiocarbon-dated as about 4100 years old. The age of the fourth postglacial shoreline is not yet known, but since it is only a few feet above present high-water mark it is presumably much younger than the third one.

The fourth shoreline, owing to its gentle gradient of 0·17 feet a mile, becomes separated by a smaller and smaller vertical interval from the other postglacial shorelines towards the east. For comparison the altitude of the margin of the modern mudflats is represented by the lowest line in Fig. 81, which falls from 6½ feet near Grangemouth to 4½ feet near Dunbar. This gentle descent reflects tidal influences, for high spring tides are about 1·6 feet higher at Grangemouth than at Dunbar. This means that, assuming past tides had a similar variation to present ones, the amount of isostatic tilting of the shorelines is very slightly less than Fig. 81 suggests. For all shorelines except the very lowest one this factor is negligible. For the lowest one, however, owing to its slight gradient, the tidal factor becomes significant and, if taken into account, reduces the isostatic slope of this shoreline to 0·12 feet a mile.

The shoreline sequence and some implications

The pattern of raised shorelines in Southeast Scotland described in the preceding pages permits various inferences to be made concerning the patterns and causes of land and sea-level changes in this region. In Fig. 82 changes of sea-level relative to the land during the last 10 000 years or so are represented by a continuous curve. Since all the raised shorelines are tilted, a diagram of this type has to be drawn for a particular location in order to allow absolute altitudes to be entered on it. In Fig. 82 a locality immediately east of the Menteith moraine has been used since detailed height information is available here for several shorelines. The heights of shorelines that do not penetrate this far west are derived by calculation from their gradients farther east.

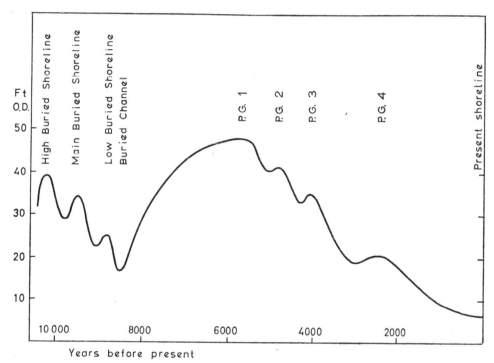

FIG. 82. Sea-level changes relative to the land during the last 10 000 years at a point immediately east of the Menteith moraine.

Inferences concerning changes in the relative levels of land and sea can be made from Fig. 74, which shows the six East Fife shorelines. The total distance the ice margin retreated while these shorelines were being formed was only 10 to 15 miles, from which it seems probable that the group of six shorelines was produced in a relatively short period of time: certainly this period of time is short when compared with the time span represented by the whole shoreline sequence of Fig. 81. Yet the first East Fife shoreline has a gradient more than twice that of the last one (6·7 as opposed to 3·2 feet a mile). This implies that half the total isostatic tilting that this area has suffered since the first shoreline was formed took place in the short space of time during which the area was freed from its cover of glacier ice. In other words, it appears that initial isostatic recovery was immediate and rapid.

Another point worthy of note is the total amount of uplift the East Fife area has undergone since the group of lateglacial shorelines was formed. These shorelines attain altitudes of 80 to 100 feet above present sea-level at their western ends. Yet we may estimate from Fairbridge's graph that when they were formed world sea-level was some 200 or more feet below its present level. Thus the shorelines at their western ends must have been elevated not only the 80 to 100 feet that they are now situated above present sea-level, but a further 200 feet or more to keep them out of reach of the eustatically-rising sea-level. These figures may seem large, yet East Fife is in the least isostatically elevated part of Southeast Scotland, for all the shorelines of the area rise westwards, indicating much greater elevation in that direction.

A rough estimate can be made of the amount of the uplift farther west. The raised shoreline data for Southeast Scotland and the available data for other parts of the country indicate that the centre of isostatic recovery was situated in the Southwest Grampians. If we assume a centre situated 70 miles from the group of East Fife shorelines we may argue that, since the steepest shoreline has a gradient of 6·7 feet a mile, its projected altitude at the centre of isostatic recovery would be about 450 feet higher than its actual altitude in East Fife. Since East Fife appears to have been elevated some 300 feet or more, we can suggest that at the centre of isostatic recovery some 750 feet of uplift has occurred since East Fife began to be deglaciated. The total amount of uplift at the centre of recovery is probably even greater, for we have no means of estimating the uplift that occurred before the first raised shoreline was formed.

The rapid initial isostatic recovery demonstrated by the East Fife evidence is also indicated by the shorelines associated with the Perth Readvance in the Tay, Earn, Forth and Carron valleys. It is most strikingly displayed in the Forth valley, where there is a drop in the level of the highest marine features of some 50 feet in a couple of miles as one passes from east to west through the Stirling gap (p. 150). This rapid drop of relative sea-level implies at least 50 feet of isostatic uplift while the ice margin still stood close to the Stirling gap. This figure is minimal, however, because it is highly probable that, at the time that extensive glacier decay was taking place in Scotland after the Perth Readvance, rapid glacier wastage was taking place in many other parts of the world also. Hence the figure of 50 feet represents the relative rise of the land: the actual amount of land uplift was greater than this figure by the amount that world sea-level rose at this time.

Rapid land uplift as ice wasted away can be demonstrated at other localities in Southeast Scotland besides those described and it appears that this was the normal occurrence. In Fig. 81 the vertical arrows give an indication of the minimal amount of this movement, for they show the relative lowering of sea-level in various places as the ice margin withdrew. This repetitive pattern leads us to pose the following question: if, as the ice withdrew, there was an initial immediate and rapid rise of the land, is it not possible that at a time when glaciers were advancing there was a similar rapid depression of the land? In particular, one may ask: when a glacial readvance occurred, did the weight of the ice cause a renewed downwarping of the earth's crust? The evidence in Southeast Scotland suggests, in fact, that it did. It is generally believed that major glacier readvances were synchronous in many parts of the world and now that more and more radiocarbon dates are becoming available this assumption is being confirmed. If we accept such synchroneity, then, at a time when glaciers were building up and their margins readvancing in Scotland, world sea-level would be falling. If we accept also the usual view that isostatic uplift is continuous, then, relative to Scotland, sea-level would be falling due also to this cause. Therefore, by the time the ice had readvanced to its maximal extent, sea-level in relation to the land would be at a particularly low level. Yet, as we have seen, the shorelines associated with the Perth Readvance do not display this characteristic at all, for, between Falkirk and Stirling, their altitude is such that they form the highest raised shorelines in the whole of Southeast Scotland. At the time of the Menteith Readvance sea-level relative to the land was much lower, but again the evidence is not what one would anticipate in terms of continuous isostatic uplift, for the sea-level associated with this readvance appears to have been preceded and followed by lower sea-levels. Thus we are forced to the conclusion that the isostatic recovery of Scotland was not a continuous process but was interrupted by periods of renewed downwarping when major readvances occurred.

While emphasis has so far been laid on the rapid and immediate response of the earth's crust to glacial loading and unloading, it must be made clear that isostatic recovery continued long after complete deglaciation, even though at a much diminished rate. The diminishing rate of uplift is in part reflected in the tilting of the shorelines. For example, the Main Buried Shoreline formed about 9500 years ago has an average gradient of 0·8 feet a mile, while the Main Postglacial Shoreline formed about 5500 years ago has an average gradient of 0·4 feet a mile. This gives an average rate of tilting for the intervening period of 0·10 feet a mile a thousand years. If we compare the slope of the Main Postglacial Shoreline with that of the present shoreline (sloping at 0·05 feet a mile owing to the tidal factor) we obtain a rate of tilting of 0·06 feet a mile a thousand years. These rates of tilting cover rather long periods of time and probably conceal a regular decrease.

Although the pattern of warping in Southeast Scotland is clearly linked intimately with glacial loading and unloading of the earth's crust, one cannot be certain that a minor element of this warping is not a result of some other cause. The most likely cause is the downwarping of the North Sea area and certain adjacent land areas. Such movements have been in progress during the last 250 million years and are reflected over a considerable part of England by the general eastward dip of the rocks of Permian and later age. This tilting is very slow indeed compared with the crustal movements caused by the weight of glacier ice. If it has had any influence on the shoreline gradients of Southeast Scotland this is likely to be proportionately most significant in the case of the most gently inclined ones. It is possible that the most recent tilting is not due directly to glacial unloading but relates to the long period warping of the North Sea area. However, until detailed information is available on the altitudes of raised shorelines in Scotland as a whole, we cannot attempt to assess the relative importance of these two factors. One point that is clear about the warping of Southeast Scotland, however, is that, so far as we can tell, it has produced an almost uniform tilting towards the east or slightly south of east from the time ice first began to withdraw from East Fife up to the present day. This is shown by the uniform gradients of the shorelines, the only exception being the very slight increase in gradient towards the western ends of some shorelines, an increase that does not necessarily indicate differential tilting.

The regular gradients of the various shorelines largely eliminate another possible complication in the pattern of uplift, namely, faulting. This is particularly interesting because the Ochil fault system, which follows the southern side of the Ochil Hills and the northern side of the Gargunnock Hills, is one of the three most active faults in Scotland today, the other two being the Highland Boundary fault and the Great Glen fault. A. T. J. Dollar (1950) found that, of 120 earthquakes that took place in Scotland between 1916 and 1949, 30 were associated with the Ochil fault. These earthquakes are minute compared with those that occur from time to time in countries like Japan or Chile, but one might expect that the cumulative effect of movements over periods of thousands of years would be demonstrated by displacements of the raised shorelines where they cross the fault. Although such evidence has been sought for, no proof of dislocation has been detected, for the various shorelines as far back as the Main Buried Shoreline formed 9500 years ago appear to be inclined as uniformly in the vicinity of the fault system as elsewhere. Very small displacements of the shorelines of, say, a foot or so, cannot be detected by the methods used, so that this is the greatest movement we can allow along the Ochil fault system in the last nine and a half thousand years.

Before leaving the raised beaches of Southeast Scotland to turn to those of the rest of the country, we may note one further aspect of Fig. 81, namely, the intersection of shorelines. All the lateglacial shorelines between East Fife and Stirling slope down towards the postglacial shorelines. This means that, not only is each lateglacial shoreline absent west of a certain point because of the presence of glacier ice when it was being formed, but each disappears beneath later deposits east of a certain point. We may expect this relationship to apply in other parts of Scotland, so that there should be a belt of country surrounding the centre of isostatic uplift in which any particular shoreline may be expected to be visible. Another interesting relationship is displayed by the East Fife group of shorelines. It will be appreciated from Figs 74 and 81 that if these six shorelines are projected eastwards without change of gradient they soon begin to intersect each other. About fifteen miles east of Fife Ness the lowest shoreline would become the highest of the series. This implies that, at the same time as the actual East Fife shorelines were being formed in response to a fall of sea-level relative to the land, fifteen and more miles to the east a relative rise of sea-level was taking place. Now in the case of East Fife these relationships are theoretical in that the area to the east is beneath the waters of the North Sea. However, it seems quite likely that the equivalents of these shorelines begin to intersect in East Lothian near Dunbar, for here there occurs a very confused series of lateglacial shorelines that has not so far been resolved. Furthermore, in other parts of Scotland, where present coastlines do not inconveniently cut off the evidence, it seems likely that the part of the pattern that has had to be inferred in the case of East Fife may well be preserved and available for study.

The crossing of shorelines is not the prerogative of the lateglacial sequence in Southeast Scotland, for it is evident in Fig. 81 that the lowest postglacial shoreline will intersect the next higher one not far from Dunbar. One might therefore expect that, in those parts of Scotland farther removed from the centre of isostatic uplift than is Dunbar, one would find only three postglacial shorelines, the third one of the Southeast Scotland sequence having been buried by the deposits associated with the lowest. Still farther from the isostatic centre other relationships may be expected. The buried shorelines of Fig. 81 will clearly not intersect the visible postglacial shorelines however far they are projected eastwards. Whether or not the Main Buried Beach emerges from beneath the Main Postglacial Beach in the vicinity of the centre of isostatic recovery is uncertain, but it appears a possibility. A further point about the buried raised beaches is that their eastward rate of descent, as shown in Fig. 81, will carry them below present sea-level before Edinburgh is reached (buried peat has in fact been found at about present sea-level in boreholes in the northern part of the city). The same relationship is true for the lateglacial shorelines, for each passes below present sea-level if its slope is projected eastwards. Thus, in terms of a particular shoreline, the net result of land and sea-level changes has been elevation west of the point where present sea-level is crossed and depression east of this point. Thus raised beaches in the more central parts of Scotland

may be equated in the more peripheral areas with buried and submerged shorelines and
with buried valleys cut down to past sea-levels lower than the present one.

Rather than discuss further what may happen in the rest of Scotland we must at this
point turn to the actual evidence. No apology is offered for having dwelt so long on the
Southeast Scotland story for, unfortunately, the former sea-levels of other parts of the
country have not as yet been studied in similar detail. We shall be obliged, therefore, from
time to time, to make analogies with the Forth and Tay region in order to try and inter-
pret the story in the rest of the country. While this approach can clearly be objected to
and may lead to misinterpretation, there is no other course available at the present time.
It is to be hoped that in the not too distant future this gap in our knowledge will be
remedied, and one looks forward to the time when it will be possible to draw isobase
maps for the whole country for each of several shorelines, to show the relationships of
each of the lateglacial shorelines to former ice-limits, and to plot the successive changes
of land, sea and ice distributions in terms of a chronology based on large numbers of
radiocarbon dates.

11

Changing sea-levels
in Scotland as a whole

MOST of the evidence in Scotland that demonstrates changes in the relative levels of land and sea is associated with the period since the last ice-sheet reached its maximal extent. However, in addition to this lateglacial and postglacial evidence, with which we have been concerned so far, there are in many parts of coastal Scotland, distinctly older marine features that are almost entirely erosional. It can be shown that many of these older features have been overwhelmed by glacier ice since they were formed. With some other features this has not been demonstrated, but there are good reasons for believing that they too are of considerable antiquity.

Ancient rock platforms and cliffs

The most remarkable elevated marine features of Scotland occur in parts of the Inner Hebrides, where they often comprise broad abrasion platforms and conspicuous cliffs standing well above present sea-level (Wright 1911, Bailey *et al.* 1924, McCann 1964). These features are strikingly developed on certain west-facing coasts, as in Islay, Jura and Mull where the platform, rising gently landwards, ranges up to half a mile in width and is backed by a cliff that occasionally attains a height of almost 300 feet (Plate XXB). The platform is cut across a variety of rocks, including lavas, quartzites, schists and gneisses. Often the rocks are abruptly truncated regardless of their dip. In some localities, as in parts of western Mull, the platform is influenced by the gently-dipping layers of lava and interbedded slag, and comprises a series of gently-inclined planes separated by steeper slopes. On smaller islands, such as Colonsay, Oronsay and the Treshnish Islands, the platform, backed by a cliff, is widely developed on all sides. The distribution of the features on Colonsay shows that at the time they were formed this island comprised a group of smaller islands separated by narrow straits. The Bac Mor, one of the Treshnish Islands, is commonly known as the Dutchman's Cap: here the platform comprises more than two-thirds of the island and surrounds a steep-sided central hill that rises nearly 200 feet above it.

The rock platform is overlain by raised beach gravels in certain areas, most notably by the shingle spreads of western Jura and Islay (p. 201). These accumulations are much younger than the platform, however, and the seas that deposited them appear to have had little effect on it. This age difference is demonstrated in places by the presence of glacial till between the beach gravels and the underlying platform. The till, which sometimes overlies considerable areas of the platform, as in Colonsay, also proves that the platform has

190

been overridden by ice since it was formed. The passage of ice is further demonstrated by striae and especially by the strongly-marked ice-moulding that is frequently observable. The ancient cliff, too, has been modified by ice in places and its outline rendered more subdued. It may seem somewhat surprising that, despite such modifications, a feature so clear as that shown in Plate XXB should have survived overriding by glacier ice. It is likely, however, that the preservation of this and certain other similar features was favoured by the protective influence exerted by high ground to the east. Furthermore, it is reasonable to assume that the ancient coastal features were originally most extensively and clearly developed on coasts exposed to strong wave attack from the west, so that their optimal development in such locations need not occasion surprise. We have, after all, no means of gauging the extensive destruction of such features that may well have been wrought by the ice in areas where they do not now exist.

The altitude of the old shoreline has been measured approximately at a considerable number of points, especially by W. B. Wright. In Islay and Jura the altitude is about 100 to 110 feet, in the Treshnish Islands 85 to over 100 feet, in Colonsay 140 feet, and in Mull 100 to 160 feet. In the island of Ulva, adjacent to Mull, the floor of a sea cave covered with till containing a variety of erratics is situated at about 150 feet above sea-level, while on the mainland coast at Kilchoan in Ardnamurchan a conspicuous rock notch occurs at 145 feet. These measurements show that the old shoreline has a range of altitude far too large to be explained merely by variations in marine erosion as influenced by rock type and exposure, so that it seems we must conclude that the feature has been distorted by earth movements.

Features caused by marine erosion at altitudes well above present sea-level have been noted at various other points along the coastline of Scotland. An old platform occurs on part of the coast of Raasay, and on the near-by mainland coast north of Applecross a platform backed by a degraded cliff is partly covered by till and bears evidence of glacial smoothing. The old shoreline is here at about 85 feet above sea-level (McCann 1961b).

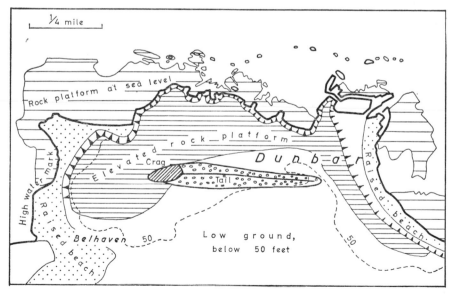

FIG. 83. Elevated marine platform with island, the latter now forming the 'crag' of a crag-and-tail.

On the opposite side of the country, on the coast of Northeast Scotland, till-covered platforms seem to be present at various points and one is clearly identifiable beneath glacial deposits in the Stonehaven area at about 75 feet. Farther south on the east coast a platform between about 60 and 80 feet above sea-level is well developed in or near North Berwick, Dunbar, Eyemouth and Berwick. It is seen very clearly from the railway a short distance north of Berwick and is particularly striking at Dunbar, a considerable part of the town being built on it. A short distance west of the town centre the platform cuts clean across a volcanic neck and rises gently inland to a craggy knoll that was clearly an island in the ancient sea. A perfectly-formed tail of till declines eastwards from this ancient island and passes below the level of the platform on its inland side where the ground is relatively low (Fig. 83). It is thus evident that the area has been glaciated since the platform was cut, for, had the delicate tail of glacial drift been formed first, it would certainly have been destroyed during the considerable period required for the production of the extensive rock platform.

At distinctly lower levels around many parts of the coast of Scotland there occur the elevated cliffs, abrasion platforms, stacks and caves that are often closely associated with the upper limit of the sea in postglacial times (Plates XVII and XVIIIb). The clarity and freshness of many of these features have already been mentioned, and it appears that the postglacial seas were in some instances at least partly responsible for them. We cannot assume, however, that these seas were entirely responsible (McCallien 1937). The amount of marine erosion represented by this platform far exceeds in many localities the erosion that has taken place along the modern shore. This was neatly demonstrated for a specific point by James Smith as long ago as 1838. He made measurements in the Clyde area of one of the many igneous dykes that stand up from the present shore as well as from the old platform. He found that the sandstone on either side of the dyke had been cut back only 13 feet more than the dyke to produce the present small cliff, but that it had been cut back 208 feet to produce the old elevated cliff. He therefore justifiably argued that at this point the elevated features represent at least 16 times as much erosion as the features of the present shore. This, and similar evidence that might be cited from many points on the coast of Scotland, implies that at some time in the past the sea stood at a fairly constant level for a very considerable period. Yet, as we have seen, the relative levels of land and sea have varied so much in lateglacial and postglacial times that it is very difficult to see how the elevated platform and cliff could have been cut either during or since the disappearance of the last ice-sheet.

The problem may be approached by referring to evidence in other parts of Britain. An ancient platform and cliff with a shoreline between about 10 and 25 feet above sea-level have been identified along many stretches of the coasts of England, Wales and Ireland. In all three countries the antiquity of the platform is proved by overlying glacial drift. The situation in Ireland is particularly relevant. Here N. Stephens (1957) pointed out that the rock platform that occurs intermittently along the length of the east coast shows no discernible tilt. The postglacial raised beach deposits, which overlie the platform in the more northern areas, are tilted, however. Thus, although the postglacial deposits rest on the rock platform in Northeast Ireland, the essential independence of the two is demonstrated, an important point that is also proved by the glacial deposits that rest on the platform in places. Now it is less than fifteen miles from Antrim to Kintyre, the nearest part of Scotland, and here rock-cut features at approximately the same altitude as in Antrim are strongly developed. In southern Kintyre the raised platform is often backed by a line of cliffs, in which may be seen chasms hewn out along the joints to depths of 40 or 50 feet, and caves up to 130 feet long and 40 feet high cut in such resistant rocks as porphyry and conglomerate. It is difficult to imagine these striking features having been formed during or since the disappearance of the last ice-sheet, and equally difficult to believe that they are not the Scottish continuation of the features that Stephens has identified along the east coast of Ireland. If this correlation be adopted in Kintyre, then there seems no reason why the extensive rock-cut features often associated with the postglacial raised beach deposits in other parts of Scotland should not be part of the same set of phenomena.

This interpretation is strongly favoured by evidence from various parts of the country. For example, at two places on the coast of Hoy in the Orkneys a cemented gravel up to 15 feet thick and containing numerous rounded boulders and stones occurs between 20 and 40 feet above sea-level (Wilson *et al.* 1935). The gravel rests on a well-defined rock platform cut into the hill side. Since the lateglacial and postglacial raised beaches of the Scottish mainland pass below sea-level before they reach the Orkneys, the gravel and platform must have been formed at a much earlier time. A rock platform at around 10 to 20 feet above sea-level occurs in the isolated island of North Rona situated some 45 miles northwest of Cape Wrath (Gailey 1959). As in the Orkneys, it seems unlikely that a platform in this distant island relates to any of the isostatically-tilted raised beaches of the mainland. J. Geikie (1878) mentioned that in Harris and Lewis, as well as in adjacent islands, rock features no more than a dozen or so feet above sea-level occur at various points. His statement that none have beach deposits enhances the probability that they pre-date the last ice-cover. A low-level rock platform also occurs in Colonsay and Oronsay and includes a considerable part of the glaciated low ground in the latter island as well as the ice-worn skerries off-shore. Although W. B. Wright (1911), who described this feature, expressed doubts as to its significance, he was more convinced by the evidence on the shores of the sound separating Iona from Mull. Here a low-level rock platform is overlain by postglacial raised beach gravels. It is clear, however, that the postglacial sea did not cut the platform, for there is no cliff at the back of it at all equivalent in magnitude to the extent of the shelf, but instead a rounded ice-worn slope. It therefore seems that the rock platform is older than the last ice-cover of this area. This interpretation is now further strengthened, for F. M. Synge and N. Stephens (1966) refer to glacial striae on the platform in other parts of Mull, while S. B. McCann (1966b) has observed ice-moulding and striae on the platform in Mull and Lismore. On the opposite side of the country, in Northeast Scotland, the antiquity of a wave-cut platform is well established, for K. Walton (1959) has described a feature at about 30 feet above sea-level that has been partly exhumed from beneath a cover of glacial drift. There is also a brief reference to similar evidence in Kintyre where W. Sinclair (1913) referred to rock stacks that are almost entirely covered by till, while others are nearly bared. Finally we may cite evidence from St Andrews described to the author by R. A. Cullingford. The rock cliff that forms the Fife coast for some distance east of St Andrews swings inland in the city, and between it and the sea are interposed thick deposits of drift including glacial outwash and lateglacial and postglacial raised beach deposits. A considerable number of commercial boreholes put down through these materials shows that the whole series rests on a rock platform that slopes gently seawards. The buried platform and the backing cliff, which latter occasionally appears briefly from beneath the mantle of drift, thus pre-date the last ice-cover of the area.

There is thus a strong indication that the low-level rock-cut features of Scotland are of considerable age. It will be noted, however, that the implied correlation of the platform remnants in various parts of the country as one feature is based essentially on their broad similarity of altitude, a method of correlation that has considerable limitations. Nevertheless it is quite clear that in many parts of coastal Scotland there exists a well-marked wave-cut platform with a shoreline between about 10 and a maximum of about 40 feet above sea-level, while in various parts of England, Wales and Ireland a platform is clearly preserved between about 10 and 25 feet. Although in these latter countries there is some difference of opinion as to the age of the platform, the majority view at present favours its formation during the last interglacial, so that we may tentatively suggest this age for the Scottish feature. In this event we might even more tentatively proceed a step further and suggest that the distinctly higher marine platform of parts of coastal Scotland was formed during the previous interglacial.

The indications of erosion of the Scottish coast by ancient seas are by no means restricted to elevated features, for it is clear that many coastal features that at first sight may be assumed to have been recently produced by the sea acting at its present level are essentially much older. This is not meant to imply that the sea today is totally ineffective as an agent of erosion: in fact, the Scottish coast has provided some remarkable instances of the achievements of storm waves. For example, on parts of the west coast of the Orkneys waves have thrown up mounds 15 feet high and tens of yards long composed of slabs of Old Red sandstone, that are to be found on cliff tops as much as 60 feet above sea-level. On the Bound Skerry in the Shetlands blocks of stone from 6 to 13 tons in weight have been dislodged at an elevation of 70 to 75 feet above the sea. The windows of Dunnet Head lighthouse, which are over 300 feet above the sea, have sometimes been broken by stones swept up the cliff by waves. At Wick harbour in 1872 a massive block of 1350 tons weight, that was intended as a protection for the seaward end of the breakwater, was torn from its place and dropped inside the pier. The block was replaced by an even larger mass with a volume of 1500 cubic yards and a weight of 2600 tons, but in 1877 waves disposed of this also. Such feats can leave us in no doubt concerning the immense power of severe storm waves on coasts exposed to their attack. Nevertheless, it remains true that the erosion of rocky coasts often appears to be extremely slow and in many places the main rock features appear to owe little to recent attack by the sea. Along the coast of Northwest Scotland glacially-smoothed Lewisian rocks often pass beneath the waters of the sea. J. A. Steers (1952) was impressed by the limited evidence of marine erosion in the Inner Hebrides and he observed that along much of the coast of Rhum the cliffs are unmodified by recent waves and are covered with scree. In East Lothian on either side of North Berwick the base of the cliff is in places masked by vegetated wind-blown sand or even separated from the sea by a strip of dunes. One may add that the survival along many parts of the Scottish coast of the low-level rock platform described already in this chapter is in itself evidence of the limited nature of later marine erosion.

Even where cliffs descend vertically to the present shore one cannot automatically assume that they are the product of recent marine attack. This can often be demonstrated by following such a cliff along the coast, when it will be frequently found that in the more sheltered locations it disappears beneath a blanket of glacial deposits, to re-emerge farther along the coastline. The impression gained from such evidence is that in many coastal areas the cliffs were buried or partially buried in glacial deposits, and that since the ice disappeared the sea has done little more than exhume them from beneath the cover of drift. Such is the case in Northeast Scotland, where ancient cliffs, stacks and platforms have been denuded of their encasing drift by marine attack. In some instances the long narrow steep-sided inlets known as goes are still partly filled with glacial drift, showing that the sea has not yet completed its task of re-excavation. The same sort of evidence is found in Caithness where, as in many other areas, the height of many of the cliffs is in itself an argument against their having been produced in the limited time available since the dissipation of the last glacier ice. Cliffs of till are present in Thurso Bay, Gills Bay and at Dunbeath, while glacial drift in many of the goes shows that they already existed before the last glaciation.

The evidence we have so far considered is almost entirely erosional and at present no confirmatory depositional evidence of the apparent pattern of events is available. There are elevated marine deposits of some antiquity in certain scattered parts of Scotland, but these are of no direct assistance and, in fact, present their own problems. These deposits, which are concealed beneath glacial drift, were discovered last century and some of them caused a great deal of controversy.

Marine deposits covered by glacial drift

One of these old marine deposits occurs at various points in the northernmost part of Lewis and is well exposed in the lower part of a cliff section on the west coast near The Butt, where it appears to be *in situ*. Here there is a three-fold sequence comprising a lower till, a bed of stratified marine deposits composed of laminated clay, sand and gravel, and an upper till. All three layers contain marine shells, which have been studied particularly by D. F. W. Baden-Powell (1938). The ice-transported shells in the lower till are fragmentary and indicate a sea temperature rather similar to that of the present day. The overlying stratified deposits contain a mixture of cold and warm forms, but among the latter *Sipho jeffreysianus* is abundant. This is particularly significant since at the present time this shell is not found farther north than the southern parts of Britain. The upper till includes transported cold forms, such as *Astarte borealis*, that are not present in the layer beneath and suggest conditions comparable with those off northern Norway at the present day. The sequence of deposits thus points to considerable climatic variations. The shells in the lower till suggest that a climate somewhat similar to that of today existed before ice advanced across the area. The glacial advance was followed by a marked amelioration to conditions that appear to have been milder than those of the present. Finally there was another period of cold climate associated with the deposition of the upper till. The warm element in the fauna of the stratified beds suggests that these may well represent an interglacial deposit (as opposed to an interstadial one) and in this respect they are unique, for no other fossiliferous interglacial deposit has yet been identified in Scotland. This, together with their isolation, makes correlation with the sequence of glacial events in other parts of the country impracticable at present.

The most anomalous of the old deposits with marine fossils is one that occurs at Clava above five miles east of Inverness. This produced a great deal of heated discussion towards the end of last century and was investigated in detail by a committee of experts set up by the British Association for the Advancement of Science (Horne *et al.* 1893). Despite their careful work the members of the committee were unable to present a unanimous report on the main point at issue, namely, whether the deposit is *in situ* or has been transported to its present position by glacier ice. The controversial deposit is a bed of blue clay containing abundant marine organisms. The bed extends for at least 190 yards and has a thickness of 16 feet at the point where it was studied in detail, its upper surface here being just over 500 feet above sea-level. Overlying the marine bed is 20 feet of sand and above this some 40 to 50 feet of till, while beneath it about 35 feet of gravel, sand and till conceal the underlying Old Red sandstone bedrock (Fig. 84). The shells in the marine layer, which include *Littorina littorea, Natica groenlandica* and *Leda pernula,* indicate subarctic conditions. Many of the shells are intact and others partly crushed, but none striated. In view of the extent of the bed and the perfect condition of some of the shells the majority of the British Association committee considered the bed to be *in situ,* thus implying a marine submergence to 500 feet above present sea-level. The view of a

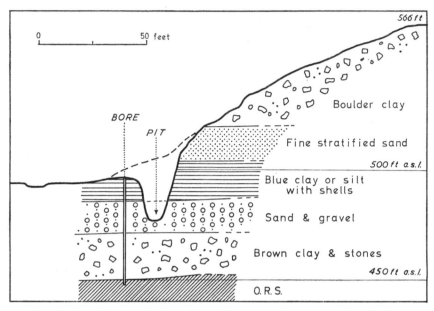

FIG. 84. Section through deposits at Clava, near Inverness. After J. Horne *et al.* 1893.

minority was that the mass of marine clay had been transported by glacier ice. Transport from a northerly point is suggested by the discovery of a piece of Jurassic grit in the clay, for the nearest known outcrop of the Jurassic rocks is situated twelve miles due north of Clava. Analyses of the stone content of the overlying till and underlying gravel show that it contains up to 76 per cent Old Red sandstone, which is not surprising since this rock crops out around Clava and in the area to the southwest. On the other hand, only 17 to 20 per cent of the stones found in the shelly clay are Old Red sandstone. Thus the Jurassic block, the small Old Red content, and the marine fossils themselves all suggest that the marine clay has been transported to the area as an erratic from a northerly point (at a time previous to the last great ice movement from southwest to northeast).

A third area where old marine deposits produced considerable discussion towards the end of last century lies on the west coast of Kintyre north of Machrihanish. These marine deposits appear to be *in situ* and were found in three small glens that lead down to the coast, being those of the Tangy and Drumore burns and of a stream near Cleongart. The first was studied by D. Robertson and H. W. Crosskey (1874), while the last was carefully investigated by the British Association committee (Horne *et al.* 1896) and shortly afterwards was further studied by two Scandinavian authorities (Munthe 1897, Jessen 1900). The marine clay at Tangy Glen is a dark grey laminated deposit at least 13 feet thick and covered by 50 feet or more of till. Shells are scarce, but they included a specimen of *Pecten groenlandicus,* a shell that is normally found only in the arctic clays of the east of Scotland. Micro-organisms are much more abundant (over 130 species of foraminifers were identified) and again there is much more resemblance to the arctic clays of the east than to the subarctic ones of the west. The deposit of clay was seen to stand up in the till as a knoll, strongly suggesting that it forms only the basal part of a formerly much thicker deposit of which the upper part was removed by the ice that laid down the till. This appears to be confirmed by studies of the deposits at Cleongart four miles to the north, where the clay is at least 27 feet thick. Again there is a thick cover of till, amounting to as much as 76 feet. It seems that the lower part of the Cleongart marine clay represents cold conditions, but in the middle part there is evidence of an amelioration of climate, for cold shells are mixed with temperate ones such as *Turritella terebra*, which becomes the most abundant shell. The top of the deposit shows a return to cold conditions. It thus appears that a sequence of climatic changes is recorded, and it may well be that a period of glacier decay is represented by the cold basal layers, an inter-stadial phase by the more temperate deposits, and a readvance of ice by the upper cold deposits, the overwhelming of the area by the ice itself being demonstrated by the thick layer of till that caps the sequence.

The earlier lateglacial sea-levels

In the description in Chapter 10 of sea-level changes in Southeast Scotland before the Perth Readvance, there emerged two broad elements in the pattern that we will now attempt to discern in the limited evidence available for the rest of Scotland. Firstly, we saw that in eastern Fife and the eastern part of East Lothian the upper limit of marine evidence (the *marine limit*) falls away quite rapidly eastwards. Secondly, farther west in the Forth valley the marine limit, although showing considerable local variations, does not vary greatly in altitude when viewed as a whole. Expressing this second point in another way, one may say that the western ends of several lateglacial shorelines where they merge into glacial outwash are not very dissimilar in altitude. Thus in order to locate other areas in Scotland with shoreline patterns similar to those that exist in Southeast Scotland to the east of the Perth Readvance limit, one must look for evidence (in terms of most of the published literature) of a horizontal '100-foot raised beach' followed, farther from the centre of isostatic recovery, by evidence of a sharp decline in the altitude of lateglacial raised beaches. There are strong indications that such a pattern exists in some parts of Scotland, although it is quite impossible at present to identify individual shorelines.

Since the marine limit begins to fall away quite rapidly in the east of East Lothian and of Fife, we might reasonably expect to find a similar pattern on the coast of Angus a short distance to the north. A hint that such a pattern exists is provided by J. Rice's descriptions of the area (1959, 1962). The highest raised beach is situated at approximately 100 feet above sea-level around Carnoustie, where marine shells have been found in it. That this sea existed while glacier ice was still in the vicinity is demonstrated in the Brothock valley at Arbroath and also in the Lunan valley, by kames and outwash deposits that descend as low as 65 feet above sea-level yet bear no sign of ever having been covered by the sea. It seems significant that Rice was able to trace the '100-foot beach' for only a short distance around Carnoustie. In the Lunan valley the highest marine deposits appear to lie at no more than 70 feet and farther north, near Montrose, the marine limit seems to be even lower. There thus appears to be a considerable decline in the marine limit northeastwards from Carnoustie. Unfortunately one cannot attempt to trace this pattern farther for the published evidence relating to the coast farther north past Aberdeen contains a variety of statements that are difficult to reconcile with each other. It does appear, however, that by the time the extreme northeast of Aberdeenshire is reached lateglacial raised beaches are absent.

Much of the north coast of Aberdeenshire and Banffshire comprises steep cliffs that preclude the existence of raised beaches. There are, however, various embayments and valleys in which raised beaches could have been preserved, yet the accounts of this coast contain only rare references to such features above the level of the postglacial beaches. Hence it seems that along much of this coast the lateglacial beaches are absent or at a low level. The situation is very different, however, westwards from around Elgin, for lateglacial beaches and fluvioglacial deposits are here abundant as far as the Beauly Firth. Much of Elgin is built on flattish-surfaced spreads of fluvioglacial sand and gravel that slightly exceed 100 feet above sea-level, and amongst which occur broad depressions passing down well below 100 feet. These materials represent the deposits of the River Lossie built out into the sea amidst the decaying ice. Farther west outwash spreads and raised beaches are common between altitudes of about 70 and 90 feet. Above the latter altitude beaches appear to be absent and kames and kettles occur unmodified by the sea, a particularly striking feature being the Fremlington esker system near Nairn, where some of the associated dead-ice hollows lie below the 100-foot contour. A similar pattern of well-developed raised beaches, often intimately associated with outwash spreads and other fluvioglacial features, characterises much of the coastal area between the outer parts of the Cromarty and Dornoch firths, and continues thence northwards from the Dornoch Firth to the vicinity of Brora. The Geological Survey memoirs and the account given by A. G. Ogilvie (1923) show that throughout the long coastal zone from the vicinity of Elgin to near Brora (but excluding the inner parts of the three major firths) raised beaches between altitudes of 70 and 95 feet are extremely common. In the Survey memoirs these are grouped together as the '100-foot beach', although this is sometimes qualified by the statement that the margin is at 80-90 feet. In all accounts the presence of an essentially horizontal feature is mentioned or implied. When we view this evidence in the light of the pattern of Southeast Scotland, however, it is clear that the existence of a horizontal lateglacial beach is extremely improbable. Furthermore, the relations of the marine features in the 70 to 95-foot range to fluvioglacial deposits show that the former are of various ages, being oldest in the more peripheral areas and youngest in the entrances to the three firths. Thus it appears that a whole series of lateglacial raised beaches is present in the Moray Firth area, each of which slopes down eastwards or northeastwards to pass below the next older in the series in the manner shown in Figs 69 and 81.

It seems likely that the outermost and most steeply inclined members of this series of beaches, comparable with the features in East Fife and the eastern part of East Lothian, lie to the east of Elgin. On the other side of the Moray Firth the comparable locality may well be about Brora. Northeastwards from here the marine limit falls away rapidly, and along the coast of Caithness which, though usually cliffed, has various re-entrants in which beaches could have survived, the lateglacial beaches are absent or at a very low level. They seem to have disappeared completely by the time the extreme northeast is reached and are absent from the Orkneys, where there are innumerable sheltered gently-sloping coasts that would have permitted their survival had they ever existed.

The lateglacial raised beaches of eastern Scotland so far described lie entirely, or almost entirely, between the limits of the Aberdeen–Lammermuir and Perth readvances as mapped in Fig. 59. They suggest that, as the ice wasted back from the earlier of these ice limits, the eustatically-rising sea-level at first overtook the isostatically-rising land, extending into present coastal areas. In the west of Scotland also a transgression into coastal areas is indicated by raised beaches at various places, but it cannot as yet be related to the glacier decay following the Aberdeen–Lammermuir Readvance, for the limit of this readvance is quite unknown in the west of the country. In the extreme north-west, towards Cape Wrath, lateglacial beaches are absent or at low altitudes. Southwards they gain in altitude, attaining between 40 and 50 feet in Enard Bay, and rising to about 60 feet near Ullapool (Kirk *et al.* 1966). From Ullapool past Gruinard Bay to Loch Ewe the general alignment of the coast changes to nearly east-west and the marine limit here appears to remain in the vicinity of 60 feet, probably because the trend of the coast is not very different from that of the isobases. Southwards, past Gairloch, the marine limit resumes its rise, attaining about 75 feet at Redpoint, 85-90 feet near Applecross, and about 100 feet in the Broadford–Kyleakin area of Skye (McCann 1961b). In the distance of about 60 miles from Enard Bay to eastern Skye the average rate of rise of the marine limit is approximately a foot a mile. The general alignment of the coast, however, is oblique to the probable trend of the isobases. A line that is probably perpendicular to the isobases is one passing northwestwards through Skye towards the Outer Hebrides, and in this direction the slope of the marine limit appears to be of the order of two feet a mile. This gradient does not, of course, apply to the actual shorelines, for it represents a generalised line through the upper limit of a series of more steeply-sloping shorelines. That such a series of shorelines exists is indicated by the numerous references in the literature to lateglacial raised beaches at altitudes below the local marine limit. Unfortun-ately no one has yet attempted detailed accurate measurement and correlation of these features.

Farther south an outward descent of the marine limit at a rate of about or more than two feet a mile is indicated by a comparison of western Mull with the southernmost islands of the Outer Hebrides. In the latter raised beaches are absent, yet in Iona and the Ross of Mull, some 60 miles distant, shingle ridges occur up to altitudes of around 110 feet above sea-level.

The pattern becomes a little clearer when we move farther south, for instead of a sea area dotted with islands there is available the coastal zone of northeastern Ireland, where the limits of the lateglacial seas are recorded by marine deposits at numerous places. Over more than 150 miles of the Irish coast, extending from near Lough Swilly eastwards to Fair Head and then southwards past Belfast to Carlingford Lough, the upper limit of marine evidence usually lies between altitudes of 50 and 70 feet (Morrison and Stephens 1965). Outside this area of near horizontality the upper limit of the lateglacial deposits falls away sharply, descending to present sea-level in about 15 miles west of Lough Swilly on the north coast (Stephens 1963) and falling to present sea-level between Dundalk and Dublin on the east coast. This pattern closely resembles that of the Moray Firth area and, as in that area, leads one to suspect that there exists a series of shorelines comparable with those of Southeast Scotland, the older and outermost members of which probably decline quite steeply. None of these shorelines has yet been accurately levelled at closely-spaced intervals.

The pattern is probably continued in the Solway area but unfortunately the Solway Firth itself largely occupies the area where the most interesting evidence should lie. Lateglacial beaches are on the whole poorly developed on the Scottish side of the firth, their maximal altitude perhaps being about 60 feet, as exemplified on the coast near Abbey Head to the southeast of Kirkcudbright. On the opposite coast, in Cumberland, the upper limit of lateglacial features appears to pass beneath the postglacial deposits

E.S.S.—O

to the north of Maryport and to descend below sea-level before St Bees Head is reached.

Taking as a whole the lateglacial marine evidence so far described for Scotland and northeastern Ireland, it is clear that it reveals a striking resemblance to the pattern in Southeast Scotland outside the Perth Readvance limit, thus permitting the inference that in other parts of Scotland outside this limit, as well as in northeastern Ireland, there exists a sequence of inclined lateglacial shorelines with gradients comparable with those of the Southeast. The line along which the outermost of these shorelines passes below present sea-level is tentatively marked in Fig. 68. The inclusion within this line of a considerable area of Ireland suggests the distortion by Irish ice of what would otherwise seem to be a fairly symmetrical area of isostatic warping caused by Scottish ice. The line does not, of course, mark the outer limit of the area affected by glacial isostasy, for world sea-level was probably at least 200 feet below its present level when the outermost shorelines were being formed. A further point about this line is that it is never very far from the limit of the Aberdeen–Lammermuir Readvance in the areas where a tentative mapping of the latter has been attempted. This leads one to suspect that the warping of the earth's crust with which we have been dealing so far was related to this readvance.

Sea-levels associated with and following the Perth Readvance

In Southeast Scotland an important aspect of the Perth shorelines is the rapid relative lowering of sea-level that they show to have occurred near the limit of the Perth Readvance or a short distance within it. We might therefore reasonably expect a similar marked displacement to be identifiable at other places where the ice of the Perth Readvance terminated in the sea.

The upper limit of marine deposits, corresponding frequently with the lower limit of sharp fluvioglacial features, that lies at around 90 feet along the south side of the Moray coastlands from near Elgin past Forres and Nairn, comes to an end in the Inverness Firth. The limit of the Perth Readvance in this area appears to have been at the entrance to the firth, where large deposits of fluvioglacial gravel form the bases of the headlands built by wave action at Fortrose and Ardesier. From here southwestwards extensive fluvioglacial deposits border the firth, especially its southeastern side, and at Alturlie Point a mass of deeply-pitted gravel that protrudes into the firth includes kettle holes that descend to altitudes of only 40 feet above sea-level. Farther up the firth, around North Kessock, a mass of fluvioglacial gravel slopes down to 90 feet and indicates that sea-level was not above this altitude when it was formed. Westwards from this deposit evidence of high sea-levels is absent and rapid relative uplift of the land thus appears to have occurred.

In the Cromarty Firth the Perth Readvance appears to have terminated near Invergordon. Evidence of a sea-level at about 80-85 feet occurs for a short distance within this limit along the shores of the firth, and at Alness and Evanton the upper parts of the great outwash fans, fed by torrents that poured down the valleys of the Alness and Glass rivers, are said to be related to this level (Ogilvie 1923). A hint that sea-level had fallen considerably by the time the ice had wasted back to Strathpeffer village is contained in Ogilvie's reference to eastward-sloping terraces that fall from over 110 feet above sea-level near the village to only 35 feet a mile and a half west of Dingwall.

The pattern is clearer in the Dornoch Firth area, through the detailed work of Ogilvie and the Geological Survey (Read et al. 1926), and there is very good evidence for a considerable relative fall of sea-level as the ice withdrew from the firth and the Kyle of Sutherland. During the Perth Readvance the ice appears to have reached its limit a few miles west of Dornoch. Immediately outside this limit raised beaches up to about 85 feet are present, but within the limit they fail to attain this altitude. On the south side of the firth near Edderton, situated close to or at the readvance limit, an outwash plain containing a kettle hole nearly 40 feet deep falls eastwards from 95 to 75 feet above present sea-level, thus indicating a former sea-level of no more than 75 feet when it was formed. A short distance farther up the firth the extensive mass of pitted gravel that terminates in Sgarbh Point lies mainly between 60 and 70 feet. Still farther west, near Fearn, another fluvioglacial spread descends from 90 to 70 feet. Together these features suggest a sea-level of no more than 60 or 70 feet. A further fall is then indicated, for between Fearn and Bonar Bridge the highest shoreline is between 50 and 55 feet. This shoreline can be traced only as far as Bonar Bridge, however, suggesting a further drop in sea-level, which is confirmed by fluvioglacial deposits. The latter border the Kyle of Sutherland from near Bonar Bridge to Shin Bridge and comprise three outwash plains, each of which commences in a kame and kettle area and declines down-valley to end at an altitude of between 27 and 38 feet. The lowest of these features thus points to a sea-level of no more than 27 feet above present level as the ice decayed in the Kyle of Sutherland.

Viewing the evidence in the three firths as a whole, it thus seems that the Perth Readvance was here associated with a maximal sea-level of about 80 to 90 feet above present level. As the ice wasted back sea-level at first fell gradually, but thereafter fell rapidly and dropped below the level it achieved at a much later time at the culmination of the major postglacial transgression.

Turning now to the opposite side of the country, there exist numerous lateglacial marine features in Islay and Jura, of which by far the most striking are the shingle ridges that occur on parts of the western coast of Jura and the northern coast of Islay where they often overlie the high marine platform referred to earlier in this chapter. These shingle ridges are far better developed along the coast of Jura immediately north of Loch Tarbert than anywhere else (and are, in fact, the best assemblage of lateglacial features of this type in the whole of Scotland). The shingle, which consists almost entirely of well-rounded pieces of quartzite mostly 4 to 8 inches across, is without vegetation over large areas, where it can be seen to form patterns of curving ridges. The latter include well-developed features at all levels from 125 feet down to 45 feet (McCann 1964). A significant aspect of the Jura ridges is the restriction of the very abundant features to a stretch of the west coast about five miles long. In part this may be a result of the presence here of the gently-sloping rock platform, which probably facilitated the construction of the ridges, but this alone does not seem an adequate explanation. An explanation is suggested, however, by evidence recorded by McCann. He noted that to the south of Loch Tarbert, where the shingle ridges are poorly developed, a great thickness of glacial till containing large quantities of quartzite is exposed in the cliff sections at the back of the postglacial beach. On the other hand, north of Loch Tarbert in the area of abundant shingle ridges he was unable to find any till. This suggests that the lateglacial sea reworked the till of the latter area to produce the shingle. It also suggests that this area suffered a much more prolonged attack by the lateglacial sea than the area south of Loch Tarbert. This difference can be accounted for if the more southern area was covered by glacier ice at the time of the highest sea-level. Since the high southern part of the island rising to 2500 feet lies close at hand it seems likely that the ice came from this high ground.

Striae and erratics, show, however, that most of the ice in Jura, as well as the ice in Islay, came from the mainland. That this mainland ice failed to cover the areas of lateglacial marine gravel in central-west Jura is implied by the evidence already described, while the abundance of similar gravels in northern Islay suggests it also remained ice-free. Yet the ice seems to have covered much the greater part of the remainder of Islay (and probably also a considerable part of Jura). The period of cold climate associated with the advance of the ice is recorded in northern Islay by a belt of solifluction deposits, up to 35 feet thick and a hundred yards or more broad, that masks the inner part of the interglacial rock platform and the lower slopes of the associated high cliff. On other parts of the Islay coast, as well as on the adjacent coast of Jura, raised beaches form flattish terraces at a number of places and the higher ones lie between 80 and 100 feet above sea-level. In central Islay, however, including the northern part of the Laggan Bay lowland and the low ground extending from Loch Indaal to Loch Gorm, the highest marine features barely exceed 50 feet. Above this altitude there occur abundant fluvio-glacial features, including well-defined eskers, that bear no sign of marine action.

It thus appears that at the time of the last major readvance of mainland ice into Jura and Islay, during which local glaciers also developed in Jura, parts of the west remained ice-free. The large difference in altitude between the highest marine features in western Jura and those in central Islay implies that considerable land uplift took place as the ice subsequently wasted away. The situation is thus similar to that in the Forth and Tay areas following the Perth Readvance and suggests that the features in Islay and Jura were also formed at this time.

In other parts of Scotland the sea-level changes associated with the maximum of the Perth Readvance are more obscure. In the Northwest the limit of the readvance is unknown but there are occasional hints of a pattern of sea-level change similar to that associated with the limit in other areas. For example, while raised beaches up to about 60 feet occur on the coast from Loch Ewe to Ullapool, an outwash fan situated where Loch Maree drains into Loch Ewe falls from 70 feet above sea-level down to 35 feet (McCann 1961b). In Southwest Scotland raised beaches at about 60-70 feet have been noted in various localities. Thus J. K. Charlesworth (1926a) described outwash merging into a beach at 60 feet by Loch Ryan, J. J. Donner (1963) measured terraces at 60-65 feet by Luce Bay, and a feature at about 60 feet near Abbey Head has been referred to above. If a sea-level at around these altitudes prevailed on the Solway coast of Scotland following the Perth Readvance one would expect to find extensive beaches close to and immediately within the readvance limit for, not only are there many long sheltered coastal indentations, but vast quantities of fluvioglacial material were laid down during the decay of the Perth ice in some of the valleys of this area. A few features are referred to by Donner in the Kirkcudbright area, but there is no sign here or elsewhere of the extensive raised beaches one would expect. In fact there are in places clear indications of a sea-level well below 60 feet following the Perth Readvance. For example, kame and kettle features, as well as meltwater channels, occur as low as the limit of the postglacial features (20-25 feet) south of Dalbeattie, and in the great kame and kettle area around Dumfries many of the dead-ice hollows descend below the 50-foot contour. In fact, to the south of Dumfries in particular there ought to be extensive beach deposits accumulated contemporaneously with the fluvioglacial landforms. Since they are not visible, one must infer that they lie buried beneath later deposits and await investigation.

The ice margin did not have to retreat very far from the Perth Readvance limit in the Moray Firth and Tay areas before it ceased to be in contact with the sea. Contact was probably maintained a little longer in the Forth area, and between Stirling and the Menteith moraine occasional raised shorelines up to a normal maximum of about 65-70 feet occur. In the Clyde area contact between sea and ice was maintained much longer, during the decay of the large ice-mass that had extended into Ayrshire, across Kintyre and, along with local ice, covered Arran. Raised beaches formed as this ice decayed occur at various points in Kintyre and Arran and are particularly extensive in Ayrshire, where the highest ones are between 80 and 100 feet above sea-level. In the valley of the Clyde itself, westwards from Glasgow, the lateglacial marine deposits attain altitudes of 70 to 80 feet, although they are most widespread below 60 feet. In this area, with an ice-mass wasting back northwestwards (i.e. down the valley), it would be interesting to know how and at what stage of deglaciation the sea managed to gain entry to the Glasgow area.

Indications of a high sea-level also occur along the Argyllshire coast between Loch-gilphead and Oban. Some of the long trains of outwash gravel deposited in valleys leading down to the coast have been described on p. 116. Towards the seaward ends of several valleys the outwash trains end well above sea-level but (contrary to recent statements) the altitude of the associated sea-level has not been established, although the Geological Survey memoirs contain references to marine features up to altitudes slightly exceeding 100 feet. It would seem that the period of high sea-level was of short duration and was probably followed by rapid emergence of the land, for lateglacial beaches at lower levels are generally poorly developed.

Low sea-levels and the Loch Lomond Readvance

While the pattern of sea-level changes following the Perth Readvance shows variations in different parts of Scotland, the eventual result in all the areas to which reference has been made was a major emergence of the land. This may be inferred also from the buried gravel layer of the Grangemouth area for, as we saw in the last chapter, this shows that around Grangemouth a sea-level no higher than the present prevailed for a con-siderable period between the time that the ice of the Perth Readvance decayed and the time of the Menteith Readvance. We may therefore presume in those areas more distant from the centre of isostatic uplift in the Southwest Grampians than is Grange-mouth, the sea stood below (and, in the most distant parts, very much below) its present level.

It is not possible to elaborate this presumption by reference to a similar buried gravel layer in other parts of the country, for the available evidence is insufficient. However, at one point on the coast of Northeast Ireland (Roddans Port) detailed studies supported by radiocarbon dates of a buried and partly submerged peat bed strongly suggest that the sea had fallen below its present level by 12 000 years ago and that it did not rise above this level until the major postglacial transgression (Morrison and Stephens 1965). A low lateglacial sea-level has also been proved at one locality on the Solway coast (Godwin et al. 1965, Godwin and Switsur 1966). At Redkirk Point, between Annan and Carlisle, a bed of peat has been radiocarbon-dated as about 12 300 years old. Slightly above this peat bed another one, situated almost exactly at present mean sea-level, has given a radio-carbon age of about 10 300 years. This latter date invites comparison with the Forth valley, where the Menteith moraine, of approximately the same age, was associated with a sea-level as high as 40 feet. The difference in altitude reflects distance from the centre of isostatic uplift, and we thus have a hint of a shoreline slightly over 10 000 years old that falls from 40 feet in the Menteith area to below sea-level in the Solway area and Northeast Ireland.

Other evidence in Scotland that relates to sea-level at this time is to be found along the west coast, where valley glaciers of the Zone III (Loch Lomond) Readvance descended to sea-level. Outwash slopes away southwards down the valley of the River Leven, which drains Loch Lomond to the Clyde, and appears to pass below the postglacial beach deposits as in the Forth valley. Since the limit of the postglacial sea was about 40 feet in this area, we can infer that sea-level at the time the outwash was laid down did not exceed this altitude. Nearby there are raised beach deposits up to an altitude of about 70 feet, related to the emergence that followed the Perth Readvance, and these can be traced intermittently along the northern side of the Clyde past Helensburgh into the entrance to the Gare Loch. They are absent, however, north of Row Point (which appears to mark the limit of the Zone III Readvance), only the postglacial beaches being visible. Thus a sea-level lower than the limit of the latter appears to have prevailed as the Zone III glacier retreated up the Gare Loch.

Rivers draining from the glacier that occupied the site of Loch Etive at the time of the Loch Lomond Readvance built an extensive plain of outwash gravel that now forms the large peninsula at the mouth of the loch (Plate XVII). The surface of the gravel, which is interrupted by several kettle holes and largely covered by peat, slopes outwards down the loch from 90 feet at its eastern margin to about 45 feet in the west (McCann 1961a). Here the gravel has been modified by the sea in postglacial times. The situation is very similar to that at Corran on Loch Linnhe, where an outwash fan falls gently seawards to about 40 feet (Fig. 65). In the same area, at Ballachulish on Loch Leven, a gravel promontory projects into the loch. It is likely that this was originally another outwash fan associated with the Loch Lomond phase, but that its surface has been completely reworked by the postglacial seas. Another glacier that reached the sea occupied the site of Loch Creran. Extensive outwash deposits were laid down near the mouth of the loch but these are not related to any visible raised beach. In all these cases the presumption must be that sea-level was relatively low when the ice of the Loch Lomond Readvance was at its maximal extent.

Several of the valley glaciers that radiated from the mountain mass in the eastern part of Mull descended to sea-level. The outwash fans associated with two of these glaciers – in Glen Forsa and in the valley containing Loch Ba – show that sea-level was not above 35 feet when they accumulated (p. 154). On the east coast of Mull valley glaciers coalesced and spread out as a large piedmont lobe occupying lochs Don and Spelve. The moraines by Loch Spelve are partly composed of clay with a subarctic shell assemblage, and those by Loch Don are in part formed of sandy raised beach deposits redistributed by the ice. It is thus evident that the sea occupied the two lochs before the ice readvanced into them. E. B. Bailey (1924) stated that 'the notch of the 75-ft raised beach is cut in the outer face of the Loch Don moraine . . . but nowhere inside the moraine is a vestige of this beach to be found'. If correct, this implies that the sea was as high as 75 feet at the time the ice stood at the moraine. This is difficult to reconcile with W. B. Wright's clear evidence (given in the same publication) of a sea-level below 35 feet at the time the outwash fans in Glen Forsa and near Loch Ba were formed. One solution of the anomaly might be that the raised beach described by Bailey was already there before the ice advanced, and that beyond the moraine (itself partly composed of similar beach deposits) the beach remains unmodified.

On the mainland coast farther north there is again evidence of a low sea-level associated with the Zone III limit. At the western end of Loch Shiel kames and kettles merge into an outwash fan that is said to slope seawards down to 16 feet above sea-level, and a similar fan at the western end of Loch Morar has been followed down to 35 feet (Summary of Progress Geological Survey 1923, McCann 1961b). Still farther north outwash gravels laid down by streams from a valley glacier at the head of Loch Carron descend to between

25 and 30 feet above sea-level, where they are obscured by postglacial deposits. On the northern side of Loch Kishorn boulder-strewn moraines descend to the level of the post-glacial raised beach deposits and even the delicate fluted moraines are unmodified by the sea above this level (Fig. 41). At the head of Loch Torridon a large arcuate moraine marking the terminus of a glacier that flowed down Glen Thrail is little above present sea-level, and this also applies to the hummocky moraines near the head of Loch Eriboll.

Thus in the west of Scotland the evidence available at present is everywhere consistent with a low sea-level at the time of the Loch Lomond Readvance (excepting perhaps only part of Mull). Beaches formed at this time have not as yet been identified since they lie below the limit of the later postglacial transgression. It seems likely, however, that the fossiliferous subarctic deposits, including the 'Clyde beds', may be in part related to sea-level about and shortly after the time of the Loch Lomond Readvance. We have so far considered these beds only in terms of the falling sea-level that was associated with the deglaciation that followed the Perth Readvance. This interpretation is certainly encouraged by the accounts of these beds that imply continuous accumulation of marine sediments following upon the retreat of the ice, commencing with the laminated clays poor in fossils and succeeded by the richly fossiliferous 'Clyde beds' or their equivalents. While this interpretation may be in part correct, it is deficient as the sole explanation in four respects. Firstly, the beds that are very rich in fossils are usually found close to present sea-level and apparently do not occur above an altitude of about 30 feet. In terms of a falling sea-level this apparently rather sudden appearance of a rich fauna seems difficult to account for. Secondly, the fossiliferous beds, as known at present, are abundantly developed in quite a restricted area. Apart from the Clyde region itself, including adjacent shores such as those of the Kyles of Bute and Loch Fyne, the beds appear to be abundantly present around or above sea-level only along the coast between Knapdale and Loch Linnhe. Now while this distribution might conceivably reflect merely the proximity of the energetic Glasgow geologists of last century (when most of the shell sites were found), it seems more likely that it relates to the proximity of the centre of isostatic uplift. Thirdly, the existence in the Forth valley at altitudes up to 40 feet of a series of buried beaches formed between about 10 300 and 8800 years ago, leads one to expect similar deposits in other parts of the country. The most likely area where such deposits might be encoun-tered is the Clyde–Loch Linnhe area. In fact, if the subarctic fossiliferous beds of this area are not in large part the equivalent of the Forth buried beaches, it is difficult to see what could be their equivalent, for the fossiliferous beds are immediately overlain by the deposits of the major postglacial transgression (and since these two series of deposits do not merge into each other a period of lower sea-level separating them is implied, again resembling the Forth region). Finally, it is significant that fossiliferous deposits closely resembling the 'Clyde beds' have been found near Fort William, well within the limit of the Loch Lomond Readvance, thus proving that the subarctic deposits continued to accumulate after the maximum of this readvance.

In brief, then, it appears that the subarctic deposits of the west of Scotland began to be laid down following the Perth Readvance, and at the time of the Loch Lomond Re-advance were incorporated in moraines by several of the glaciers. They continued to accumulate for a time following the latter readvance and it may well be that they are in part equivalent to the buried raised beaches of the Forth valley. The latter, as we have seen, are usually overlain by deposits of peat, which began to develop during the oscilla-tory fall of sea-level that followed the Loch Lomond Readvance. It is to these and other peat deposits of significance for sea-level changes that we now turn.

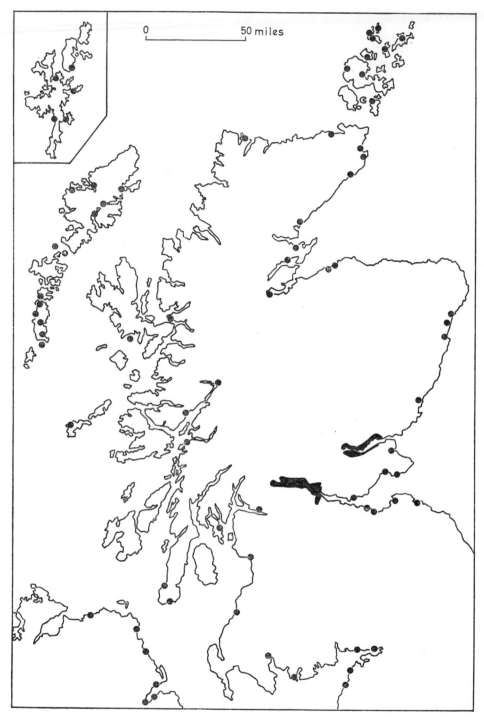

FIG. 85. Localities where peat beneath marine deposits or beneath high-water
mark is known to occur. Based on numerous sources.

Buried and submerged peats and related evidence

Peat buried beneath later deposits or submerged beneath the sea is found in coastal areas throughout Scotland, as well as in inland localities where the sea formerly penetrated. The places at which such peat is definitely known to occur are shown in Fig. 85, but the actual occurrences must be far more numerous. In the Outer Hebrides, Orkneys and Shetlands in particular peat below sea-level is so common that published accounts often cite only one or two occurrences as examples of a widespread phenomenon. In general, around most of the mainland the peat is often covered by marine or estuarine deposits related to the higher sea-levels of later postglacial times, while in the more peripheral areas (especially in the outer islands and Caithness) it is often covered only by the sea or by recent coastal accumulations. The various coastal peat deposits extend over a long period of time. The oldest one so far dated in Scotland has given a radiocarbon age of about 12 300 years (p. 203). On the other hand, peat that is still growing at the present time is now being submerged in the outer islands.

The burial of many low level peat deposits in Scotland by marine and estuarine sediments was a consequence of the major postglacial transgression. Quite often the peat accumulated owing to the rising water-table caused by this transgression. On the other hand, in some areas the peat had begun to build up long before the transgression occurred. In the Forth valley near the Menteith moraine it began to accumulate, in fact, during the preceding regression as the now-buried beaches were exposed. Here the ideal peat succession is present, comprising a basal part that began to accumulate as the sea withdrew from the now-buried beach beneath, a middle part with abundant tree remains formed when sea-level was low, and an upper part related to the transgression of the carse sea over the peat (p. 178). Thus a particular layer of peat sandwiched between marine deposits may vary very considerably in age, so that a peat sample for radiocarbon dating has to be taken from a particular horizon if the dates of the variations in sea-level are to be accurately determined. Unfortunately, most of the radiocarbon dates so far obtained for the buried peats in Scotland do not fulfil this requirement, while the peats themselves have not been related to buried raised beaches. However, taken as a whole, the dates give a good general picture of the relative changes of sea-level in the southern half of the country.

As we saw in the last chapter, the buried peat that rests on the Main Buried Beach in the western part of the Forth lowlands began to accumulate around 9500 years ago, while the change-over from a falling to a rising sea-level occurred about 8500 years ago. A series of radiocarbon dates obtained by H. Godwin and E. H. Willis (1960–62) for buried peat at other points in Southeast and Southwest Scotland and in Northeast Ireland accords with the pattern in the western part of the Forth valley. These dates are as follows:

Forth valley, near Airth	8400
Lower Earn valley (two sites)	8350 and 8400
Irvine (one site)	9600 and 9500
Girvan (two sites)	9400 and 9000
Brighouse Bay, Kircudbrightshire	9650
Redkirk Point, Dumfriesshire	8100
Ballyhalbert, Co. Down	8100

Together these dates suggest that the main deposits of buried peat accumulated between about 9700 and about 8000 years ago and had been covered by the deposits of a transgressing sea by about the latter date.

In places, however, peat was not buried till later by the rising sea, and in some localities in the Forth valley where it built up as fast as the sea rose it was not buried at all (p. 181). It may be that Lochar Moss, the large area of surface peat southeast of Dumfries, is in some ways similar to these Forth peats. A sample from near the base of the moss, which rests on fine sand, gave a radiocarbon age of about 6650 years. Not far away the carse clay occurs to a higher level than the base of the moss (Jardine 1964), so that it seems possible that the growth of the moss, perhaps triggered off by the rising sea-level, was sufficiently rapid to exclude the sea. Another sample from Southwest Scotland that proved younger than the main mass of the peat was a piece of drifted wood found in the carse clay and associated deposits at Newton Stewart. This gave a radiocarbon age of about 6150 years.

The buried peats reflect the influence of isostatic warping just as do the raised beaches. In considering the peats from this point of view it is most useful to note the lowest altitude of peat in a particular locality (so far as this is known). In the extreme west of the Forth lowlands peat is not found below an altitude of about 25 feet. Eastwards the minimal altitude gradually declines, so that at Edinburgh peat is found at sea-level, and on the opposite side of the Forth farther east at Largo it has been seen at low-tide mark. In the Earn and Tay valleys a similar decline is evident, for the lowest buried peat appears to be between 5 and 10 feet above sea-level in the lower Earn valley, but passes down below low-water mark as it is followed down the Firth of Tay, while it extends well below low-water mark at Montrose (Howden 1870). We may also make a comparison between the minimum of 25 feet in the western part of the Forth valley and peat as low as 6 feet above sea-level at Girvan. Farther from the centre of isostatic uplift buried peat at Belfast has been found at 23 to 24 feet below sea-level (Praeger 1892). Still farther away sea-level was even lower and considerable parts of the present floor of the southern North Sea were land. This is shown by a radiocarbon date of about 8400 years obtained for peat taken from the sea-bed off the Norfolk coast at a depth of 120 feet. H. Godwin and E. H. Willis (1959) suggested that 30 feet should be allowed for tectonic lowering of the sea-bed since the peat formed, making the subsequent rise of sea-level at least 90 feet. Thus at a time when the sea was probably slightly above its present level near to the centre of isostatic recovery in Scotland it was at least 90 feet below its present level off Norfolk. Although this outward slope of the old sea-level can only be demonstrated so clearly in a southward direction, there is every reason to believe that a similar outward slope from the Southwest Grampians prevailed in other directions also. The more peripheral areas of Scotland, such as the outer islands, probably stood far higher above sea-level than they do now.

At this point it is convenient to refer to sea-level changes in these peripheral areas. We have made little mention of them so far, since raised beaches are scarce or absent and the pattern of changes through lateglacial and postglacial times has been very different from that in the rest of Scotland. The dominant theme has been one of rising sea-level with the inevitable consequence that the evidence is now submerged beneath the sea. Proof of the final stages of submergence abounds, but evidence of the earlier stages is nowhere precise. J. S. Flett (1925) plotted submarine contours for the Orkney area and came to the conclusion that at a depth of 8 to 10 fathoms and again at 18 to 20 fathoms there are considerable areas of flattish sea-floor. He suggested that these flats may reflect former sea-levels lower than the present. In Caithness deep water comes close in to some of the cliffs and suggests the possibility that such cliffs extend below sea-level (Crampton *et al.* 1914). Here, too, the valley of the Wick River is infilled with sand and mud to a depth of at least 70 feet near its mouth, implying that the river has excavated its valley in relation to a sea-level at least this amount below present level. There are also records of 'fossil' arctic and subarctic shells dredged up from the sea floor at many points around Scotland. Sometimes shallow-water species have been found as, for example, at depths as great as 250 feet 40 miles off the coast of Aberdeenshire (Dawson 1866). Such shells may, of course, have reached the places at which they have been found in various ways, perhaps having been transported by glaciers, ice-bergs, ice-floes or turbidity currents, but doubtless many of them thrived on now submerged shores whose existence we can as yet only infer.

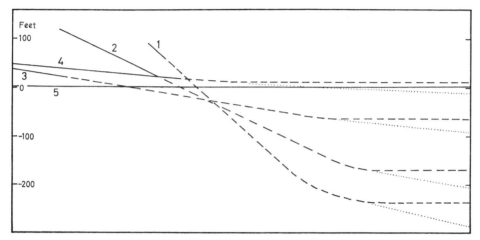

FIG. 86. Some possible shoreline relationships. For explanation see text.

Fig. 86 shows in simplified form the type of shoreline relationships we might expect. On the left of the diagram four of the raised shorelines of Southeast Scotland (comprising one of the East Fife group, the Main Perth, the Main Postglacial and the Main Buried Shoreline) are shown by continuous lines. In the remainder of the diagram each of these shorelines is projected with the same gradient until it approaches the contemporary world sea-level as shown on R. W. Fairbridge's graph (Fig. 70). The diagram need not apply only to Southeast Scotland and the area of the North Sea bed to the east, but may well be generally applicable to Scotland as a whole. For this reason no horizontal scale is shown, but the horizontal distance represented may be taken to be between about 200 and 300 miles, depending on which line radiating from the centre of isostatic uplift the diagram is related. The right-hand side of the diagram, where the shorelines are shown as broken horizontal lines, is presumed to lie beyond the area of isostatic uplift. Here the sequence of sea-level changes should be as in Fig. 70 (assuming, of course, that no other complicating factors such as local earth-movements have occurred). In terms of the pattern of sea-level changes we are dealing with here (those associated with and following the oscillatory retreat of the last ice-sheet), it is probable that only the Shetland Islands belong in this part of the diagram. Thus when the last ice-sheet was at its maximal extent some 17 000 to 20 000 years ago the Shetlands, covered by their own ice-cap, probably stood far higher in relation to the sea than they do now, the present islands forming part of one land mass that may have been joined to the Orkneys. Since that time the islands have been subjected to an oscillatory rise of sea-level, during the later stages of which the present islands were severed from one another by the encroaching sea.

Part or all of the Orkneys and the main island group of the Outer Hebrides, along with the northeastern parts of Caithness and Aberdeenshire, come within the area affected by isostatic uplift. The amount of uplift has been smaller, however, than the world rise of sea-level, so that all the lateglacial shorelines are now drowned. Consequently the dominant pattern in these areas has been one of rising sea-level interrupted by temporary regressions. The present Orkney Islands and the main island chain of the Outer Hebrides were each a single large island, and the shallow straits separating the islands of each group indicate that final separation into the many islands we see today occurred during the later stages of the transgression, as in the Shetlands.

In Fig. 77 the Main Postglacial Shoreline is shown by the broken line to level out above the present shoreline. This construction has been adopted to accord with Fairbridge's view that at the time this shoreline was formed world sea-level was above its present level. Thus, if Fairbridge is correct – and it must be pointed out that other views exist (p. 211) – then the fact that in the Shetlands, Orkneys and much of the Outer Hebrides the shoreline has not been found, must mean that these areas have subsided since the shoreline was formed five and a half thousand years ago. This means that to show the actual situation the broken lines of Fig. 77 should be modified, and the nature of this modification is hinted at by the dotted lines.

The most recent part of the rise of sea-level is amply demonstrated in the outer islands by various types of evidence and is even suggested by local legend. According to tradition the Outer Hebrides were at one time linked with St Kilda and this land is reputed to have been the hunting ground of a former princess of Harris. More reliable evidence is provided by archaeological remains. Neolithic chambered cairns in North and South Uist are now partly submerged at high water. 'Duns' believed to have been constructed in the early part of the Christian era are also partly under water. In North Uist the sill and outer entrance of one dun are submerged as much as 18 inches at spring tides and in another instance the interior and part of the enclosing stone wall are permanently submerged (Callander 1929). From the same locality comes the record that in 1721 complaints about the sea overflowing several parts of the island were sent to the Forfeited Estates Commissioners. In the upper reaches of some of the sea lochs of the Outer Hebrides all stages can be observed in the gradation from truly freshwater lochs, through examples that are only brackish to a slight degree, to those that are now entered by the ordinary tides (Jehu and Craig 1926). In Shetland there are numerous local traditions of submergence in historic times. Thus there is a tradition that Roe Sound, now spanned by a bridge 100 yards long, was once fordable at low tide and that a crofter's steading on its shores is covered by shingle, while Pictish buildings in the neighbourhood are completely submerged.

The most obvious evidence of submergence in the outer islands is the peat very frequently found below high-water mark. How far below sea-level the peat goes is unknown, but it has often been seen at the limit of lowest tides, sometimes including the stumps of rooted trees. During storms chunks of peat may be thrown up on the shore, while peat has also been brought up on ships' anchors, having been discovered in this manner several miles from the west coast of North Uist. In the Orkneys about a century ago peat was ploughed up by a wreck and afterwards an iron bar was put down 15 feet into the peat without passing through it. A similar thickness of peat has also been found in

Stornoway Bay, while in the original *Statistical Account* the following description appears: 'In the island of Pabbay, where the sea ebbs out in spring tides to a great distance, there are visible, at the very lowest ebb, large trunks of trees; the roots of which, spread out widely and variously, are fixed in black moss, which might be dug for peat to a great depth'. Near Finstown in the Orkneys peat below sea-level was found to rest on an unknown thickness of freshwater marl from which the antlers and bones of a deer were obtained (Wilson *et al.* 1935). Submerged peat has also been found at a number of places on the Caithness coast and here some of the caves appear to relate to a sea-level rather lower than prevails today. This is clearly shown in a cave at Balnakeil Bay close to Durness in Northwest Sutherland, for here stalactites extend about four feet below the sea even at mid-tide (Ford 1959).

In Benbecula peat situated about 9 feet below high spring tides (almost 2 feet below Ordnance Datum) has given a radiocarbon age of about 5700 years (Ritchie 1966). This peat site lies on the west coast where, behind the machair, peat is accumulating today as low as Ordnance Datum. Thus only a slight submergence, if any, can be demonstrated by this dated peat. Submergence is indicated, however, by pollen analysis of a peat deposit in Loch Eynort in South Uist. This layer of peat is about 6 to 7 feet thick and is completely exposed only at low tide. It began to accumulate during Zone VI of the pollen sequence and continued to build up through Zones VII and VIII (Harrison and Blackburn 1946). Since the postglacial transgression culminated in Zone VIIa in many other parts of Scotland, it would seem that at this time the sea failed to cover this peat site. This implies that sea-level was at least ten feet lower then than at present. In Shetland a considerably lower sea-level at that time has been demonstrated. Here it has been shown that peat off the shore of the island of Whalsay probably accumulated in a fen, and five radiocarbon dates range between 5400 and 7000 years ago (Hoppe 1965). Since the peat was obtained from about 29 feet below high-water mark, at least this amount of relative sea-level rise has occurred in this part of Shetland in the last 5500 years or so. If we adopt Fairbridge's view that world sea-level was 10 feet above its present level 5500 years ago, it follows that Whalsay has subsided at least 40 feet or so since then, and this represents a movement of the land itself.*

The situation in the outer islands and some other peripheral areas of Scotland is thus very different from that in the rest of the country, for whereas submergence has dominated the one region, emergence has dominated the other. Since the emergence has been essentially a result of glacial unloading, one wonders if the apparently quite rapid submergence is also partly related to this cause. Perhaps subcrustal transfer of material from one region to the other has been taking place. A further cause of land depression, which may well have been particularly effective in the outer islands, may be the additional weight of water on the surrounding sea-beds caused by the eustatic rise of sea-level that resulted from widespread deglaciation in many parts of the world.

* Fairbridge's figures for eustatic sea-level changes have been used here and elsewhere in this book since his is the only really comprehensive attempt to correlate evidence on a world scale. Although his interpretations have been strongly criticised, these criticisms are concerned more with details than with the broad pattern of eustatic sea-level changes, and the inferences made in the preceding pages are not significantly affected thereby. However, the differences of opinion are more important in relation to sea-level changes during the last few thousand years. In particular, it must be pointed out that whereas Fairbridge concluded that about 5500 years ago world sea-level was about 10 feet above its present level, others have concluded that it was below its present level at that time, several giving figures of between 15 and 25 feet below (Fig. 70). Even if we accept figures in this range, however, it is still necessary to postulate a downward movement of Shetland (or, at least, of Whalsay) during the last 5500 years.

The postglacial raised beaches

The great rise of world sea-level that culminated in much of Scotland with the production of the Main Postglacial Shoreline occupied about 3000 years from about 8500 to 5500 years ago. So far as is known at present the sea encroached continuously on the land, although future work may show that the transgression was more complicated. There are localities in the Tay, Forth and Solway areas where peat occurs within the deposits laid down during the transgression, but it has not yet been shown that such peat is of anything more than local significance.

The rise of sea-level relative to the land was least near the centre of isostatic uplift, since the sea here suffered strong competition from the rising land. For example, at the head of the Forth lowlands the total amount of submergence – as given by the difference in altitude between the Main Postglacial Shoreline and the lowest occurrence of peat – was approximately 25 feet. On the other hand, the comparable figure for Belfast is about 45 feet, and this figure is minimal since it is not certain that the lowest part of the Belfast peat has been located. Throughout the area of its occurrence, however, the Main Postglacial Raised Beach clearly demonstrates the rise of the sea in the way it penetrates innumerable valleys. The altitude of the shoreline is shown by isobases in Fig. 87, where its outward slope from the Southwest Grampians is clearly portrayed. From the map it seems that the actual centre of uplift was probably in the vicinity of Rannoch Moor.

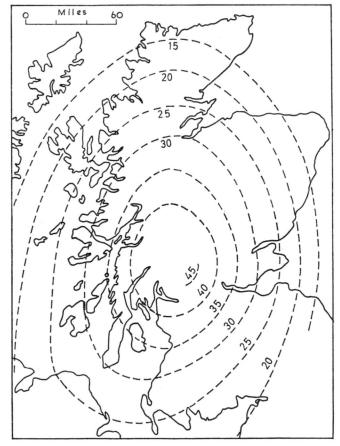

FIG. 87. Isobases for the Main Postglacial Shoreline. Based on various sources.

The only radiocarbon date related to the Main Postglacial Shoreline in Scotland gives an age of approximately 5500 years (p. 184), which accords with the end of the main eustatic rise of ocean level as shown on Fairbridge's graph (Fig. 70). It also accords with radiocarbon dates for the culmination of this rise obtained in the Somerset Levels by H. Godwin and E. H. Willis (1959, 1961), these being about 5600, 5500 and 5400 years before present. Pollen analyses reveal a story that is consistent with these dates, for on the small island of Soay near Skye and also near Dunbar it has been shown that the transgression culminated in Zone VIIa of the pollen sequence (Newey 1965).

We saw in the last chapter that in Southeast Scotland continued isostatic uplift was associated with the formation of three lower postglacial features. We cannot attempt to trace these three features through the rest of Scotland since present data are inadequate. It is certain, however, that raised beaches below the Main Postglacial Beach exist on many parts of the coasts of the mainland and adjacent islands, for they are obvious in numerous places. It is perhaps significant that frequent references have been made in the literature to a raised beach at about 15 feet, which causes one to suspect that there may be a rather widespread feature a few feet above high-water mark. Such a feature may be in part equivalent to the lowest shoreline in Southeast Scotland, which has a very gentle gradient.

Although it is probable that over a considerable part of Scotland the maximal post-glacial sea-level occurred about 5500 years ago, it cannot be assumed that this is true of the whole country. We have already seen, in fact, that in the outer islands the maximal sea-level is the present one. We might reasonably expect, therefore, that in some areas the highest postglacial sea-level has occurred at some intermediate time. Thus one might anticipate that the highest sea-level would be oldest near the centre of isostatic recovery, becoming younger farther away from the centre. W. B. Wright (1937) believed that this pattern prevailed and F. M. Synge and N. Stephens (1966) consider that on the east coast of Ireland the evidence is conclusive that the postglacial marine limit becomes younger southwards. Such differences in age may arise partly through younger postglacial shore-lines intersecting older ones as they are traced outwards from the isostatic centre.

Finally, in tracing the pattern of sea-level changes we come to the present day. The average rate of eustatic sea-level rise in recent years has been estimated at about 0·5 feet a century. In the outer islands any tendency of the land to subside is therefore being emphasised by this movement of the sea itself. On the mainland the evidence points to a very slight upward movement of the land. One indicator of this is the geodetic levelling undertaken by the Ordnance Survey, which suggests that the mainland of Scotland is rising relative to Newlyn in Cornwall. Similar evidence is provided by comparison of the long period trend of the Aberdeen and Newlyn tide-gauge records (Gordon and Suthons 1963). This shows that in the period 1916 to 1962 the average rate of sea-level rise at Newlyn was 0·81 feet a century but at Aberdeen only 0·38 feet a century. Thus Aberdeen is rising at 0·43 feet a century relative to Newlyn. If we assume a world sea-level rise of 0·5 feet a century, a rise of the land itself at Aberdeen of 0·12 feet a century is implied, a figure that agrees fairly well with the rise of 0·17 feet a century at Dunbar calculated from the Ordnance Survey levelling. Whether these movements indicate that isostatic recovery from the ice load is still going on very slowly or whether they are a result of other factors is not known. However, that isostatic recovery is at least very nearly complete is implied by the small variation in altitude of the low-level rock platform believed to have been formed during the last interglacial (p. 194).

12

Periglacial and postglacial changes

WHILE glaciers have had a pronounced effect on the surface of much of Scotland and the consequences of sea-level changes are prominent in many coastal areas, other agencies that have operated during and since the time glaciers existed have had a small but often very significant influence on the land surface. One important development has been the formation of soils, a subject that lies outside our scope except in its effect on landforms. Another has been the spread of different types of vegetation, a detailed picture of which is beginning to emerge through pollen studies. Again the details are not our concern, but the pattern of changes with its implications of marked climatic changes, and the influence of the plant cover on the exposure of the ground surface to denuding agencies are very relevant. Of particular interest are weathering and the mass transfer of debris down slopes, the effectiveness of which have changed greatly since glacial times. In some coastal areas one important change has been the accumulation of sand by wind. Finally, man himself has become one of the principal agents influencing the evolution of the land surface.

Changing vegetation and changing climate

Great changes in climate and vegetation have taken place in Scotland during and since the disappearance of glaciers. Thus on the one hand remains of trees occur in abundance in peat bogs at considerable altitudes in the mountains. On the other hand plants that are now found only in the high mountains of Scotland are found in peat and lake deposits even on the lowest ground.

The best-known of the low-level sites is the former loch of Corstorphine in Edinburgh. From the lower part of the deposits of this loch have been obtained remains of dwarf birch (*Betula nana*), mountain avens (*Dryas octopetala*) and the three arctic willows (*Salix herbacea, S. polaris* and *S. reticulata*), as well as the bones of a lemming and numerous specimens of the arctic freshwater crustacean *Lepidurus arcticus* (Tait 1934). At the present day *Betula nana* is restricted to the Highlands, *Salix reticulata* occurs very sparsely in Scottish mountains above an altitude of 2000 feet, while *Salix polaris* apparently no longer grows naturally in the British Isles (Godwin 1956). Lepidurus is now found in the freshwater pools of Spitsbergen and Greenland, only thawed during the brief summer of these lands (Bennie 1891, 1896b). Similar evidence of a cold climate has been obtained at two other sites in Edinburgh, namely the abandoned Hailes Quarry and the former Broughton Loch, while in Fife a former loch near Auchtertool provided, along with remains of arctic willows, thousands of specimens of Lepidurus. These various remains were doubtless interred in lateglacial times but their age has not yet been determined by radiocarbon dating.

An ancient lake that has been dated is the one at Loch Droma, situated at 900 feet above sea-level in Ross-shire, where a radiocarbon age of about 12 800 years has been obtained. Detailed studies show that the vegetation of this area was then comparable with that existing today on the lower alpine slopes of Swedish Lappland. Trees were absent except perhaps in copses, with birch dominant, although there was a great variety of other plants. The plant communities included acidic *Empetrum* (crowberry) heath and snow-patch vegetation, while there were also marshy areas, as well as stony areas probably affected by solifluction giving fresh soils of somewhat calcareous nature carrying a richly varied herbaceous plant cover. Among the plants typical of snow-patches was *Polytrichum norvegicum*, which is now found in Britain in only a few areas exceeding 3000 feet (Kirk and Godwin 1963).

About 12 000 years ago, at the beginning of Zone II of the pollen analysts, the climate appears to have ameliorated, although it remained colder than the present climate. G. Manley (1951) has tentatively suggested that during Zone II mean July temperatures

Years before present	Pollen zones	Blytt-Sernander periods	Climate	Man
— 1000	VIII	Sub-Atlantic		
— 2000			Deterioration	Iron Age
— 3000	VIIb	Sub-Boreal		Bronze Age
— 4000				
— 5000			Climatic Optimum	Neolithic
— 6000	VIIa	Atlantic		
— 7000				Mesolithic
— 8000	VI	Boreal		
— 9000	V		Rapid Amelioration	
—10 000	IV	Pre-Boreal		
	III	Upper Dryas	Cold	
—11 000	II	Alleröd	Cool	

E.S.S.—P

exceeded 10° C only in the southernmost part of Scotland, and that mean January temperatures were below minus 7° C except along the west coast of the Highlands and in the western islands. Under these conditions trees were absent from most of the country and there were wide areas of heathland dominated by plants such as crowberry and heather, although there was a great variety of herbaceous plants along with an abundance of grasses and sedges. In the south this tundra vegetation appears to have given way to park tundra with patches of birch trees and here and there willow and pine (Donner 1957).

There followed a brief but important period of colder climate (Zone III) that caused glaciers to build up once again and to extend, as the Loch Lomond Readvance, to the limits shown in Fig. 59. Little is known of the vegetation at this time, for the Zone III deposits are poor in pollen. In lakes they often occur as a layer of pink clay sandwiched between the organic muds of Zone II and the postglacial zones, suggesting that there were considerable areas with little vegetation.

This harsh open landscape was soon transformed, however, for about 10 300 years ago the glaciers that had extended to the Loch Lomond limit began to decay and a period of rapid climatic amelioration commenced. In the early part of the pre-Boreal period (Zone IV) the vegetation was similar to that of Zone II, but this open landscape was rapidly replaced on low ground by birch forests along with some pine and willow. In Southeast Scotland birch continued to be dominant in the early part of the Boreal period (Zone V) and hazel was also important, but in the later part (Zone VI) birch declined somewhat as the continued rise of temperature allowed first elm and then oak to increase in importance (Fig. 88). In the Highlands oak and elm never achieved the status they attained in the southeast and instead, over a large area, pine forests were dominant with birch usually of secondary importance.

Towards the end of the Boreal period and in the succeeding Atlantic period (Zone VIIa) the climate was distinctly milder than it is at present. This Climatic Optimum marks the culmination of a period of remarkable climatic change, for only 3000 years or so before it was ushered in large glaciers had occupied many of the valleys of western Scotland. It has been estimated that mean temperatures perhaps two degrees Centigrade above present ones were attained. Part of the evidence for the Optimum comes from shells in postglacial raised beach deposits (p. 159). The milder climate is also demonstrated by the presence of pollen of holly and ivy in Zones VI and VIIa in East Lothian (Newey 1965). It has also often been noted that layers of tree remains, especially pine, occur widely in peat bogs in the Highlands well above the level at which trees exist today. For example, stools of pine are usually abundant in the peat bogs of eastern Ross-shire up to an altitude of 2000 feet (Peach *et al.* 1912). While the present upper limit of trees in Scotland is almost entirely artificial, a result of man's depredations, it is nevertheless apparent that the tree-line at the Climatic Optimum was above the present natural tree-line. N. V. Pears (1965) has suggested that the natural limit of trees in the Cairngorms is now between 2000 and 2250 feet, but he has found abundant remains of pine along with some birch remains up to an altitude of 2600 feet. This high tree-line appears to have been achieved in the later part of the Boreal period. In the succeeding Atlantic period the wetter climate resulted in the rapid accumulation of peat and consequent destruction of the high-level trees in the Cairngorms.

There was doubtless a general lowering of the tree-line in Scotland as a whole at this time. Many spreads of hill peat began to accumulate during the Atlantic period and they built up rapidly over wide areas. Many basin peats, however, are older, some dating back to lateglacial times. During a particularly dry phase that occurred towards the end of

Boreal times these basin peats had been encroached upon by trees, but with the wetter conditions that followed peat growth resumed with renewed vigour and often the peat encroached on the surrounding forests. Large areas of lowland and hill side nevertheless remained tree-covered, for the mild damp conditions favoured dense forests. These conditions also caused changes in the forest composition, alder rapidly increasing in importance in the south, although in most of the Highlands it remained subsidiary to pine and birch.

During at least part of the sub-Boreal period (Zone VIIb) climate became somewhat drier and trees extended over peat bogs. In many peat sections in the Highlands a second layer of pine stumps can be seen as a record of this phase. Pears has found that the second layer of tree remains in the Cairngorms extends up to 2300 feet but no higher, implying that the sub-Boreal tree-line was at this altitude. With the return to wetter conditions in the sub-Atlantic period, beginning about 500 BC, the tree-line once again receded. Manley (1964) has estimated that around this time lowland summer temperatures fell by about 2° C and that upland summer temperatures dropped rather more. Precipitation and cloudiness increased, especially on the mountains, and evaporation decreased. Consequently peat began to accumulate rapidly again, not only in bogs that had been temporarily colonised by trees during part of the sub-Boreal period, but also over large tracts that had till then been free of peat.

The beginning of the sub-Atlantic period is often recorded in pollen diagrams by a marked decline in the proportion of tree pollen to non-tree pollen, this decline continuing up to the present day. Among the non-tree pollen, that of heather and allied plants in particular increased rapidly in amount (Fig. 88). The implication is that the wide open moorlands that now characterise so much of Scotland have expanded immensely in the last two and a half thousand years. The mountain tops above the highest tree-line have, of course, always remained open and windswept, while in some areas the decline in the proportion of tree pollen dates from the beginning of the sub-Boreal period, about 5000 years ago. The later stages of this decline in the tree cover are clearly the work of man, the effect of whose depredations, culminating in the extensive cutting of timber during two world wars, is at last being sharply reversed by the Forestry Commission. It is possible that man's influence on the vegetation began about 5000 years ago with the arrival of Neolithic settlers. This is suggested by the regular occurrence in some peat deposits of pollen of *Plantago lanceolata* (ribwort plantain) from the beginning of sub-Boreal times onwards (Donner 1962, Durno 1965). This plant is today commonly associated with pasturage and cultivation and has come to be regarded as an indicator of the beginning of forest clearance by man. In some pollen diagrams *Plantago lanceolata* does not appear till later in sub-Boreal times, and then only sparsely, or it may be restricted entirely to sub-Atlantic times, suggesting that important forest clearances were initiated by Iron Age man. This Iron Age influence is strongly represented in some pollen diagrams from the Edinburgh area (Newey 1965 and Fig. 88), while in Northeast Scotland it has been found that in early sub-Atlantic times the proportion of tree pollen falls much more rapidly at coastal sites than at inland sites, suggesting that the former were favoured by agriculturalists (Durno 1957).

Thus while the climatic deterioration that marked the beginning of the sub-Atlantic period brought about a reduction in the area of forests and an extension of peat mosses, man's influence also increased rapidly about this time. In part the two have worked together to the detriment of much of the land surface. Thus forest clearance by man has exposed the ground to the elements, allowing plant nutrients to be leached out of the soil, so that regeneration of trees has been hampered and the extension of heath and bog encouraged by the increasing soil acidity. In this partnership man's influence has for some time been dominant over much of the surface of Scotland, a point that is emphasised when we remember that, but for his activities, the greater part of the country away from the windswept northern and western margins would probably be forested to an altitude of around 2000 feet.

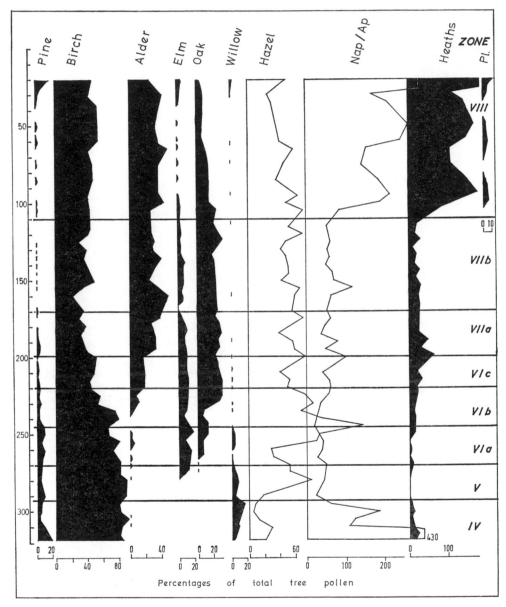

FIG. 88. Pollen diagram for a peat moss in the Eddleston valley, northern Peeblesshire, after W. W. Newey 1965. Depths in cms. Nap/Ap = non-arboreal pollen expressed as a percentage of arboreal pollen. Pl = *Plantago lanceolata*.

Some discoveries of animal remains

Among the larger animals that existed in Scotland during glacial times were woolly rhinoceros, mammoth, Giant Deer, elk and reindeer. The radiocarbon date of 27 500 years for a woolly rhinoceros bone from Bishopbriggs (p. 145) shows that this animal was present in Scotland at least during the long interstadial that preceded the last great build-up of glacier ice. Mammoth survived until the time of the Perth Readvance, as is shown by the radiocarbon-dated tusk from the Kilmaurs area (p. 145). Remains of Giant Deer have been obtained from the lateglacial deposits of the former Corstorphine Loch in Edinburgh and from Maybole in Ayrshire and it seems likely that, as in Ireland, this animal became extinct when glacial conditions came to an end around 10 000 years ago (Mitchell and Parkes 1949). Elk may have suffered similarly: it has been found in lateglacial deposits at Whitrig Bog in Berwickshire as well as at Airleywight (8 miles northwest of Perth) in deposits of unknown age. The reindeer apparently survived longer but the time of its extinction is uncertain. Although almost all the sites at which these animal remains have been found lie south of the Highlands, this may well reflect the availability of artificial sections and of people to investigate them rather than their true distribution. One major discovery has been made at the other end of the mainland, for in a limestone cave near Inchnadamff in western Sutherland B. N. Peach and J. Horne (1917) found an abundance of faunal remains. A layer of angular limestone fragments contained remains of lemming, vole, bear and birds, including hundreds of ptarmigan. A higher layer composed of red clay with occasional splinters of limestone provided lynx, reindeer, red deer and otter as well as remains of frog and toad in large numbers.

Weathering and mass-wasting

The effects of climatic change are seen in many landforms. Like the arctic plants some of these landforms reflect the harsh climatic conditions that prevailed on even the lowest ground in glacial times, but they are now being produced only on high ground or not at all. These cold climate features are usually referred to as 'periglacial' even though the term is not strictly applicable to those forming now on our mountain tops far distant from modern glaciers.

Among the various types of evidence of the severe climates of the past are involutions and fossil frost wedges. The former are seen as intricate folds in stratified deposits and usually occur in the uppermost few feet of such materials. They are believed to have been formed when the ground was permanently frozen, except for the top few feet that thawed out in summer. The often sharp lower boundary to a zone of involutions is thought to correspond with the upper surface of the permafrost at the time of their formation. Unfortunately periglacial involutions can be confused with structures formed in quite different ways, so that records of their occurrence have to be treated with caution. On the other hand, well-developed fossil frost wedges are much more reliable indicators of past climate. They are most commonly observed in sand and gravel pits, where they often appear as vertical wedges that taper from a width of a foot or two at the top to end in a point or in a narrow vein at a depth of 5 to 15 feet. The beds of sand and gravel bordering a wedge are usually bent and slightly faulted, while within the wedge most of the stones stand vertically. The wedges were originally tapering masses of ice that gradually grew in frozen ground as it contracted and cracked under conditions of intense cold. Later, as the ice melted, debris replaced it to provide the fossil features we now see.

The distribution of frost wedges, so far as it is known at present, is shown in Fig. 89. The wedges close to Glasgow and some of those south of Edinburgh occur in sands or gravels overlain by glacial till and relate to cold interstadial times, probably having been formed when glacier ice was advancing into these areas. Almost all the remainder, however, extend almost to the present ground surface and show that a severe climate has existed in the areas in which they occur since these areas were last covered by glacier ice.

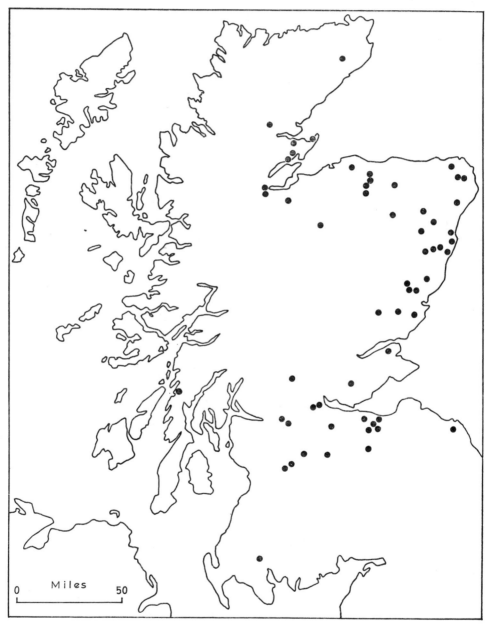

FIG. 89. Known locations of fossil frost wedges. Based mainly on R. W. Galloway 1961a and on unpublished observations by E. A. Fitzpatrick, J. C. C. Romans, J. S. Smith and the author.

It is likely that these wedges also were formed mainly at times of glacial advance or re-advance. Their dominant eastern distribution suggests a relationship to the various re-advances shown in Fig. 59, when the west was largely or entirely ice-covered and part or all of the east remained ice-free. Most of the wedges occur outside the limit of the Perth Readvance and none have yet been found within the limit of the Loch Lomond Readvance, for the latter was followed by the rapid warming up of early postglacial times. The distribution of involutions is apparently very similar, except that a single example is reported to have been found within the Loch Lomond limit (Galloway 1961a). While the distribution of frost wedges shown in Fig. 89 thus exhibits a significant pattern, it must be pointed out that to some extent it reflects the distribution of sand and gravel pits and of people who are interested in examining them.

The influence of the cold conditions of glacial times is also seen in the frost-shattered rock debris that covers the ground in various parts of Scotland, for intense break-up of bedrock occurred even in the lowest areas. Where glacier ice advanced over the fragmented rocks it usually incorporated them in its till, but beyond the glacier limits of various times the frost-shattered debris survived widely. The permafrost and sparse vegetation encouraged movement of this debris by solifluction, so that we may envisage the thawed surface layer in late spring and summer as saturated with water and moving down-slope much more readily than at the present time. Today this debris masks many slopes to a depth of a few feet, concealing minor irregularities and thus giving the slopes a smoother form. At the base of slopes, where the debris accumulated, it is thicker and may attain depths of 20 to 25 feet. Small valley-heads in particular often have a considerable infilling of the angular debris and the streams have had to cut down into it afresh.

Although solifluction deposits are of limited volume in Scotland compared with southern England where, beyond all the glacier limits of Quaternary times, accumulations of soli-flucted debris locally reach fifty or even a hundred feet in thickness, they are important in that they have often provided the parent material on which soils have developed. Peri-glacial conditions also appear to have given rise to an indurated layer that occurs beneath freely-drained soils in many parts of eastern Scotland. This compact layer usually occurs at a depth of 16 to 24 inches and it has been suggested that it marks the former junction between permafrost and the surface layer that thawed in summer. This 'fossil permafrost' has a detrimental effect on plant growth, particularly by inhibiting root penetration. It is also somewhat impermeable to water, sometimes resulting in waterlogging of the soil, while in years of low rainfall the shallow depth of soil above it may dry out and cause plants to suffer (Fitzpatrick 1956, 1958).

The degree to which frost shattering and solifluction have affected the land surface appears to be closely related to the limits of the glacial readvances. Thus in Northeast Scotland beyond the limit of the Aberdeen–Lammermuir Readvance the effects of soli-fluction are particularly marked, while bedrock shattered to depths as great as 25 feet has been observed (Galloway 1961b). The effectiveness of solifluction outside the limit of the Perth Readvance can be gauged from glacial meltwater channels that run along hill sides. That many quite small channels survive in such locations implies that the period of soli-fluction that accompanied the Perth Readvance, although probably severe while it lasted, was too short to infill them. It is noticeable, however, that while complex systems of very small channels occur inside the limit of the Perth Readvance (e.g. Fig. 45), they are absent outside it, suggesting that many of the very minor features have been obliterated. A difference in the forms of kames and related depositional features is also apparent on either side of the Perth limit, for those within it are usually more sharply defined. The most marked change, however, takes place at the limit of the Loch Lomond Readvance, for solifluction has not operated at all on low ground since the glaciers of this stage disappeared, with the consequence that within this limit features such as kames and moraines are extremely sharp and clear. Rock outcrops too are often fresh and little affected by weathering so that minor features such as striae are often much better preserved than elsewhere.

That periglacial processes were active at the time of the Loch Lomond Readvance is indicated by evidence beyond its limit. For example, as mentioned already, the layer of mineral matter deposited in some lakes at this time implies a sparse vegetation cover and active solifluction. Peat near Keith in Banffshire, situated at about 550 feet above sea-level and radiocarbon-dated as between about 11 900 and 10 800 years old, is overlain by a layer of stones and clay that is probably solifluction debris that moved downslope over it during Zone III (Godwin and Willis 1959). The operation of this process during this cold phase has been clearly demonstrated by radiocarbon dating of material from a section at about 500 feet above sea-level situated by the Bigholm Burn, near Langholm, in Dumfriesshire. Here a layer of organic mud beneath thick solifluction gravels gave dates of about 11 800 and 11 600 years before present. From within the gravels themselves a lens of organic mud provided a date of about 10 800 years, while a similar deposit on top of the gravels gave ages of about 9600 and 9500 years (Godwin and Willis 1964).

This dated evidence allows one to speculate on the possible significance of certain evidence related to former lake sites that was described last century. In Edinburgh at the foot of the steep scree slope that descends from Salisbury Crags the former existence of a small postglacial lake referred to as Holyrood Loch is well known. Beneath the deposits of this lake, however, is a thick bed of angular boulders up to two feet across. Still farther down (some 40 feet beneath the ground surface) is a layer of peat and beneath this a bed of marl with many water plants and freshwater shells (Taylor 1888). From this evidence it seems very probable that a lake existed here in lateglacial times and that its deposits were buried beneath scree from Salisbury Crags when frost-shattering was very active during a cold phase (probably Zone III). The lateglacial lake deposits at Corstorphine (p. 214) are extensively covered by a layer of sand and gravel above which are the deposits of a postglacial lake whose final reclamation was completed in 1837. The sand and gravel layer is clearly water-laid and represents flood deposits spread out by the Water of Leith as it debouched onto the flat ground. Since only postglacial deposits overlie the sand and gravel layer it seems likely that the latter was laid down largely or entirely during the Zone III cold period.

If such a modest-sized stream as the Water of Leith could deposit great quantities of sand and gravel at this time, one wonders what volumes of debris were laid down by other rivers elsewhere in Scotland. Unfortunately specific evidence on this point is lacking, for the matter has not been investigated. Yet we may imagine that, while the cold climate would probably be associated with a reduction of precipitation, this would be more than compensated in spring as winter snows began to melt and the ground surface thawed out. The sparse vegetation, feeble soil development and absence of a protective cover of hill peat would all encourage rapid run-off, while glacial till would be particularly susceptible to gullying and solifluction and was probably stripped off many of the steeper slopes to provide abundant debris for the rivers. Under these conditions frequent flooding in spring and rapid deposition of coarse debris on low ground must have occurred, and it seems very probable that many of the alluvial fans that are common where upland streams debouch onto valley floors were largely formed or greatly augmented at this time.

Another probable result of periglacial stream action is the erosion of valleys in sandy deposits. Spreads of fluvioglacial sand are quite often dissected by small dry valleys, occasionally forming dendritic systems, and it seems likely that these valleys were excavated when the sand was rendered impervious owing to its interstitial water being frozen. Similar valleys are widely developed in the Forth and Tay regions in the raised beach deposits associated with the Perth Readvance. Here they occasionally attain a depth of 60 feet and a width between their upper edges of 300 yards. That they have not been excavated recently is evident from the fact that the carse clay and the sub-carse peat (Chapter 8) extend some distance along their floors, the peat having been dated close to one of the valleys as about 8400 years old. The valleys are therefore at least this old and it seems probable that they were excavated under the cold conditions of lateglacial times before the ground became stabilised by a dense cover of vegetation (Sissons *et al*. 1965).

The marked amelioration of climate and the rapid spread of a dense cover of vegetation as the ice decayed following the Loch Lomond Readvance halted abruptly the operation of periglacial processes on low ground, but some of these processes have continued to operate on high ground. There is also evidence on high ground that implies that in earlier times, when glacier ice still covered adjacent lower ground, conditions were extremely severe. The principal evidence is the great extent of intensely-shattered rock. Plateaux are sometimes covered with accumulations of angular debris so abundant that it is difficult to find an exposure of solid rock. Frequently this debris is itself covered by peat, effectively demonstrating that the break-up of the rock relates to past times. On granite summits boulders are numerous but in addition there are spreads of gritty sand that may be several feet deep and the coarser elements of which are the individual quartz crystals from the disintegrated granite. On some rocks, such as the gabbro of the Cuillins, frost action has produced serrated ridges whose contrast with the glacier-smoothed slopes at lower levels is extreme. Quartzite mountains have proved particularly susceptible to frost attack. Thus the conical summit of Schiehallion in the central Grampians is covered in a mass of boulders, while in Caithness quartzite hills such as Scaraben have great quantities of scree that descends far down their slopes. The consequences of severe frost action are also very evident on the conglomerate of Morven in Caithness, for its summit is almost covered by gravel while its flanks are buried in blocks of enormous dimensions (Crampton *et al*. 1914). On moderate to steep slopes the angular debris has often moved down hill as lobes, which are fully exposed around the mountain summits but may be buried in peat farther down the slopes. On Lochnagar the frontal faces of the lobes are as much as 15 feet high and are composed of granite boulders up to 4 feet long. Sometimes the frost-riven debris is arranged in terraces and again some of those of the Lochnagar area are large, occasionally forming steps 10 to 15 feet high. Among the minor forms that the debris occasionally assumes are rings and stripes. At the northern end of Ben Wyvis the presence of such patterned ground is revealed by variations in the vegetation. On level ground rings of fresh green moss 5 to 10 feet in diameter correspond with shallow circular depressions occupied by angular stones. Within the circles the slightly higher ground is occupied by withered brown moss, while stones are scarce. On slopes the rings become elongated into ovals, which in turn pass into stripes of sorted debris when the gradient exceeds about six degrees (Galloway 1961c). Similar stripes occur in the Cairngorms, while in western Sutherland bare stone circles up to 13 feet in diameter occur on Beinn an Fhurain (Godard 1965).

These various mountain-top features probably ceased to form when the climate improved following the Loch Lomond Readvance. J. M. Ragg and J. S. Bibby (1966) found abundant frost-shattered debris on the summit and upper slopes of Broad Law in the central Southern Uplands, and recorded a thickness of more than 11 feet at an altitude of 1700 feet, a thousand feet or so below the summit. On the other hand, at a similar altitude in the corrie of Loch Skene, only a few miles away, comparable deposits appear to be absent and steep-sided hummocky moraines of presumed Zone III age are beautifully preserved. A similar relationship is often apparent in the northwestern Highlands. For example, in the areas covered by Figs 60 and 61 the high ground that overlooked the glaciers often abounds in fossil periglacial features, but on the ground occupied by the glaciers well-developed examples are lacking. The contrast can be readily examined on the high ground of the Applecross peninsula, for the road to the village reaches just over 2000 feet at its highest part. Here on either side of the road are large areas of bare gently-inclined beds of Torridon Sandstone dotted with stones and boulders left by the ice. The rock is but little weathered and is almost as it was when glacier ice last left it. However, only a few hundred yards from the road and some 200 to 300 feet above it, on the higher ground to the east, a complete change occurs. Above this level large areas have been completely shattered by frost action to produce great accumulations of slab-like boulders, some of them 5 or 6 feet long, that are piled on top of each other at all angles and often in precarious positions. This sharp change in so short a distance can hardly be due to climatic causes and it appears that below a certain level the glaciers shown in Fig. 60 either swept away the debris that had accumulated earlier, or protected the ground they covered from frost action.

Tors provide another group of features whose existence is related to climatic conditions of the past, although different opinions have been expressed in recent years concerning their origin and significance. The largest assemblage of tors occurs on the granite of the Cairngorms, where the individual masses of rock rise abruptly from relatively smooth slopes to heights ranging from 10 to 70 or 80 feet (Plate XXIIIB). Most of them occur on summits or the crests of spurs, but some are on slopes as great as 20 degrees and at altitudes as low as 2300 feet. Vertical joint planes in the granite usually correspond with the sides of the tors and give rise to deep clefts in them, while pseudobedding parallel with the slope of the ground divides them into a series of slabs. The conspicuous isolated tor of Clachnaben in Kincardineshire, the Oxen Craig on Bennachie in Aberdeenshire, and the tors of Ben Rinnes in Banffshire are also developed in granite. On the other hand, the tor-like mass on The Buck, in Banffshire, is developed in metamorphic rock, the tors on the summits of Morven, Smean and Maiden Pap in Caithness are formed of conglomerate, while those on Ben Loyal in Sutherland are composed of syenite (Linton 1955).

It is sometimes assumed that the presence of tors indicates that an area has not been covered by glacier ice. However, as we have seen (Chapter 7), it appears that the whole or virtually the whole of the mainland has been overwhelmed. In some instances there is clear local evidence that tors were buried beneath the ice: for example, the Argyll Stone, a small granite tor in the western Cairngorms, is surrounded by schist erratics (Sugden 1965). The tors do reflect the work of glacier ice in their distribution, however, for they appear to be absent from the intensely-glaciated west. Within the Cairngorms they are most numerous and largest on the northern and northeastern slopes of the mountain mass, where they were most sheltered from ice that came from the southwest. It therefore seems likely that tors were once far more numerous than they are now, most of them having been destroyed by glacier ice except in some relatively-protected eastern and northern areas. It may be, therefore, as D. L. Linton has suggested, that the tors have resulted largely from weathering in Tertiary times, their specific location being determined by a wider spacing of joints. The removal of the more readily-weathered rock around the tors may well have taken place mainly in Tertiary times also, but a final modelling under periglacial conditions probably put the finishing touches to the features we now see.

In emphasising the different climates of past times, we must not forget that the present climate of the mountain summits is very different from that of the low ground. The records of the former observatory on the summit of Ben Nevis show that the mean annual temperature from 1884 to 1896 was below freezing (− 0.4° C.), ranging from − 4.6° in February to + 4.7° in July. These temperatures are comparable with those of the coast of east-central Greenland. The high precipitation (144 inches), much of which falls as snow, and the very frequent gales make the climate much harsher than such Arctic areas, however. Even on the summit of Broad Law in the Southern Uplands, a mere 2750 feet above sea-level, the soil is often frozen from late December until early April apart from the diurnal thawing of a thin surface layer, while ice lenses have been observed in April at a depth of $1\frac{1}{2}$ feet (Ragg and Bibby 1966). Under such conditions it is not surprising to find that periglacial features are still forming on the mountains, although they are much smaller than those formed in past times. Among these features are small lobes and terraces with frontal faces up to 3 or 4 feet high. Quite often the presence of 'bow-waves' in front of large boulders and hollows in their wakes shows that they are still moving down hill. Small stone polygons up to about 2 feet across (and occasionally reaching 4 feet) form on flat ground, while examination of scree slopes may show that they are composed of alternate stripes of coarse and finer debris aligned down the slope and spaced at intervals of about 9 to 18 inches. That such stripes are still active was proved on Tinto Hill in Lanarkshire by destroying a small area of them, it being found on visiting the site two years later that they had re-formed (Miller *et al.* 1954). On some mountain tops the sparse vegetation and strong winds encourage the formation here and there of sand dunes, although these are very tiny features only a few feet high. Much larger sand dunes, comparable to some on the present coast, that occur on the plateau between An Teallach and Mac' us Mathair in Wester Ross relate to past times, for they are covered by vegetation except in occasional scars.

The level down to which periglacial features are being formed today is very variable, depending on such factors as aspect, slope, rock type and precipitation, as well as on the type of feature being considered. In general, however, over most of the mainland and inner islands polygons and stripes are not found below about 1800 to 2000 feet, although there are local exceptions. For example, while the stone stripes on the south side of Tinto Hill descend to 1900 feet, those on the north side are found as low as 1300 feet where burning and overgrazing have destroyed the vegetation. In the north and west the altitude down to which periglacial processes operate appears to fall quite rapidly, a change that R. W. Galloway (1961c) attributes mainly to high winds and their inhibiting influence on vegetation. He points out that the features forming at 1200 to 1400 feet on the wind-swept summit of Ronas Hill in the Shetlands are comparable with those forming at 3500 to 4000 feet on the Cairngorms and Ben Nevis, while on the island of Unst small stone stripes occur even at sea-level where bad soil conditions have inhibited vegetation growth.

Such evidence leads one to ask: by what margin do the highest mountains in Scotland now fail to carry glaciers? and, have glaciers existed in Scotland since the Zone III glaciers disappeared? The latter question has been partly answered by J. J. Donner (1962), for he analysed the pollen in lake deposits situated at an altitude of 2350 feet in the corrie of Lochan nan Cat on the northeastern side of Ben Lawers in Perthshire. He found a continuous sequence of deposits from Zone IV onwards, implying that in this corrie, and hence in many others, glaciers have not existed since the decay of those nourished during the climatic recession of Zone III. This does not, however, exclude the possibility of glaciers having existed at higher altitudes. It is well known that snow usually persists throughout the year in sheltered spots such as Garbh Choire in the Cairngorms and the Observatory Gully on Ben Nevis. It is said that in 1933 Ben Nevis was entirely free from snow for the first time since 1840 at least, while the Cairngorm snow-beds completely disappeared in that year for the first time since before 1864 (Manley 1949). Since 1933 the snow-beds have melted occasionally, a change that reflects the recent slight amelioration of climate that has taken place in the North Atlantic region. Glaciers in countries such as Iceland and Norway were considerably more extensive in the eighteenth and nineteenth centuries than they are now, so that one wonders what conditions were like in the highest Scottish mountains at that time. There are hints that snow-beds were larger and more persistent, for eighteenth-century travellers commented on the survival in late summer of beds large enough to be conspicuous from a distance on Ben Nevis and the Cairngorms. T. Pennant (1771) considered these beds, as well as one on the northern side of Ben Wyvis, to be permanent. Recently D. E. Sugden (1965) has found that the diameter of the largest lichens (*Rhizocarpon* genus) growing on boulders inside the moraines of five Cairngorm corries is only half the diameter of the largest ones growing outside the moraines. From the estimated rate at which lichens grow in the Cairngorms he suggests that large snow-beds (and perhaps even glaciers) occupied the corries in the eighteenth century and were perhaps responsible for the innermost moraines. Whether this suggestion is warranted or not, there is no doubt about the interesting evidence on Ben Nevis described by V. Gatty in 1906. He found that a tiny lochan in Corrie na Ciste was held up by a small 'moraine' composed of blocks up to 4 feet across. Fresh fractures on the corrie walls showed that some of these blocks had fallen very recently and it was clear that the 'morainic' dam was being added to each spring when debris slid down the snow-bed that then covered the site of the lochan. Not far away, in the Observatory Gully, Gatty found that a snow-bed was in fact composed of hard ice, while a tunnel 4 or 5 feet high at its lower end presumably marked the course of a stream that had emerged from beneath the ice. From such evidence it appears that the highest Scottish mountains were at least very close to having glaciers not along go (and, also, probably during the sub-Atlantic recession about 500 BC). Despite the very recent amelioration of climate a drop in temperature of only 2° C. or so would probably be sufficient to establish glaciers in the highest corries.

Among the processes of slope modification, one to which we should make special reference is large-scale land-slipping, for it has been very important on many steep slopes. In some instances land-slipping has been greatly assisted by favourable rock structure. The prime example is northern Skye where, below the great escarpment that culminates in The Storr and Quirang, huge masses of basalt, that have collapsed owing to the incompetence of the underlying clays, now lie in a belt up to half a mile wide as a series of remarkable tilted blocks forming pinnacles and crags with lakelets or ill-drained hollows between (Plate XXI). In neighbouring Raasay landslips are again common, and at and near the margin of the eastern cliffs fissures 1 to 10 feet wide and tens of feet deep in sandstone appear to have been caused by movement of this well-jointed rock on the underlying shales (Lee 1920). Great slips have occurred on the island of Eigg, some of them facilitated by thick shales underlying sandstones and lavas. Many landslips have been induced by glacial oversteepening of slopes, as witness the numerous examples that occur along the sides of glacial troughs. Sometimes these landslips are revealed by arcuate scars on a valley side, sometimes by great masses of tumbled blocks littering a slope, or by a sea of hummocks that to some extent resembles a morainic landscape. In Glen Shira, not far from Inveraray, a vast landslip has involved the hill side for over a square mile (Hill *et al.* 1905). Another large slide in the valley of Allt Coire Gabhail on the south side of Glen Coe produced a temporary lake now represented by the flat valley floor (Bailey *et al.* 1916). A slip in Glen Fintaig, tributary to Glen Gloy, has formed a massive pile of debris some 40 or 50 feet high that extends down one side of the glen from a fractured rocky scar. An important factor in the opening out of glacial troughs, much of this land-slipping probably took place in glacial and lateglacial times. Doubtless some masses tumbled down onto the glaciers themselves and contributed to the morainic debris. Probably the main time of collapse was when the glaciers decayed and thus removed their support from the valley walls, at which time also the process would be assisted by the thawing of permafrost. Land-slipping still continues, though doubtless at a reduced rate, as can be seen from the occasional fresh scars on the sides of Highland glens. One relatively recent landslip in northern Arran is known as the Scriden and comprises an accumulation of sandstone and conglomerate blocks, above which several parts of the hill side have moved slightly to produce deep and narrow rents in the ground. This fall is said to have occurred some 250 years ago, producing a concussion that shook the earth and was heard in Bute and Argyllshire.*

Coastal changes

By far the greatest changes that have taken place in coastal areas of Scotland in lateglacial and postglacial times are the changes in relative levels of land and sea that we have discussed in earlier chapters. In the broadest terms, the major result of these changes was to reduce greatly the extent of the outer islands and to add considerable areas of land to the more central parts of Scotland, especially the Central Lowlands. Compared with such changes others in coastal areas have been small, although they have often been of great significance to the local inhabitants.

Most of the solid rock coastlines of Scotland have altered very little through erosion in postglacial times. Along many stretches of the west coast of the Highlands the virtual absence of erosion is shown by glacially-smoothed rocks and striae between tide-marks. Coastal erosion in the country generally has been essentially of soft drift deposits, and raised beach materials in particular have been stripped away. This has happened, for example, at many places along the East Fife coast, as at St Monans, Crail and St Andrews. The menace of this process today is seen here and elsewhere in the sea-walls that protect many towns and villages built on unconsolidated deposits.

Erosion in some areas has been more than counterbalanced by deposition in others. The infilling towards the head of the Solway Firth is evident from the vast sand flats that are exposed at low tide. Small coastal indentations such as Rough Firth, Auchencairn Bay and Fleet Bay are completely vacated by the sea at low water, and it is clear that the flats thus exposed will in due course become permanently part of the land as the salt-marsh vegetation that occurs here and there at their margins extends its influence. Infilling of the deep fjords of the Highland west coast is naturally less marked, but at the head of many there is a considerable delta continued beneath the waters of the fjord by a zone of shoals. On the west coast of the Outer Hebrides and on the east and south coasts of the Orkneys

---

* It is probable that land-slipping is responsible for the presence of glacial till on top of stratified deposits containing plant and animal remains in Cowdon Glen about 10 miles southwest of Glasgow. These deposits gave rise to a great deal of controversy in the late nineteenth century, some writers maintaining that the stratified deposits accumulated during the warm climate of an interglacial.

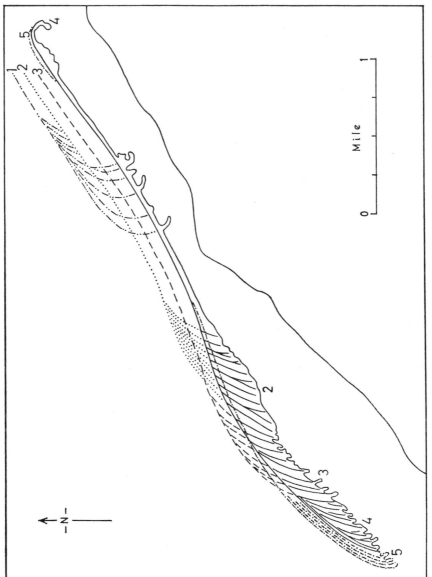

FIG. 90. Successive stages (1 to 5) in the evolution of The Bar, near Nairn. After J. A. Steers 1937.

shingle ridges have been thrown up by storm waves across many bays and inlets. In the Orkneys the ridges are called 'ayres' and the lagoons behind them are referred to as 'oyces'. Some of the lagoons, such as the Peerie Sea at Kirkwall, are salt while others, such as the Roos Loch in Stronsay, are fresh water. Occasionally the ayres have joined islands together as, for example, the one linking Deerness to the rest of Mainland and that between Hoy and Walls (Wilson et al. 1935).

Among the coastal storm ridges are some of the most rapidly-changing landforms of Scotland. The Bar, near Nairn, is the most elaborate feature in this category and consists of a narrow strip of sand and pebbles 4 miles long situated a short distance off-shore (Plate XXIVb). The major part is composed of parallel wave-built ridges of shingle, as many as 18 in number, in the shelter of which salt-marshes occur. Some ridges aligned at an angle to the main direction are the curved ends of earlier ridges that once existed to seawards of the present feature (Fig. 90). As these outer features have been destroyed, new ridges have been thrown up to landwards and have also extended The Bar farther and farther towards the southwest, this extension amounting to five-sixths of a mile between 1835 and 1937 (Steers 1937). In the same locality the River Findhorn was formerly deflected by a long narrow spit to enter the sea about 6 miles west-southwest of the present village of Findhorn, part of this old river course now being occupied by Buckie Loch. In the year 1702 this spit was breached during a severe storm to give the river its present mouth. During the next few years the old village of Findhorn was destroyed and was re-established on its present site about a mile to the east. Farther along the coast the westward transport of beach material is again shown by the prominent spit that deflects the mouth of the River Lossie, while still farther along the Spey has suffered many changes through the same cause and according to tradition once entered the sea 3 miles west of its present outlet. The shingle accumulates as a spit across the mouth of the Spey, impeding the river in times of flood. The spit was breached during the great flood of 1829 and has been subsequently cut through artificially, but each time this is done it builds up again. Thus between 1903 and 1933 the spit grew in length from 180 yards to three-quarters of a mile. It was cut through in 1938, but in 1946 was 200 yards long and by 1953 500 yards (Grove 1955). The last cut was made in 1962 and it is estimated that the next one will be required in 1982.

Sand dunes comprise another group of landforms that in certain coastal areas have changed rapidly. Narrow belts of dunes are common along many coasts with sandy beaches, and dunes occasionally cover large areas, as at Tents Muir in eastern Fife, at Torrs Warren at the head of Luce Bay, and around Balnakeil Bay near Durness. In many of the western islands blown sand is very widespread and often consists almost entirely of comminuted shell fragments. It gives rise to the sandy plains, or machair, that lie between the coastal dune belt and the hills and bogs of the interior (Fig. 40). The machair has contributed greatly to the fertility of Tiree but reaches its optimum development along the west coast of the Outer Hebrides, especially in the more southern islands. Here the wide sandy beaches exposed at low tide supply abundant material for the winds to carry landwards. This material has buried many of the coastal shingle ridges built by storm waves and has filled the lagoons within them to form the valuable machair.

The blowing of sand has not always favoured human activity, however, and there are certainly two localities in the Northeast where it has had grave consequences for the inhabitants. Between Peterhead and Fraserburgh lie the remains of the Royal Burgh of Rattray, only the ruined chapel now being visible. This small port grew up at the edge of a lagoon formed behind a two-mile-long spit built in postglacial times when sea-level was slightly higher than now. Around the year 1720 the port ceased to function, for the entrance to the lagoon had become blocked with blown sand to form the Loch of Strathbeg. The level of the loch has risen since, partly owing to the accumulation of mud and aquatic vegetation, while an artificial outlet has been made to the sea, which is now almost half a mile away as a result of further deposition of sand by wind and waves (Walton 1956). Until recently the greatest spread of blowing sand in Scotland was the Culbin Sands, now largely stabilised through the work of the Forestry Commission (Plate XXII). The sand in places attains a thickness of a hundred feet and has been built into large dunes that are mostly transverse to the prevailing wind and have steep leeward slopes and gentler windward slopes (Steers 1937). The material has been picked up by the wind from the extensive beaches of the adjacent coast and much of it was probably brought to the coast by the River Findhorn, which carries great quantities of sand. Some three hundred years ago the area now occupied by the Culbin Sands was mostly fertile farmland. The years 1694 and 1695, however, appear to have marked the culmination of a period of sand accumulation that resulted in the overwhelming of the Culbin estate comprising a mansion house, 16 farms (of which only Earnhill escaped destruction) and crofters' cottages. Today the only signs of this once fertile land are plough furrows and cart tracks occasionally revealed when the wind moves the sand.

Recent changes and the influence of man

By far the most obvious changes that take place in the land surface at the present time are those resulting from exceptionally heavy rainfalls. The floods of August 1948 in South-east Scotland accompanied a fall of more than 5 inches in one day over part of the area, while in 72 hours at the end of July 1956 5 inches of rain fell over a wide area around the Moray Firth with 10 inches attained in a small part of Nairnshire (Learmonth 1950, Green 1958). The floods associated with such downpours inevitably make news headlines and the emphasis is on the inundation of buildings and the disruption of lines of communication. Serious and costly as this damage may be (in 1953 a thunderstorm caused £130 000 of road damage in Argyllshire), it represents but a small part of the effects of heavy rains on the land surface. Thus the 1948 downpour in Southeast Scotland caused hundreds of small landslides, while the swollen rivers undercut their banks at numerous places and spread a layer of gravel over many stretches of floodplain. It is estimated that in the 1956 flood roughly 1500 acres of fertile haughland in the Laich of Moray alone were covered with gravel. While the 1953 thunderstorm resulted in 6000 tons of debris being deposited on the main road by Loch Lochy, it also produced scores of long narrow debris slides starting in round-headed landslip scars on many steep valley slopes in southern Inverness-shire and northern Argyllshire (Common 1954). The sides of some Cairngorm valleys have a corrugated appearance owing to thick deposits of glacial till having been scarred by numerous, closely-spaced, V-shaped ravines 10 to 30 feet deep. Such ravines on the southern slope of Glen Geusachan were greatly deepened during a downpour in August 1956 when more than 6 inches of rain probably fell in one day. On the gentler slopes towards the valley floor each ravine is continued by two parallel walls of debris up to 20 yards apart and 3 feet high containing boulders up to 6 feet across. Many of these deposits were greatly augmented during the 1956 storm, and it appears that they and the ravines that lead down to them have been formed mainly by the flowage of tongues of water-soaked debris down the valley sides. Each pair of boulder ridges represents the coarser debris pushed aside as a bulging tongue with its more quickly moving centre of finer material continued down the slope (Baird and Lewis 1957).

The most famous flood in Scotland, and the best-documented through the efforts of T. D. Lauder, occurred in 1829. Heavy rain fell over a wide area from Strath Nairn to the valley of the Dee, almost a sixth of the normal annual total falling in 24 hours in part of the Findhorn basin. At the height of the flood 20 square miles of the plain of Forres were inundated and the River Dee was 33 feet higher than normal at the Linn of Dee, while the River Findhorn reached 40 feet above its usual level in the gorge spanned by Dulsie Bridge and 50 feet above in the very narrow gorge a mile above Sluie. Hundreds of acres of land formed of unconsolidated material were swept away from valley floors, the coarser materials subsequently being spread widely as thick layers of sand and gravel over low-lying land, while large masses of debris were accumulated where mountain streams debouched on valley floors. Some of the latter are still very evident today as, for example, the mass of sand and granite blocks a quarter of a mile long and up to 150 yards broad laid down by the Luibeg Burn in the Cairngorms.

There is no doubt that flooding has been greatly aggravated by man's activities. This was appreciated long ago by Lauder and his opinion, expressed in 1830, is well worth quoting: 'Any given quantity of rain must now produce a much greater flood than it could have done before the country became so highly improved. Formerly the rain drops were either evaporated on the hill side, or were sucked up by an arid or spongy soil, before so many of them could coalesce as to form a rill. But when we consider the number of open cuts made to dry hill pastures – the numerous bogs reclaimed by drainage – the ditches of enclosure recently constructed – and the long lines of roads formed with side drains, back drains and cross conduits, we shall find that, of late years, the country has been covered with a perfect net-work of courses to catch and to concentrate the rain drops as they fall, and to hurry them off in accumulated tribute to the next stream.'

Apart from his influence on flooding, man has affected the land surface in many other ways and is now one of the most important factors in its evolution. Some results of his activities, such as the urban sprawls, the lines of communication, the quarries and sand and gravel pits, and the piles of waste from coal or oil-shale mines are obvious and require no comment here. So also are some of the changes he has wrought in coastal areas such as the constriction and deepening of the Clyde estuary or the reclamations from the sea that still continue along the shores of the Forth. The consequences of man's actions are far from fully appreciated, however, and in some instances are far-reaching. The construction of sea-walls may protect one stretch of coastline from attack but, by depriving an adjacent stretch of its supply of beach material, may cause it to suffer erosion instead. On the other hand, some of man's works have unintentionally resulted in new land being produced. For example, a wall set up in an attempt to control the meanderings of the Nith at its mouth was probably responsible for the increase of 480 acres in the area of Kirkconnell Marsh and of 1020 acres in Caerlaverock Marsh between 1856 and 1946 (Marshall 1962).

That much of Scotland away from the western and northern margins would probably be forested up to an altitude of around 2000 feet but for man's depradations has already been mentioned. Man has also removed large areas of peat, especially from low ground. Of many of these former bogs there is now no sign, although the straight boundaries and sharp corners of others show that they are the remnants of features that were once more extensive. While innumerable small lakes that existed in early postglacial times have since been largely or entirely infilled by the accumulation of peat and mineral matter, their final draining to produce flat fertile farmland has often been carried out by man. He has also removed great quantities of stones and boulders left behind by the glaciers. While all these achievements have improved or extended the land available for crops or animals they have also exposed it to the elements to a far greater degree than at any time since forests spread rapidly in early postglacial times. On hill slopes matters have often been made worse by burning and over-grazing so that the protective cover of vegetation has been breached and debris that was once relatively stable is now actively moving again. Some of the hill-side gullies are clearly recent additions to the landscape, for they form straight gashes along artificial drainage lines. It is equally apparent that many others are growing rapidly, for their slopes are steep and composed of loose debris that lacks vegetation. Many hill slopes are scarred by innumerable small irregularities: they include tiny 'sheep rubbings', each with its tail of debris trailing away down the slope (Plate IIB), and patches where water-soaked debris has moved down hill. Sometimes the movement of surface material has exposed the bare rock beneath and rendered the land useless, a process that was seen by R. Common (1954) to have operated in Glen Nevis and the Great Glen during the heavy rain of May 1953. On the higher hill slopes many peat mosses are dissected by innumerable channels floored by angular rock fragments. The cause of this dissection is not established, but it would be surprising if man himself were not the main agent through his flocks and through burning and forest destruction. Whatever the cause, the result is that many peat bogs have lost much of their capacity to absorb heavy rains so that run-off is far more rapid than in earlier times. On lower ground many alluvial fans that have probably received little increment since lateglacial times are now actively growing again.

It would be misleading to represent man's activities as entirely detrimental to the land surface, for the construction of dams for hydro-electricity and water supply, with their feeding channels running round the contours of the hills, have helped to regulate some rivers, while the recent marked extension in the area of forested land will, when the trees are well established, help to stabilise slopes and reduce the rate of run-off. Important as these activities are, however, they as yet affect only a small part of the total surface of Scotland. Over much of the country, especially on hill and mountain slopes and on valley floors, man's activities are of great significance not only for landform evolution but also for his own existence.

Looking back to glacial times, the situation may be summarised as follows. Glacial and periglacial processes produced a layer of loose unconsolidated debris of varying thickness that concealed the solid rocks over much of the country. While glaciers still existed, the sparse vegetation and cold climate facilitated the movement of this debris towards the valley floors, but this process was greatly retarded with the rapid spread of forests in early postglacial times. Especially during the last two and a half thousand years, however, man has almost destroyed this protective forest cover and in numerous ways, albeit often unintentionally, has encouraged the down-slope movement of the unconsolidated deposits to valley floors. Since the glacial and periglacial deposits are a product of times past, and the weathering of rock under present climatic conditions is a very slow process, this loss is irreplaceable. The ultimate result of this interference with nature will be the production of vast areas of bare infertile rock on hill slopes and of huge accumulations of coarse debris on valley floors. Although the day may be far off when this dismal forecast could be fulfilled, these final changes in the evolution of Scotland's scenery to date are certainly well established already. It is now up to man to reverse the unfortunate consequences of his actions and thus conserve his heritage.

BIBLIOGRAPHY

ABSALOM, R. G., and HENDERSON, S. M. K.	1947	A tooth of *Elephas primigenius* from Headswood, Larbert, Stirlingshire. *Geol. Mag.*, **84**, 181-4.
AGASSIZ, L.	1840	On the evidence of the former existence of glaciers in Scotland, Ireland and England. *Proc. geol. Soc., Lond.*, **3**, 327-32.
ANDERSON, F. W.	1947	The fauna of the '100 feet beach' clays. *Trans. Edinb. geol. Soc.*, **14**, 220-9.
ANDERSON, J. G. C.	1949	The Gare Loch Readvance moraine. *Geol. Mag.*, **86**, 239-44.
	1951	Geology of the Glen Tromie hydro-electric tunnels, Inverness-shire. *Geol. Mag.*, **88**, 133-9.
BADEN-POWELL, D. F. W.	1938	On the glacial and interglacial marine beds of northern Lewis. *Geol. Mag.*, **75**, 395-409.
BAILEY, E. B.	1934	The interpretation of Scottish scenery. *Scott. geogr. Mag.*, **50**, 308-30.
BAILEY, E. B., *et al.*	1916	The geology of Ben Nevis and Glen Coe. *Mem. geol. Surv.* 2nd ed. 1960.
	1924	Tertiary and post-Tertiary geology of Mull, Loch Aline and Oban. *Mem. geol. Surv.*
BAIRD, P. D., and LEWIS, W. V.	1957	The Cairngorm floods, 1956. *Scott. geogr. Mag.*, **73**, 91-100.
BARROW, G., *et al.*	1905	The geology of the country round Blair Atholl, Pitlochry and Aberfeldy. *Mem. geol. Surv.*
BATTEY, M. H.	1960	Geological factors in the development of Veslgjuv-botn and Vesl-Skautbotn. *Norwegian cirque glaciers*, edited by W. V. Lewis, *Roy. geogr. Soc.*, 5-10.
BENNIE, J.	1891	The ancient lakes of Edinburgh. *Proc. roy. Phys. Soc. Edinb.*, **10**, 126-54.
	1896a	On the occurrence of peat with Arctic plants in boulder-clay at Faskine near Airdrie, Lanarkshire. *Trans. geol. Soc. Glasg.*, **10**, 148-52.
	1896b	Arctic plant-beds in Scotland. *Ann. Scott. nat. Hist.*, **17**, 53-6.
BISHOP, W. W.	1963	Late-glacial deposits near Lockerbie, Dumfriesshire. *Trans. J. Proc. Dumfries. Galloway nat. Hist. Antiq. Soc.*, **40**, 117-32.
BOULTON, G. S., and WORSLEY, P.	1965	Late Weichselian glaciation in the Cheshire-Shropshire basin. *Nature*, **207**, 704-6.
BREMNER, A.	1916	The Vat near Loch Kinord, Aberdeenshire. *Trans. Edinb. geol. Soc.*, **10**, 326-33.
	1921	The physical geology of the Don basin. *Aberdeen Univ. Stud.*

BREMNER, A.   1932   Further problems in the glacial geology of north-eastern
                                Scotland. *Trans. Edinb. geol. Soc.*, **12**, 147-64.
                         1934a The glaciation of Moray and ice movements in the north
                                of Scotland. *Trans. Edinb. geol. Soc.*, **13**, 17-56.
                         1934b Meltwater drainage channels and other glacial pheno-
                                mena of the Highland border belt from Cortachy to the
                                Bervie Water. *Trans. Edinb. geol. Soc.*, **13**, 174-5.
                         1939   The late-glacial geology of the Tay basin from Pass of
                                Birnam to Grandtully and Pitlochry. *Trans. Edinb. geol.
                                Soc.*, **13**, 473-4.
                         1942   The origin of the Scottish river system. *Scott. geogr.
                                Mag.*, **58**, 15-20, 54-9, 99-103.

BUCKLAND, W.   1840   On the former existence of glaciers in Scotland. *Edinb.
                                New phil. J.*, **30**, 194-8.

BUIST, G.   1841   Outline of the geology of the south-east district of
                                Perthshire. *Trans. Highland agric. Soc. Scott.*, **13**, 17-49.

BURKE, M. J.   1966   *Ice-moulded forms in the Forth valley*. M.Sc. thesis,
                                Edinburgh.

CADELL, H. M.   1886   The Dumbartonshire Highlands. *Scott. geogr. Mag.*, **2**,
                                337-47.
                         1913   *The story of the Forth*. Glasgow.

CALLANDER, J. G.   1929   Land movements in Scotland in prehistoric and recent
                                times. *Pro. Soc. Antiq. Scott.*, **63**, 314-22.

CAMPBELL, A. C., and   1910   Notes on a transported mass of igneous rock at Comi-
ANDERSON, E. M.   ston sand-pit, near Edinburgh. *Trans. Edinb. geol. Soc.*,
                                9, 219-24.

CAMPBELL, R.   1934   On the occurrence of shelly boulder clay and interglacial
                                deposits in Kincardineshire. *Trans. Edinb. geol. Soc.*, **13**,
                                176-83.

CARRUTHERS, R. G.   1911   On the occurrence of a Cretaceous boulder of unusual
                                size, at Leavad, in Caithness. *Summ. Prog. geol. Surv.*,
                                80-4.

CHAMBERS, R.   1853   Glacial phenomena in Scotland and parts of England.
                                Edinb. New phil. J., **54**, 229-81.

CHAPELHOW, R.   1965   On glaciation in North Roe, Shetland. *Geogr. J.*, **131**,
                                60-70.

CHARLESWORTH, J. K.   1926a The glacial geology of the Southern Uplands, west
                                of Annandale and upper Clydesdale. *Trans. roy. Soc.
                                Edinb.*, **55**, 1-23.
                         1926b The readvance marginal kame-moraine of the south of
                                Scotland and some later stages of retreat. *Trans. roy.
                                Soc. Edinb.*, **55**, 25-50.
                         1955   Lateglacial history of the Highlands and islands of Scot-
                                land. *Trans. roy. Soc. Edinb.*, **62**, 769-928.

COMMON, R.   1954   A report on the Lochaber, Appin, and Benderloch
                                floods. *Scott. geogr. Mag.*, **70**, 6-20.

COOPE, G. R.   1962   Coleoptera from a peat interbedded between two boulder
                                clays at Burnhead, near Airdrie. *Trans. geol. Soc. Glasg.*,
                                24, 279-86.

CRAIG, E. H. C., *et al.* 1911 The geology of Colonsay and Oronsay with part of the
                                Ross of Mull. *Mem. geol. Surv.*

CRAIG, R.   1874   On the boulders found in cuttings on the Beith branch
                                railway, considered in relation to their parent rock.
                                Trans. geol. Soc. Glasg., **4**, 45-56.

CRAMPTON, C. B., *et al.* 1914 The geology of Caithness. *Mem. geol. Surv.*

CROSSKEY, H. W. 1886 Note on the glacial geology of the district around Loch Sween, Argyllshire. *Proc. Birmingham phil. Soc.*, **5**, 219.

CULLINGFORD, R. A., and SMITH, D. E. 1966 Late-glacial shorelines in eastern Fife. *Trans. Inst. brit. Geogr.*, **39**, 31-51.

DAVIDSON, C. F. 1932 The arctic clay of Errol, Perthshire. *Trans. Perthshire Soc. nat. sci.*, **9**, 55-68.

DAVIES, G. L. 1956 The parish of North Uist. *Scott. geogr. Mag.*, **72**, 65-80.

DAWSON, R. 1866 On the occurrence of dead littoral shells in the bed of the German Ocean, forty miles from the coast of Aberdeen. *Geol. Mag.*, **3**, 130.

DE GEER, G. 1935 Dating of late-glacial clay varves in Scotland. *Proc. roy. Soc. Edinb.*, **55**, 23-6.

DOLLAR, A. T. J. 1950 Catalogue of Scottish earthquakes, 1916-1949. *Trans. geol. Soc. Glasg.*, **21**, 283-361.

DONNER, J. J. 1957 The geology and vegetation of late-glacial retreat stages in Scotland. *Trans. roy. Soc. Edinb.*, **63**, 221-64.
1959 1963 The late- and post-glacial raised beaches in Scotland. *Annal Acad. sci. Fenn.*, **53**, 25 pp.; **68**, 13 pp.
1962 On the post-glacial history of the Grampian Highlands of Scotland. *Soc. sci. Fenn.*, *Comm. biol.*, **24**, 29 pp.

DRYSDALE, W. S. 1956 Firth of Forth seismic refraction survey. *Trans. Inst. min. Eng.*, **115**, 435-54.

DURNO, S. E. 1957 Certain aspects of vegetational history in North-East Scotland. *Scott. geogr. Mag.*, **73**, 176-84.
1965 Pollen analytical evidence of 'Landnam' from two Scottish sites. *Trans. bot. Soc. Edinb.*, **40**, 13-19.

DURY, G. H. 1953 A glacial breach in the north-western Highlands. *Scott. geogr. Mag.*, **69**, 106-17.

ELDER, S., *et al.* 1935 The drumlins of Glasgow. *Trans. geol. Soc. Glasg.*, **19**, 285-7.

ESMARK, J. 1827 Remarks tending to explain the geological history of the earth. *Edinb. New phil. J.*, **2**, 107-21.

FAIRBRIDGE, R. W. 1961 Eustatic changes in sea-level. *Phys. and Chem. of the Earth*, **4**, 99-185.

FITZPATRICK, E. A. 1956 An indurated soil horizon formed by permafrost. *J. Soil Sci.*, **7**, 248-54.
1958 An introduction to the periglacial geomorphology of Scotland. *Scott. geogr. Mag.*, **74**, 28-36.
1963 Deeply weathered rock in Scotland, its occurrence, age and contribution to soils. *J. Soil Sci.*, **14**, 33-43.
1965 An interglacial soil at Teindland, Morayshire. *Nature*, **207**, 621-2.

FLEET, H. 1938 Erosion surfaces in the Grampian Highlands of Scotland. *Rapp. Comm. Cartog. des Surf. d'Appl. tert.*, *Union geogr. Internat.*, 91-4.

FLETT, J. S. 1925 The submarine contours around the Orkneys. *Trans. Edinb. geol. Soc.*, **11**, 42-9.

FLETT, J. S., and READ, H. H. 1921 Tertiary gravels of the Buchan district of Aberdeenshire. *Geol. Mag.*, **58**, 215-25.

FLINN, D. 1964 Coastal and submarine features around the Shetland Islands. *Proc. Geol. Assoc.*, **75**, 321-40.

FORBES, J. D.   1845   Notes on the topography and geology of the Cuchullin
                                   Hills in Skye, and on the traces of ancient glaciers which
                                   they present. *Edinb. New phil. J.*, **40**, 76-99.

FORD, T. D.   1959   The Sutherland caves. *Trans. cave Research Group of Gt.
                                   Brit.*, **5**, 139-90.

FRANCIS, E. H.   1965   Carboniferous-Permian igneous rocks. In *The geology of
                                   Scotland*, edited by G. Y. Craig, Edinburgh, 359-82.

GAILEY, R. A.   1959   Glasgow University Expedition to North Rona. *Scott.
                                   geogr. Mag.*, **75**, 48-50.

GALLOWAY, R. W.   1961a   Ice wedges and involutions in Scotland. *Biul. Peryglac.*,
                                   10, 169-93.
                          1961b   Periglacial phenomena in Scotland. *Geogr. Ann., Stockh.*,
                                   43, 348-53.
                          1961c   Solifluction in Scotland. *Scott. geogr. Mag.*, **77**, 75-87.

GATTY, V.   1906   The glacial aspect of Ben Nevis. *Geogr. J.*, **27**, 487-92.

GEIKIE, A.   1863   On the phenomena of the glacial drift of Scotland.
                                   Trans. geol. Soc. Glasg., **1**, 1-190.
                          1901   *The scenery of Scotland.* London. 1st ed. 1865, 2nd ed.
                                   1887.

GEIKIE, J.   1873 1878   On the glacial phenomena of the Long Island or
                                   Outer Hebrides. *Quart. J. geol. Soc.*, **29**, 532-45; **34**,
                                   819-66.
                          1894   *The great ice age.* London. 1st ed. 1874, 2nd ed. 1877.

GEORGE, T. N.   1955   Drainage in the Southern Uplands: Clyde, Nith, Annan.
                                   Trans. geol. Soc. Glasg., **22**, 1-34.
                          1965   The geological growth of Scotland. In *The Geology of
                                   Scotland*, edited by G. Y. Craig, Edinburgh, 1-48.
                          1966   Geomorphic evolution in Hebridean Scotland. *Scott. J.
                                   Geol.*, **2**, 1-34.

GODARD, A.   1965   *Recherches de géomorphologie en Ecosse du Nord-Ouest.*
                                   Paris.

GODWIN, H.   1956   *The history of the British flora: a factual basis for phyto-
                                   geography.* Cambridge.
                          1961   Radiocarbon dating and Quaternary history in Britain.
                                   Proc. roy. Soc. B., **153**, 287-320.

GODWIN, H., and   1966   Cambridge University natural radiocarbon measure-
   SWITSUR, V. R.   ments VIII. *Radiocarbon*, **8**, 390-400.

GODWIN, H., and   1959-1962 1964.   Cambridge University natural radiocarbon
   WILLIS, E. H.   measurements I-III, V, VI. *Radiocarbon*, **1**, 63-75; **2**,
                                   62-72; **3**, 60-76; **4**, 57-70; **6**, 116-37.

GODWIN, H., WILLIS,   1965   Cambridge University natural radiocarbon measure-
   E. H., and SWITSUR, V. R.   ments VII. *Radiocarbon*, **7**, 205-12.

GOODLET, G. A.   1964   The kamiform deposits near Carstairs, Lanarkshire,
                                   Bull. geol. Surv., **21**, 175-96.

GORDON, D. L., and   1963   Mean sea level in the British Isles. *Admiralty Marine
   SUTHONS, C. T.   Sci. Publ.*, **7**, Admiralty, London.

GREEN, F. H. W.   1958   The Moray floods of July and August 1956. *Scott.
                                   geogr. Mag.*, **74**, 48-50.

GREGORY, J. W.   1913   *The nature and origin of fiords.* London.
                          1915   The Tweed valley and its relation to the Clyde and
                                   Solway. *Scott. geogr. Mag.*, **31**, 478-86.
                          1926   The moraines, boulder clay, and glacial sequence of
                                   south-western Scotland. *Trans. geol. Soc. Glasg.*, **17**,
                                   354-76.

GREGORY, J. W., and CURRIE, E. D. — 1928 — The vertebrate fossils from the glacial and associated post-glacial beds of Scotland in the Hunterian Museum, University of Glasgow. *Mon. geol. Dept. Hunterian Mus. Glasg. Univ.*, **2.**

GROVE, A. T. — 1955 — The mouth of the Spey. *Scott. geogr. Mag.*, **71,** 104-7.

HALL, J. — 1815 — On the revolutions of the earth's surface. *Trans. roy. Soc. Edinb.*, **7,** 139-211.

HARKER, A. — 1899 — Notes on subaerial erosion in the Isle of Skye. *Geol. Mag.*, **36,** 485-91.

1901 — Ice-erosion in the Cuillin Hills, Skye. *Trans. roy. Soc. Edinb.*, **40,** 221-52.

HARRISON, J. W. H., and BLACKBURN, K. B. — 1946 — The occurrence of a nut of *Trapa natans* L. in the Outer Hebrides, with some account of the peat bogs adjoining the loch in which the discovery was made. *New Phytol.*, **45,** 124-31.

HILL, J. B., *et al.* — 1905 — The geology of Mid-Argyll. *Mem. geol. Surv.*

HINXMAN, L. W., *et al.* — 1902 — The geology of lower Strathspey. *Mem. geol. Surv.*

1923 — The geology of Corrour and the Moor of Rannoch. *Mem. geol. Surv.*

HOLLINGWORTH, S. E. — 1938 — The recognition and correlation of high-level erosion surfaces in Britain: a statistical study. *Quart. J. geol. Soc.*, **94,** 55-84.

HOPKINS, W. — 1852 — On the granite blocks of the south Highlands of Scotland. *Quart. J. geol. Soc.*, **8,** 20-30.

HOPPE, G. — 1965 — Submarine peat in the Shetland Islands. *Geogr. Ann. Stockh.*, **47A,** 195-203.

HOPPE, G., *et al.* — 1965 — Från fält och forskning naturgeografi vid Stockholms Universitet. *Ymer*, 109-25.

HORNE, J. — 1899 — The intercrossing of boulders in the Applecross Mountains. *Trans. Edinb. geol. Soc.*, **7,** 38-44.

HORNE, J., *et al.* — 1893 — The character of the high-level shell-bearing deposits at Clava, Chapelhall and other localities. *Rept. brit. Assoc.*, 483-514.

1896 — The character of the high-level shell-bearing deposits in Kintyre. *Rept. brit. Assoc.*, 378-99.

HOWDEN, J. C. — 1870 — On the superficial deposits at the estuary of the South Esk. *Trans. Edinb. geol. Soc.*, **1,** 138-50.

HUTTON, J. — 1795 — *The theory of the earth.* 2 vols. Edinburgh.

IMRIE, —. — 1814 — On the dressed rocks of the Campsie Hills. *Mem. Wernerian Soc.*, **2,** 24-50.

JAMIESON, T. F. — 1862 — On the ice-worn rocks of Scotland. *Quart. J. geol. Soc.*, **18,** 164-84.

1863 — On the parallel roads of Glen Roy, and their place in the history of the glacial period. *Quart. J. geol. Soc.*, **19,** 235-59.

1865 — On the history of the last geological changes in Scotland. *Quart. J. geol. Soc.*, **21,** 161-203.

1866 — On the glacial phenomena of Caithness. *Quart. J. geol. Soc.*, **22,** 260-81.

1874 — On the last stage of the glacial period in north Britain. *Quart. J. geol. Soc.*, **30,** 317-37.

1906 — The glacial period in Aberdeenshire and the southern border of the Moray Firth. *Quart. J. geol. Soc.*, **62,** 13-39.

JARDINE, W. G.
1959 River development in Galloway. *Scott. geogr. Mag.*, **75**, 65-74.
1964 Post-glacial sea levels in South-West Scotland. *Scott. geogr. Mag.*, **80**, 5-11.

JEHU, T. J., and CRAIG, R. M.
1923 1926 1934 Geology of the Outer Hebrides. *Trans. roy. Soc. Edinb.*, **53**, 419-41; **54**, 467-89; **57**, 839-74.

JESSEN, A.
1905 On the shell-bearing clay in Kintyre. *Trans. Edinb. geol. Soc.*, **8**, 76-86.

KING, C. A. M., and WHEELER, P. T.
1963 The raised beaches of the north coast of Sutherland, Scotland. *Geol. Mag.*, **100**, 299-320.

KIRBY, R. P.
1966 *The glacial geomorphology of the Esk basin.* Ph.D. thesis, Edinburgh.

KIRK, W., and GODWIN, H.
1963 A late-glacial site at Loch Droma, Ross and Cromarty. *Trans. roy. Soc. Edinb.*, **65**, 225-49.

KIRK, W., RICE, R. J., and SYNGE, F. M.
1966 Deglaciation and vertical displacement of shorelines in Wester and Easter Ross. *Trans. Inst. brit. Geogr.*, **39**, 65-78.

KYNASTON, H., *et al.*
1908 The geology of the country near Oban and Dalmally. *Mem. geol. Surv.*

LAUDER, T. D.
1830 *An account of the great floods of August 1829 in the Province of Moray and the adjoining districts.* Edinburgh.

LEARMONTH, A. T. A.
1950 The floods of 12th August, 1948, in South-East Scotland. *Scott. geogr. Mag.*, **66**, 147-53.

LEE, G. W.
1920 The Mesozoic rocks of Applecross, Raasay and North-East Skye. *Mem. geol. Surv.*

LEWIS, W. V.
1954 Pressure release and glacial erosion. *Union Geod. et Geophys. Internat. Assoc. Int. d'Hydrol. Sci.: Comm. des neiges et glaces*, **4**, 393.

LINTON, D. L.
1933 The origin of the Tweed drainage system. *Scott. geogr. Mag.*, **49**, 162-75.
1940 Some aspects of the evolution of the rivers Earn and Tay. *Scott. geogr. Mag.*, **56**, 1-11, 69-79.
1951a Problems of Scottish scenery. *Scott. geogr. Mag.*, **67**, 65-85.
1951b Watershed breaching by ice in Scotland. *Trans. Inst. brit. Geogr.* **15**, 1-15.
1954 Some Scottish river captures re-examined III. The beheading of the Don. *Scott. geogr. Mag.*, **70**, 64-78.
1955 The problem of tors. *Geogr. J.*, **121**, 470-87.
1959 Morphological contrasts between eastern and western Scotland. In *Geographical essays in memory of Alan G. Ogilvie*, edited by R. Miller and J. W. Watson, Edinburgh, 16-45.
1963 The forms of glacial erosion. *Trans. Inst. brit. Geogr.*, **33**, 1-28.

LINTON, D. L., and MOISLEY, H. A.
1960 The origin of Loch Lomond. *Scott. geogr. Mag.*, **76**, 26-37.

LYELL, C.
1840 On the geological evidence of the former existence of glaciers in Forfarshire. *Edinb. New phil. J.*, **30**, 199-202.

McCALL, J., and GOODLET, G. A.
1952 Indicator stones from the drift of south Midlothian and Peebles. *Trans. Edinb. geol. Soc.*, **14**, 401-09.

McCALLIEN, W. J.
1937 Late-glacial and early post-glacial Scotland. *Proc. Soc. Antiq. Scott.*, **71**, 174-206.

McCANN, S. B.   1961a Some supposed 'raised beach' deposits at Corran, Loch Linnhe, and Loch Etive. *Geol. Mag.*, **98**, 131-42.

1961b *The raised beaches of western Scotland.* Ph.D. thesis. Cambridge.

1964 The raised beaches of North-East Islay and western Jura, Argyll. *Trans. Inst. brit. Geogr.*, **35**, 1-16.

1966a The limits of the Late-glacial Highland, or Loch Lomond, Readvance along the West Highland seaboard from Oban to Mallaig. *Scott. J. Geol.*, **2**, 84-95.

1966b The Main Postglacial Raised Shoreline of western Scotland from the Firth of Lorne to Loch Broom. *Trans. Inst. brit. Geogr.*, **39**, 87-99.

MACGREGOR, M.,   1940 Early glacial remains of reindeer from the Glasgow district. *Proc. roy. Soc. Edinb.*, **60**, 322-32.
   and RITCHIE, J.

MACKIE, W.   1905 Some notes on the distribution of erratics over eastern Moray. *Trans. Edinb. geol. Soc.*, **8**, 91-7.

MACKINDER, H. J.   1902 *Britain and the British seas.* London.

MACLAREN, C.   1866 *Geology of Fife and the Lothians.* 2nd ed. 1st ed. 1839. Edinburgh.

MACNAIR, P.   1908 *Geology and scenery of the Grampians.* Glasgow. 2 vols.

MANLEY, G.   1949 The snowline in Britain. *Geogr. Ann. Stockh.*, **31**, 179-193.

1951 The range and variation of the British climate. *Geogr. J.*, **117**, 43-68.

1964 The evolution of the climatic environment. In *The British Isles: a systematic geography*, edited by J. W. Watson and J. B. Sissons, 152-70, Edinburgh.

MARSHALL, J. R.   1962 The morphology of the upper Solway salt marshes. *Scott. geogr. Mag.*, **78**, 81-99.

MATHIESON, J., and   1925 The glacial strand-lines of Loch Tulla. *Trans. Edinb. geol. Soc.*, **11**, 193-99.
   BAILEY, E. B.

MILLER, H., Snr.   1850 On scratched boulders. *Rept. brit. Assoc.*, **19**, 93-6.

1864 *Edinburgh and its neighbourhood.* Edinburgh.

MILLER, H., Jnr.   1884 On boulder-glaciation. *Proc. roy. Phys. Soc. Edinb.*, **8**, 156-89.

MILLER, R.,   1954 Stone stripes and other surface features of Tinto Hill. *Geogr. J.*, **120**, 216-19.
   COMMON, R., and
   GALLOWAY, R. W.

MILNE-HOME, D.   1871 *The estuary of the Forth and adjoining districts viewed geologically.* Edinburgh.

MITCHELL, G. F.   1952 Late-glacial deposits of Garscadden Mains, near Glasgow. *New Phytol.*, **50**, 277-86.

MITCHELL, G. F.,   1949 The Giant Deer in Ireland. *Proc. roy. Irish Acad.*, **52B**, 291-314.
   and PARKES, H. M.

MORRISON, M. E. S.,   1965 A submerged late-Quaternary deposit at Roddans Port on the north-east coast of Ireland. *Phil. Trans. roy. Soc. Lond. B.*, **249**, 221-55.
   and STEPHENS, N.

MORT, F. W.   1914 The sculpture of North Arran. *Scott. geogr. Mag.*, **30**, 393-404.

1918 The rivers of south-west Scotland. *Scott. geogr. Mag.*, **34**, 361-8.

MUNTHE, H.   1897 On the interglacial submergence of Great Britain. *Bull. geol. Inst. Upsala*, **3**, 369-411.

MURRAY, J.,   1910 *Bathymetrical survey of the Scottish freshwater lochs.*
  and PULLAR, L.   Edinburgh. 6 vols.

NEWEY, W. W.   1965 *Post-glacial vegetational and climatic changes in part of
                                   South-East Scotland.* Ph.D. thesis, Edinburgh.

                             1966 Pollen analysis of sub-carse peats of the Forth valley.
                                   Trans. Inst. brit. Geogr., **39,** 53-9.

OGILVIE, A. G.   1923 The physiography of the Moray Firth coast. *Trans. roy.
                                   Soc. Edinb.,* **53,** 377-404.

                             1930 *Great Britain: essays in regional geography.* Cambridge.

PEACH, A. M.   1909 Boulder distribution from Lennoxtown, Scotland. *Geol.
                                   Mag.,* **46,** 26-31.

PEACH, B. N., and   1879 The glaciation of the Shetland Isles. *Quart. J. geol. Soc.,*
  HORNE, J.   **35,** 778-811.

                             1880 The glaciation of the Orkney Islands. *Quart. J. geol.
                                   Soc.,* **36,** 648-63.

                             1881 Glaciation of Caithness. *Proc. roy. Phys. Soc. Edinb.,* **6,**
                                   316-52.

                             1892 The ice-shed in the North-West Highlands during the
                                   maximum glaciation. *Rept. brit. Assoc.,* 720.

                             1917 The bone-cave in the valley of Allt nan Uamh (Burn of
                                   the Caves) near Inchnadamff, Assynt, Sutherlandshire.
                                   Proc. roy. Soc. Edinb., **37,** 327-49.

                             1930 *Chapters in the geology of Scotland.* London.

PEACH, B. N., *et al.*   1911 The geology of Knapdale, Jura and north Kintyre.
                                   Mem. geol. Surv.

                             1912 The geology of Ben Wyvis, Carn Chuinneag, Inchbae
                                   and the surrounding country. *Mem. geol. Surv.*

                             1913a The geology of the Fannich Mountains and the country
                                   around upper Loch Maree and Strath Broom. *Mem.
                                   geol. Surv.*

                             1913b The geology of central Ross-shire. *Mem. geol. Surv.*

PEARS, N. V.   1965 *The present tree-line in the Cairngorm Mountains of Scot-
                                   land and its relation to former tree-lines.* Ph.D. thesis,
                                   London.

PENNANT, T.   1771 *A tour in Scotland, 1769,* London.

PHEMISTER, T. C.,   1949 Pleistocene deep weathering in north-east Scotland.
  and SIMPSON, S.   *Nature,* **164,** 318-19.

PLAYFAIR, J.   1802 *Illustrations of the Huttonian theory of the earth.* Edin-
                                   burgh.

                             1822 *The works of John Playfair.* Edited by F. Jeffrey. Edin-
                                   burgh.

PRAEGER, R. L.   1892 Report on the estuarine clays of the north-east of Ireland.
                                   Proc. roy. Irish Acad., **2,** 212-89.

PRICE, R. J.   1960 Glacial meltwater channels in the upper Tweed drain-
                                   age basin. *Geogr. J.,* **126,** 483-9.

RAGG, J. M., and   1966 Frost weathering and solifluction products in southern
  BIBBY, J. S.   Scotland. *Geogr. Ann., Stockh.,* **48,** 12-23.

RAMSAY, A. C.   1862 On the glacial origin of certain lakes in Switzerland, the
                                   Black Forest, Great Britain, Sweden, North America
                                   and elsewhere. *Quart. J. geol. Soc.,* **18,** 185-204.

READ, H. H.   1923 The geology of the country around Banff, Huntly and
                                   Turriff. *Mem. geol. Surv.*

READ, H. H., *et al.*   1925 The geology of the country around Golspie, Sutherland-
                                   shire. *Mem. geol. Surv.*

	1926	The geology of Strath Oykell and lower Loch Shin. *Mem. geol. Surv.*
RICE, R. J.	1959	The glacial deposits of the Lunan and Brothock valleys in south-east Angus. *Trans. Edinb. geol. Soc.*, **17,** 241-59.
	1962	The morphology of the Angus coastal lowlands. *Scott. geogr. Mag.*, **78,** 5-14.
RICHEY, J. E., and THOMAS, H. H.	1930	The geology of Ardnamurchan, North-West Mull and Coll. *Mem. geol. Surv.*
RICHEY, J. E., *et al.*	1930	The geology of North Ayrshire. *Mem. geol. Surv.*
RITCHIE, J.	1928	The fauna of Scotland during the Ice Age. *Proc. roy. Phys. Soc. Edinb.*, **21,** 185-94.
RITCHIE, W.	1966	The post-glacial rise in sea-level and coastal changes in the Uists. *Trans. Inst. brit. Geogr.*, **39,** 79-86.
ROBERTSON, D.	1877	Notes on a raised beach at Cumbrae. *Trans. geol. Soc. Glasg.*, **5,** 192-200.
ROBERTSON, D., and CROSSKEY, H. W.	1874	On the post-Tertiary fossiliferous beds of Scotland. *Trans. geol. Soc. Glasg.*, **4,** 128-37.
ROBINSON, A. H. W.	1949	Deep clefts in the Inner Sound of Raasay. *Scott. geogr. Mag.*, **65,** 20-5.
ROLFE, W. D. I.	1966	Woolly rhinoceros from the Scottish Pleistocene. *Scott. J. Geol.*, **2,** 253-8.
SIMPSON, J. B.	1933	The late-glacial readvance moraines of the Highland border west of the River Tay. *Trans. roy. Soc. Edinb.*, **57,** 633-45.
SIMPSON, J. B., *et al.*	1936	The geology of the Sanquhar coalfield and adjacent basin of Thornhill. *Mem. geol. Surv.*
SIMPSON, S.	1948	The glacial deposits of Tullos and the Bay of Nigg, Aberdeen. *Trans. roy. Soc. Edinb.*, **61,** 687-98.
	1955	A re-interpretation of the drifts of North-East Scotland. *Trans. Edinb. geol. Soc.*, **16,** 189-99.
SINCLAIR, W.	1913	The relationship between the raised beach and the boulder clay of the west coast of Kintyre. *Trans. geol. Soc. Glasg.*, **14,** 170.
SISSONS, J. B.	1958	Supposed ice-dammed lakes in Britain with particular reference to the Eddleston valley, southern Scotland. *Geogr. Ann., Stockh.*, **40,** 159-87.
	1960a	Erosion surfaces, cyclic slopes and drainage systems in southern Scotland and northern England. *Trans. Inst. brit. Geogr.*, **28,** 23-38.
	1960b 1961a	Some aspects of glacial drainage channels in Britain. *Scott. geogr. Mag.*, **76,** 131-46; **77,** 15-36.
	1961b	A subglacial drainage system by the Tinto Hills, Lanarkshire. *Trans. Edinb. geol. Soc.*, **18,** 175-93.
	1961c	The central and eastern parts of the Lammermuir-Stranraer moraine, *Geol. Mag.*, **98,** 380-92.
	1963a 1964	The Perth Readvance in central Scotland. *Scott. geogr. Mag.*, **79,** 151-63; **80,** 28-36.
	1963b	The glacial drainage system around Carlops, Peeblesshire. *Trans. Inst. brit. Geogr.*, **32,** 95-111.
	1966	Relative sea-level changes between 10 300 and 8300 B.P. in part of the Carse of Stirling. *Trans. Inst. brit. Geogr.*, **39,** 19-29.
	1967	Glacial stages and radiocarbon dates in Scotland. *Scott. J. Geol.* (in the press).

SISSONS, J. B.,   1965a   Raised shorelines associated with the Perth Readvance
and SMITH, D. E.   in the Forth valley and their relation to glacial isostasy. *Trans. roy. Soc. Edinb.*, **66,** 143-68.

1965b   Peat-bogs in a post-glacial sea and a buried raised beach in the western part of the Carse of Stirling. *Scott. J. Geol.,* **1,** 247-55.

SISSONS, J. B.,   1965   Some pre-carse valleys in the Forth and Tay basins. CULLINGFORD, R. A.,   *Scott. Geogr. Mag.,* **81,** 115-24.
and SMITH, D. E.   1966   Late-glacial and post-glacial shorelines in South-East Scotland. *Trans. Inst. brit. Geogr.,* **39,** 9-18.

SMITH, James   1838   On the last changes in the relative levels of the land and (of Jordanhill)   sea in the British Islands. *Edinb. New phil. J.,* **25,** 378-94.

SMITH, J.   1893   The Great Ice Age in the Garnock valley. *Trans. geol. Soc. Glasg.,* **9,** 151-91.

1896   The geological position of the Irvine whale bed. *Trans. geol. Soc. Glasg.,* **10,** 29-50.

1898   The drift or glacial deposits of Ayrshire. *Trans. geol. Soc. Glasg.,* Suppl., **11,** 134 pp.

1902   Marine shells. *Geol. Mag.,* **39,** 479.

SOMERVAIL, A.   1880   Observations on *roches moutonnées* and other points of geological interest in the valley of the Urr, Kirkcudbrightshire. *Trans. Edinb. geol. Soc.,* **3,** 247-50.

SOONS, J. M.   1958   Landscape evolution in the Ochil Hills. *Scott. geogr. Mag.,* **74,** 86-97.

1960   The sub-drift surface of the lower Devon valley. *Trans. geol. Soc. Glasg.,* **24,** 1-7.

STEERS, J. A.   1937   The Culbin Sands and Burghead Bay. *Geogr. J.,* **90,** 498-528.

1952   The coastline of Scotland. *Geogr. J.,* **118,** 180-90.

STEPHENS, N.   1957   Some observations on the 'interglacial' platform and the early post-glacial raised beach on the east coast of Ireland. *Proc. roy. Irish Acad.,* **58B,** 129-49.

1963   Late-glacial sea-levels in North-East Ireland. *Irish Geogr.,* **4,** 345-59.

STEWART, M.   1933   Notes on the geology of Sula Sgeir and the Flannan Is. *Geol. Mag.,* **70,** 110-16.

STONE, J. C.   1959   A description of glacial retreat features in mid-Nithsdale. *Scott. geogr. Mag.,* **75,** 164-8.

SUGDEN, D. E.   1965   *Aspects of the glaciation of the Cairngorm Mountains.* D. Phil. thesis, Oxford.

SYNGE, F. M.   1956   The glaciation of North-East Scotland. *Scott. geogr. Mag.,* **72,** 129-43.

1963   The Quaternary succession round Aberdeen, North-East Scotland. *Rept. VIth Internat. quat Cong.,* Geomorph. Sect., **3,** 353-61.

SYNGE, F. M., and   1966   Late- and Post-glacial shorelines, and ice limits in Argyll STEPHENS, N.   and North-East Ulster. *Trans. Inst. brit. Geogr.,* **39,** 101-25.

TAIT, D.   1934   Excavations in the old lake deposits at Corstorphine during 1930-32. *Trans. Edinb. geol. Soc.,* **13,** 110-25.

TAYLOR, A.   1888   On a lacustrine deposit near Holyrood. *Trans. Edinb. geol. Soc.,* **5,** 44-8.

THOMPSON, H. R.   1950   Some corries of north-west Sutherland. *Proc. Geol. Assoc.,* **61,** 145-55.

TING, S.

1936 Beach ridges and other shore deposits in South-West Jura. *Scott. geogr. Mag.*, **52**, 182-7.

1937 The coastal configuration of western Scotland. *Geogr. Ann., Stockh.*, **19**, 62-83.

TIVY, J.

1957 Influence des facteurs biologiques sur l'érosion dans les Southern Uplands écossais. *Rev. Géomorph. dynam.*, **8**, 9-19.

TULLOCH, W., and WALTON, H. S.

1958 The geology of the Midlothian coalfield. *Mem. geol. Surv.*

TURNER, W.

1872 On the bones of a seal found in red clay near Grangemouth, with remarks on the species. *Proc. roy. Soc. Edinb.*, **7**, 105-14.

WAGER, L. R.

1953 The extent of glaciation in the island of St Kilda. *Geol. Mag.*, **90**, 177-81.

WALTON, K.

1956 Rattray: a study in coastal evolution. *Scott. geogr. Mag.*, **72**, 85-96.

1959 Ancient elements in the coastline of North-East Scotland. In *Geographical essays in memory of Alan G. Ogilvie*, edited by R. Miller and J. W. Watson, Edinburgh, 93-109.

WILSON, G. V., *et al.*

1935 The geology of the Orkneys. *Mem. geol. Surv.*

WRIGHT, J.

1896 Boulder-clay, a marine deposit. *Trans. geol. Soc. Glasg.*, **10**, 263-72.

WRIGHT, W. B.

1911 On a pre-glacial shore-line in the western isles of Scotland. *Geol. Mag.*, **48**, 97-109.

1937 *The Quaternary Ice Age*. London. 2nd ed.

INDEX